SCIENCE AS HISTORY

*The Story of Man's Technological Progress
from Steam Engine to Satellite*

by

HEINZ GARTMANN

Translated from the German by
Alan G. Readett

London
HODDER & STOUGHTON

Originally published in German under the title of Sonst stünde
die Welt still. *Copyright by Econ Verlag G.m.b.H.,
Düsseldorf, Pressehaus. English translation — Copyright
© 1960 by Hodder and Stoughton Limited*

*Printed in Great Britain
for Hodder and Stoughton Limited
by Richard Clay and Company Limited
Bungay, Suffolk*

CONTENTS

Page

PREFACE   xi

Chapter

I   MACHINES IN PLACE OF MUSCLES   .   .   I

Machines instead of men — The revolt of the workmen — The end of the 'abhorred vacuum' — "Down with the fire engine!"— A very important document — Watt begins to make money — "He multiplied the power of men."

II   REVOLUTION ON WHEELS   .   .   .   27

Captain Dick gets up steam — Early experiments — The steam carriage — Mr. Stephenson's absurd plan — The beginning of world-wide transport — Gloomy prophecies — The locomotive race at Rainhill — The railway becomes accepted — The end of the struggle — The internal combustion engine — The four-stroke engine — Petroleum — From the velocipede to Benz's patent coach — The petrol carriage.

III   WINGS FOR ADAM   .   .   .   71

A dream come true — The hazards of flying — Prophecies false and true — Man-made wings — By-paths of fancy — "The most wonderful things in the world" — The balloon — Adventurous balloonists — The dirigible airship — The Heroic Era — First steps in aeronautics — The beginnings of aerial travel — The last laugh.

IV   THE INVISIBLE NET   .   .   .   122

Rapid communications — The cabled word — The telephone — Opposition to the telephone — Patent disputes — The electric waves — Radio telephony — The spread of broadcasting — The face of the world — Seeing by radio — Waves from space — Fifty years of radio progress.

V   NEW FIRE FOR PROMETHEUS   .   .   182

The revolution in physics — The bricks of the universe — A new type of radiation — The Curies and radium — Splitting the atom — A world-shaking discovery — The Bomb — The sorcerer's apprentice.

VI   ROBOTS EVERYWHERE.   .   .   .   229

The crowning achievement of technology? — "Artificial men with a little intelligence . . ." — Robots everywhere — Calculating machines — Machines with consciousness? — The automatic factory — Automation, with or without tears? — Visions.

v

Chapter   Page
VII   PENETRATION INTO SPACE 261
      The Sputnik — The consequences — The road into space —
      Project Vanguard — What does science gain? — Future trends
      — Feelings in space — The American satellites — Where will it
      end?

VIII THE RACE TO THE STARS 304
      First steps with rockets — Relativistic flight and photon rockets
      — The photon-rocket controversy — We need not give up.

      POSTSCRIPT   333

      BIBLIOGRAPHY 337

      INDEX OF NAMES 345

LIST OF PHOTOGRAPHIC ILLUSTRATIONS

Facing page

Erecting the Obelisk in St. Peter's Square, Rome, in 1586. (The Mansell Collection, London) 14

Trevithick's tram engine of 1803. (Crown Copyright, Science Museum, London) 15

The opening of the Stockton and Darlington Railway in 1825. (Crown Copyright, Science Museum, London) 30

The 'Puffing Billy' at work at a colliery in 1813. (Science Museum, London) 31

The Alweg Monorail, an experimental installation near Cologne. (Alweg) 31

The first Benz car of 1885–6. (Daimler-Benz) . . 62

The first Daimler car of 1885–6. (Daimler-Benz) . . 62

The third Rover prototype of a gas-turbine powered car. (Rover Gas Turbines Ltd.) 62

A Scottish motor rally, held at Selkirk in 1901. (A. R. Edwards & Son, Selkirk) 63

A poster from the early days of ballooning. (Crown Copyright Reserved) 78

R.101, Britain's last dirigible airship. (*Flight*) . . 79

The end of the German airship 'Hindenburg'. (Associated Press) 79

The Lockheed 'Starfighter' F.104. (Lockheed) . . 94

Testing a Comet IV by the water-tank method. (The De Havilland Aircraft Co. Ltd.) 95

The Comet IV, a triumph of engineering skill. (The De Havilland Aircraft Co. Ltd.) 95

Flight refuelling of a Valiant bomber by a Valiant tanker. (Vickers Ltd.) 110

The De Havilland 'Spectre' rocket motor on test. (The De Havilland Engine Co. Ltd.) 111

Facing page

Wind-tunnel testing at the Royal Aircraft Establishment, Bedford. (Crown Copyright Reserved) . . . 111

Studio No. 1 at the B.B.C., Savoy Hill, in 1928. (The British Broadcasting Corporation) 142

King George V making his Christmas broadcast from Sandringham in 1934. (*The Times*) . . . 142

The original Baird television apparatus as used in 1925. (Crown Copyright, Science Museum, London) . . 143

The first Telefunken experimental television unit of 1926. (Telefunken) 143

An outside broadcast television camera at the 1936 Olympic Games in Berlin. (Telefunken) . . . 158

A modern studio camera. (The British Broadcasting Corporation) 158

Smaller and smaller valves. (Telefunken) . . . 159

Progressive reduction in the size of rocket packages. (The Author) 159

A printed-circuit television receiver. (Telefunken) . 159

An early spark transmitter used by Marconi in 1897. (Marconi's Wireless Telegraph Co. Ltd.) . . . 190

The huge Jodrell Bank radio-telescope. (Aero Films Ltd.) 190

Rocket observation and remote control aerials. (U.S. Information Service) 191

Rocket tracking aerials. (U.S. Information Service) . 191

An aerial view of London Airport. (Fairey Air Surveys Ltd. and Hilger & Watts Ltd.) 206

The radar display of London Airport in the control tower. (Decca Radar Ltd.) 206

Calder Hall, the world's first full-scale atomic power station. (U.K. Atomic Energy Authority) . . 207

General view of the charging deck of No. 1 reactor at Calder Hall. (U.K. Atomic Energy Authority) . 222

Facing page

Loading fuel elements into the machine which lowers
them into the core of the reactor. (U.K. Atomic
Energy Authority) 222

Adjusting a vacuum pump inside the magnet of a one-
fourth size working model of the 10,000-ton bevatron
at the University of California. (U.S. Information
Service) 223

The control panel of the synchrocyclotron at the Joint
Nuclear Research Institute at Dubna near Moscow.
(*Soviet Weekly*) 238

Series production of Atar turbojet engines. (*La Photo-
thèque*, Paris) 239

A Beta thickness gauge for testing steel strip. (U.K.
Atomic Energy Authority) 239

Automation; an in-line transfer machine for making
crankshafts. (The Austin Motor Co. Ltd.) . . 254

Punched paper tape for programming a fully automatic
machine. (U.S. Information Service) . . . 255

The earth's first artificial satellite, Sputnik I. (*Soviet
Weekly*) 270

A view of a satellite showing the interior closely packed
with miniaturised instruments. (U.S. Information
Service) 270

Testing a Vanguard satellite. (U.S. Information Service) 270

Sputnik III, the largest man-made satellite. (*Soviet
Weekly*) 271

Pioneer III installed on its carrier rocket at Cape Canaveral. (U.S. Information Service) 271

A Vanguard rocket on its launching pad at Cape Canaveral. (U.S. Information Service) 302

The Black Knight at Farnborough. (Crown Copyright
Reserved) 303

The Thunderbird surface-to-air guided weapon on its
automatic launcher. (The English Electric Co. Ltd.) 318

Man on the threshold of space; a photograph taken by
Major David Simons from his balloon at a height of
over 50,000 feet. (Associated Press) . . . 319

PREFACE

THE successive stages in man's technical progress are readily associated with particular well-known periods in his historical development: fire . . . writing . . . the wheel . . . sails . . . bronze . . . iron . . . water power . . . steam . . . explosives . . . electricity . . . light alloys . . . wireless . . . television . . . nuclear energy . . . automation . . . flight . . . rockets . . . space travel . . .

In any age, people view each major discovery or achievement as the inventor's final answer to an old question. Real 'progress' is only achieved when certain problems, some of them centuries old, have been solved.

Wherever we can penetrate the darkness which hides the early history of mankind, we find traces of astonishing technical achievements. Remember, for instance, such examples as the gigantic age-old stone monuments, the Hanging Gardens of Babylon, and the clay tablets, weapons, jewellery, fortifications, palaces, burial chambers, ships and tools unearthed by archæologists — and then think of the most outstanding discovery of all — the wheel.

These technical achievements presuppose technical means such as fire, tools for working hard stone or the finest jewellery, and levers and rollers to move heavy weights.

Very little is known of the science and technology of those days. We do not know who discovered the lever, the roller or the wheel. Nor can we say when these fundamental achievements of man's brain and hand became the daily tools of his craft; the wheel must have been 'discovered' and forgotten again many times.

How often was the lever reintroduced, or the inclined plane — which eventually gave rise to the screw — employed, before they were generally accepted?

For various reasons man's ideas did, nevertheless, triumph and his efforts throughout the ages did ultimately take effect, although only slowly at first. His artifacts furthered and supported his authority and glorified him in the wielding of it. The

development of a kind of everyday technology was therefore
directed to the construction of houses, to the manufacture of
clothes as a protection against the elements, to the manufacture
of weapons for hunting or for defence against enemies — human
or animal. This emphasis on means of survival led man to
change the world around him in many ways.

We live in an artificial technological world from which it is
now virtually impossible to escape, since it provides all the
material aids to our existence, whether they be clothing, houses,
lighting, heating, cooling, air-conditioning and sanitation, or
supplies of drinking water, gas, electricity, vitamins, medicines
or vaccines.

*   *   *

Neither do we know anything of the pattern of thinking of
those early 'technologists'. It is probable that they observed
and copied animals and natural phenomena, unceasingly seeking to perfect the knowledge gained and the methods derived
thereby; chance discoveries, laborious trials and the association
of ideas all contributed to this process. Many advances must
have been due to the creative powers of ingenious inventors and
thinkers who opposed the inertia of the traditionalist and un-
adventurous. In this way they assisted the gradual unfolding of
what we now know as science and technology.

Technology, in the modern sense, originated in the 17th century, when men like Johannes Kepler and Galileo Galilei
advocated the measurement of natural processes and the deriva-
tion of laws from such measurements as the proper field of the
natural sciences, and so prepared the way for experimental
science. Once natural laws had been formulated, they were increasingly used to replace investigation by trial and error, and
soon came to determine the limits of possible technical achievement.

Innumerable examples can be given of the advances achieved
by thus establishing technology on a scientific basis. The baro-
meter led directly to the suction pump, the law of the pendulum
to the pendulum clock, and Kepler's law of planetary motion to
the balance movement in clocks; the vacuum pump gave rise to
the principle of the steam engine, Faraday's law of induction
was the forerunner of Werner Siemens' dynamo. Hertzian

waves made wireless telegraphy possible, and the theory of gravitation preceded space rockets — to name only a few.

The concept of applied research developed in a relatively short time. Co-operation between the research worker and the designer became closer and they could no longer afford to ignore their mutual dependence; for, while the research worker studies the new territories he can conquer by technical means, the technologist can do nothing in opposition to the natural laws formulated by the scientist. Indeed, fundamental research cannot proceed without large-scale technical apparatus, such as is now indispensable for probing the structure of the atomic nucleus or studying thermonuclear reactions, or in the development of radio-astronomy.

Confident assertions are frequently made regarding the future, and the progress of technology, because research has already revealed the foundations of such advances, which are based on a new pattern of scientific thinking. As Dr. Walter Gerlach wrote in 1956: "The key is the quantum theory of light, which governs the direct transformation of radiant energy into electric energy and the photo-chemical reactions which make use of the sun's rays, whether in the test-tube or in the organism. Both these effects have been known for a long time, but modern thinking — aided by the quantum theory — has turned a mass of observations into a fruitful field of research for the future."

Predictions of this kind are solidly founded and bear no relation to those fantastic dreams, whose authors have ignored hard-won scientific knowledge, preferring to give free rein to their imagination. For centuries, innovators and traditionalists have opposed each other; today the possibility of transforming the world around us by material inventions has turned this opposition into a conflict over technology.

Most of us are directly affected by the impact of technology on our homes and on agriculture. The historian Jacob Burckhardt, who cannot be considered as whole-heartedly favourable to a technicalised life, wrote in the 19th century: "I wish that everything that can may be mechanised as quickly as possible, so as to give man more power and liberty of mind to devote to higher things."

"Technology is a demon, which destroys everything human," said its opponents. "The human spirit cannot withstand this

demon and will be conquered by it, like the sorceror's apprentice, who could not control the powers he called up."

A few years after the First World War, Friedrich Dessauer
began his campaign against the widespread misunderstandings
regarding the possibilities, intentions and limitations of technology. "Is it really devilish," he wrote in 1956, "that technology should provide a proper standard of living for millions
of men? Thirty years ago, when I wrote my *Philosophy of
Technology*, I calculated how many slaves we should need to
maintain our living standard without motors. At that time the
figure was 2,000 to 2,500 million, but today it would be twice
as many."

In other words, if we had, without motors, to maintain production, to keep our trains running and to ensure our water
supplies and lighting, 2,000 million human beings would have
to pass their lives turning wheels and lifting or dragging loads.

In the past, many millions did, in fact, do just this. "They
are now freed," says Dessauer, "technology having relieved
mankind from some of that degrading servitude which made
use of only his lowest capacities, stultifying thereby his higher
powers. The microscope alone has revealed so much that, in
one century, far more persons have been kept alive than were
killed in two World Wars."

Oswald Spengler, in 1931, described man, in his book *Man
and Technology*, as "a little creator in opposition to nature, en-
slaved by his own creations. The beast of prey has trapped
itself, and all man's handiwork is a proof of it."

In the Second World War, Friedrich Jünger analysed technology from a cultural and philosophical viewpoint, expressing
his outspoken opposition, in his *Perfection of Technology*, in the
following terms: "Even the smallest technical operation requires more power than it yields . . . It is wasteful exploitation
such as the world has not seen before . . . Technical processes
no longer allow of any leisure. The philanthropist who, in the
era of technological progress, deplored the slaves at the treadmill, is a fool if he cannot see that this progress is only leading
to the erection of a treadmill of enormous dimensions."

Luigi Pirandello says in his novel, *Cranks*: "This is the
triumph of folly. So much genius and so much zeal is devoted
to the creation of this monstrous thing, which ought to remain

a tool, but instead becomes our master. The machine, which knows no rest, will swallow up our life and soul."

                    *   *   *

It is difficult to discover the deeper reasons for this hostility to technology, if we try to look beyond the eternal conflict between the old and the new, between the conservative and the innovator, between the past and the future. Among the major causes we may find scepticism, honest doubt, ignorance, error, vanity, self-opinionation, fear of the unknown and inertia, and often no more than the spirit of 'what was good enough for my grandparents is good enough for me'. The superficial judgment and condemnation of the latest achievements of science and technology are often based on ideas of the 'good old days' which contrast with over-optimistic views of progress, particularly those held in the 19th century.

Of course, it would be naïve to ask how we would fare if we had to live — as did our forbears — in rooms without window panes, freezing cold in winter or with closed shutters keeping out the light, with only smoky pine shavings to give a dim light. What if we had to live in a world without electricity or gas, with no water mains, no railways, no cars, neither cinema nor radio nor television, and that not only for a short holiday, but summer and winter, year after year, our whole life through? After all, that life was as familiar and as natural to those who lived it as our modern life is to us, however great the difference between the two. We must not imagine that the people who led such lives felt as we would if we were transported from our modern world into those — far from good — old days.

There are plenty of objective indications as to what the good old days really were like and how much better we live in our technical era. Machines and motors, which have only existed for the last 200 years, have gradually eliminated the enormous discrepancy between demand and possible production. In this respect, technical progress has shown man for the first time that poverty is not inescapable, but is only an inconvenience which can be done away with. Technical advances have increased the chances of survival for mankind as a whole. Whereas, before 1600, the population of the world increased very slowly, after that time it rose quickly, and since the beginning of the 19th

century its growth has been so rapid that it has tripled in the
last 150 years. This was only made possible by considerable
improvements in living conditions.

Moreover, the average expectation of life has changed. In
the Bronze Age, some 4,000 years ago, it was less than 20 years,
and rose — over a period of 3,750 years — very slowly to 35
years. Since then it has, in a little more than 200 years,
increased to nearly 70 years.

Many similar facts can be quoted: body size, a rising level of
sporting records, our highly-developed living conditions, our
rising consumption of calories, increased interest in reading and
large editions of books; attendance at theatres, concerts and
other cultural activities has expanded greatly and there are far
greater opportunities for self-education. These very rapid developments have taken place only most recently because technical achievements have freed a great deal of man's mental
energy. Professor Otto Kraemer describes the present situation
as follows: "Nowadays our slaves come from the plug in the
wall. We consume more kilowatt-hours, every one of us — low
and high — than were available to a Roman with 30 or 40
slaves at his command." This development began once man
learned to utilise the strength of other creatures to draw wagons
and ploughs or drag loads for him, as the term horse-power,
which we apply to our machines, still reminds us.

No one can say what point we would have reached today
without the eternal conflict between the innovator and the
traditionalist. If the progressive inventor had not been constantly opposed by the conservatives, the history of technology
would present a chaotic picture. Had the traditionalists always
carried the day — and there were long periods in history when
they did so — we would today perhaps not have progressed far
beyond the discovery of the lever, the roller and the wheel.
Without the conservative we would have had chaos, but without
the innovator the world would have stood still — not indeed the
physical world of the astronomer, but the world of man's
making. The history of technology is full of examples of this
incessant action and reaction, to which we owe the pattern of
our modern life, if not our very existence.

For many centuries man worked first with his hands, later
with the aid of the beasts he tamed and made his servants. Not

200 years ago he made a significant step in his development, no less important than that which, millennia before, brought Stone Age man out of his cave for the first time, to build houses and till the land. This turning-point was reached with the development of a device without which our modern world would be unthinkable, and which we perhaps take far too much for granted — the steam engine.

"The steam engine produces noises which hinder reflection and greatly damages human health by poisoning the air."

Opponents of the steam engine, about 1800.

"This cast-iron monster makes manufactures dearer and interferes with trade."

Berlin manufacturers at the beginning of the 19th century.

CHAPTER I

MACHINES IN PLACE OF MUSCLES

Machines instead of men — The revolt of the workmen — The end of the 'abhorred vacuum' — "Down with the fire engine!" — A very important document — Watt begins to make money — "He multiplied the power of men"

ON 4th July 1776, the thirteen rebellious English colonies in Northern America proclaimed their independence, and constituted themselves 'States'. While the whole world watched the first great war for self-determination and Britain lost for ever her colonies in North America, Matthew Boulton and James Watt were founding a machine works in Soho, near Birmingham, with the intention of building steam engines. These two men were about to introduce something which was to make England richer than any of her colonies had ever been able to do.

Step by step man's inventiveness had been applied to improving his living conditions, and now he was, by the use of machines, to multiply the power of his muscles. At the beginning of this long development was one of the finest 'tools' ever conceived by Nature — the human hand. As he used his first, primitive tools of wood and stone, man learned how to concentrate his forces; by applying the bodily strength of several men to one task he was able to increase his efforts. Then came the lever, the roller and the wheel. In order to pool forces in this way, it was necessary to understand each other, and thus, hand, language and tool were brought together at the outset, till they made it possible for man to modify the face of the Earth.

*   *   *

I

The rapid technical developments of the 19th century — and even more of the 20th — lead us to forget that mechanical engineering has for centuries been satisfied with simple, conventional, well-tried apparatus. Even in the 16th century large-scale, difficult technical operations could only be carried out by the skilfully concerted efforts of numbers of men.

In 1586 Pope Sixtus V commissioned the Italian architect Domenico Fontana to move — from a place behind St. Peter's to a site in the Piazza San Pietro — an obelisk, weighing 327 tons, which had been brought to Rome from Heliopolis, under Caligula, forty years after the birth of Christ. This was an impressive engineering achievement, though we would today admire the organisation rather than the technique.

A special authority from the Pope made the operation possible, almost one thousand men being employed, as well as over one hundred horses. "We, Sixtus V, empower Domenico Fontana, architect to the Holy Apostolic Palace, to make use of any hand-worker or workman, and of his goods, whatever they be, and if need be to compel them to lend or sell them unto him, for the duration of this work of transport . . . And that he may likewise use all the instruments and goods of the building of St. Peter's, with its servants and officers, that they clear the place around the obelisk within a given time, to bring it thither and to make all ready for this task. That he may, at need, raze the houses near the obelisk, albeit the compensation therefor must be determined beforehand . . ."

Fontana calculated the whole operation very carefully, and decided that it would need 40 winches with good ropes and pulley-blocks, as well as 5 levers — consisting of beams 42 feet long — to lift and move the obelisk.

The experts were sceptical as to the practicability of the operation, as Fontana himself described in his final report, published in 1590: "When my discovery was made known, almost all the experts doubted whether one could cause so many winches to work in conjunction to lift so great a weight. They said that the winches would not pull uniformly, that the most heavily loaded winches would break and thus disorder arise and the machinery be brought into confusion . . ."

Since the Pope threatened excommunication and heavy punishment to anyone who dared hinder the work or trouble

Fontana and his men, the task was completed in spite of all the doubters.

On 30th April 1586, two hours before daybreak, the lowering of the great monument was begun. "Since much people came together to see so uncommon a sight, the streets were barred to avoid disorder, and notice given that none save the workmen might pass the barrier. He who should force his way would be punished with death."

The watch stood by to execute this order immediately, and so the crowd gathered to see this "remarkable undertaking" looked on in silence. At a trumpet signal the 5 levers and 40 winches began to move, under the efforts of 907 men and 75 horses. "At the first movement," wrote Fontana, "it seemed that the earth shook, and the frame groaned as all the timbers became compressed by the weight . . ." After eight days' hard work the obelisk was safely in its framework, none of the workmen having been hurt; the tension eased, and Fontana was conducted home with "drums and trumpets".

On 10th September of the same year — more than four months after the lowering — the operation of re-erecting the obelisk was commenced, and seventeen days later it stood on its new site "300 ells away". The task was over, after much toil, but mankind was accustomed to such labours.

*   *   *

Even in the 17th century man's technical methods were archaic; he had at his disposal simple means, such as water-wheels, windmills, treadmills and winches, to harness water and wind, or utilise the power of his own muscles or those of his domestic animals. In undertaking large-scale technical operations, he tried to simplify the existing means and to 'organise' the work, as in the case of the obelisk at Rome.

Equally typical of the time was the huge water-works at Marly, which fed the fountains at Versailles. An engineering book of 1739 describes this gigantic installation as follows: "It would seem that no machine has ever been built which has made so much noise as the machine at Marly."

Fourteen water-wheels, each 40 feet across and driven by the waters of the Seine, actuated 221 pumps, which lifted the water in stages through a total height of 526 feet. The power of this exceedingly expensive plant was some 80 horse-power, the same rating as that of a $3\frac{1}{2}$-ton lorry 220 years later.

*   *   *

MACHINES INSTEAD OF MEN

Fontana's great but relatively inefficient concentration of human and animal muscle-power and the gigantic 'machine' at Marly indicate the boundaries of technology at that time, when men were used far more widely than machines.

Nevertheless, early in the 17th century Francis Bacon began to call for a new science which should have as its object "to endow human life with new powers and inventions". In 1627, he attempted to foresee the future, in his picture of "Nova Atlantis". "We have also engine-houses, where are prepared engines and instruments for all sorts of motions. There we imitate and practise to make swifter motions than any you have, either out of your muskets or any engine that you have . . . We imitate also flights of birds; we have some degrees of flying in the air. We have ships and boats for going under water and brooking of seas, also swimming-girdles and supporters. We have divers curious clocks and other like motions of return, and some perpetual motions. We imitate also motions of living creatures by images of men, beasts, birds, fishes and serpents; we have also a great number of other various motions, strange for equality, fineness and subtilty." Thus Bacon envisaged entire branches of 20th-century technology as forming an enormously extended field of human activities, including factories, ships, submarines, vehicles, aircraft and robots.

Some 250 years later the Austrian poet Adalbert Stifter wrote: "What will happen when we can transmit news with lightning speed or travel ourselves rapidly to the furthest corners of the world, and transport heavy loads at the same speed? . . . I am convinced that in time we shall be able to do this. How far this progress will extend, how it will come, and how it will end, are things which human intelligence cannot fathom; but it seems certain to me that a new way of thinking and a new manner of life will come, even though all that is deepest in man's physical and spiritual nature remains unchanged." Since then, science and technology have largely transformed our world, but how much opposition they have had to overcome before reaching this point!

THE REVOLT OF THE WORKMEN

Only five years after the founding of Boulton and Watt's factory in Birmingham, the first steam engine to operate continuously in Germany was installed. The component parts had been made separately in workshops all over Prussia, and its erection created great interest. It had an output of 75 horsepower, and was in service until 1845.

The introduction of this new-fangled steam engine met with much opposition. When a 'fire engine' — as these machines were then called — was to be built at the Royal Porcelain Works at Berlin, there was great public indignation. The objectors' spokesman was a Freiherr von der Recke, who is said to have protested in the following terms: "A machine driven day and night by coal is now to be erected. Who can tell how many more such inventions and discoveries will be put into our hands? Can we afford to undermine our health and life by the constant noxious coal fumes? I am responsible to protect the health of my family and to preserve my goods, by doing all in my power to keep this calamity from our house."

This protest served to defer the installation of the engine for twelve years.

About ten years later, the Westphalian joiner and engineer Franz Dinnendahl had a similar experience, when he began to construct steam engines. "The entire staff of the Brandenburg Mining Office, even foreign mining men who had seen steam engines, doubted whether I could succeed. Some of them vowed that it was impossible, whilst others said that, although all was well with me while I stayed a simple workman, I would now ruin myself by interfering in things which were beyond me . . ."

*   *   *

Many contemporaries of these pioneers of the early days of the Machine Age must have felt — consciously or unconsciously — that the days of the 'poor workman' were numbered. "No historian," writes Friedrich Dessauer, "can imagine, much less prove, that the ordinary man had fared well in the past. Without exaggerating, we can say that there was a kind of enforced lack of necessary things, in most cases amounting to poverty, from which only a few groups were free, and it is largely they who gave us the picture of the past which is taught us. Think for a moment how many of Grandmother's tales began 'There was once a poor workman, a poor farmer, a poor wood-cutter . . .' Does that indicate that they were the good old days for the majority of people? Our idea of those days is like our stories of our childhood, in which we only speak of what was good and beautiful, and our children are rightly indignant that Father should mention only the good reports he had at school."

As the steam engine gradually spread, the revolt of the workmen began — the first industrial revolution in history. It started principally in England, which at that time — thanks to the fortunate concurrence of several factors — had a leading place. The loss of her North American colonies had less profound effects than did the establishment of Boulton and Watt's works at Soho. This factory ensured that Britain's mines and her growing industry had immense quantities of power at their disposal, and she rapidly became the leading industrial country, dominating the world markets with an ever-increasing variety of products.

The germ of the Industrial Revolution came from those men who had studied the natural sciences, whose object had been to combat poverty and to eliminate the shortages of fuel, food and means of transport. In fact, after the introduction of the steam engine, the face of England altered, decade by decade, but not without growing pains. The living conditions of large masses of human beings cannot be changed overnight. What use was it to know that it was not the steam engine but the old social order which was responsible for the misery of the masses? So the feeble wrath of those about to be freed from want and misery was vented on the machines; in 1812 the British Parliament was forced to apply the death penalty for machine-breaking.

Was there anyone then who could look into the future with confidence that progress would be made? Did the innovators who had begun the transformation see that help was near?

In 1830 Goethe wrote: "The advance of machines troubles

and frightens me; it rolls forward slowly, like a storm, but its course is fixed; soon it will reach us, and then break . . ."

Most people of the time were frightened, like Goethe, over-looking the fact that the whole purpose behind the machines was to lighten or eliminate their heavy labour.

THE END OF THE 'ABHORRED VACUUM'

In 1844 a German encyclopædia contained the following entry, headed 'Steam Engines': "The discovery is claimed by several countries; the first wide use and the majority of improvements we owe, without a doubt, to the British and to the Americans. Robert Stuart, in his *History of Steam Engines*, and Arago, in an *Examination of the Question of Priority in the Discovery of Steam Engines*, state that, as early as 1543, the Spanish captain

The Aeolipile.

Blasco de Garay showed a steamship of his devising in Barcelona Harbour; he kept his secret to himself, but it was probably based on an adaptation of the steam ball . . ."

The steam ball was the age-old device utilising the fact that steam issuing from a narrow tube sets up a thrust by reaction. A theory regarding the origin of the wind was based on this fact, and the ball was therefore called the 'Aeolipile'. The Egyptians are said to have gone one stage further by using the issuing steam to produce simple movements. It is unfortunate that we know so very little about this, since — if certain historians are right in their assumptions — we should have evidence of the first mechanical application of the reaction produced by a jet of steam. It is, however, certain that about 100 years after the birth of Christ, the Alexandrian mechanician Hero, who had achieved fame by his air-driven and water-powered de-

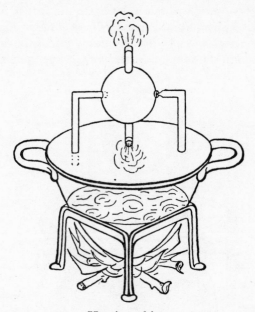

Hero's turbine.

vices, suggested a way of utilising the energy of a steam jet. In his experiments he had observed that steam issuing from a tube occasioned a pressure acting in the opposite direction. He therefore attached to a water-filled globe two tubes, bent at right-angles and facing in opposed directions. When the water was heated, the jets of steam caused the globe to rotate. This elegant physical and mechanical experiment was never put to practical use. The fuel consumption exceeded the power produced; in modern terms, the Aeolipile was inefficient. Nevertheless, this simple apparatus — Hero's globe — was the first practical demonstration of the reaction principle.

*　　　*　　　*

The steam engine was still a long way off. In 1562 the preacher Mathesius prayed for a man who "raised water with fire and air", which seems to point to the use of steam power for pumping.

The German engineer de Caus, who worked for the Palatinate Princes at Heidelberg, described in his book — published at Frankfurt in 1615 and entitled *The Reasons for the Moving Forces in Different Machines* — a steam engine of his own design, which was simply a modified Hero's turbine. The steam issuing from the pipes struck the paddles on a sort of turbine wheel, rotating the wheel, which drove a gear system. The inventor is believed to have been put into a madhouse by Cardinal Richelieu, because of 'the madness of his ideas'; however, other chroniclers say that he returned to France in 1619 and died there. Obviously he fared as almost all innovators — before and since — have done, when they have tried to change the conventional world with their inventions: he was treated as mad. Even if he was not left to die in an asylum, the bare rumour tells us enough of the difficulties he met as an engineer in a world without engineering.

Three years later Giovanni Branca described this steam turbine, and, as early as 1630, David Ramsay patented a steam engine in Britain. In his *Century of Inventions* published in 1655 (the manuscript is in the British Museum), the Marquis of Worcester described a steam engine which he himself used to throw a jet of water to a height of 40 feet; he called this the "most remarkable work in the world", although his contemporaries took little notice of him. Nevertheless, he was granted a patent for his design in 1663. Twenty years later Sir Samuel Morland submitted to Louis XIV a proposal to lift water by steam, complete with tables and drawings.

It was clear that the time was ripe for the machine which was soon to stir the world and change it completely. As early as 1666, the Dutch physicist and mathematician Christiaan Huyghens — who discovered the pendulum and improved the telescope — had suggested to Colbert, the French Minister, tests to compare the power of gunpowder and of steam, "To undertake experiments in a vacuum (using the air-pump) and elsewhere, and determine the weight of the air." These experiments led eventually to the development of a new motive machine. The allusion to the air-pump referred to the work of the German physicist Otto von Guericke, who in 1661 showed that a piston driven by air pressure into an exhausted cylinder could perform work. Guericke exhausted the cylinder by means of the air-pump he had invented. After another three years — scientific results were not so rapidly publicised then — this piston of Guericke's became known. Huyghens made the suggestions cited above two years later still.

We are apt to take these developments for granted, but in fact they were epoch-making. They led to an intellectual revolution, which liberated men from scholasticism and taught them to think for themselves. Until then it was Aristotle's natural science which had stood supreme and unchallenged. For almost 2,000 years the Greek philosopher — a pupil of Plato — had dominated the scene with his teaching. He held that there were only four elements in Nature — Earth, Air, Fire and Water; he also taught that Nature abhorred a vacuum, a principle which governed all thinking and precluded the invention of a steam engine.

Would the steam engine have been discovered, and the history of the world have been different, had it not been for the teaching of Aristotle and the principle of 'abhorring a vacuum'? It may be pointless to speculate in this way, and yet it is not without interest, for the philosopher's work was almost lost. The whole of his writings passed uncollated to his pupil Theophrastus; the collection was later hidden in a cellar in Alexandria, where it was finally found, although partly spoiled, and given to Apellikon of Teos. The manuscript copies made — arbitrarily altered and added to — were taken to Rome after the fall of Athens. As Christian philosophy grew in importance, the influence of Aristotle's teaching waned, so that the early scholastics knew no more than a few of his writings on logic. Only several hundred years later did the remaining logical works, followed by his writings on the natural sciences, become known again, so that — taken with the Arabic commentaries — they regained influence. Thomas Aquinas, theologian and philosopher, finally established Aristotle as the highest philosophical authority of the age.

The spirit of free knowledge which was now increasing in importance could no longer be reconciled with Aristotelian philosophy. But before that Helmont had to prove that Air and Water are not indivisible elements, but mixtures of very different components; Torricelli must investigate air pressure and thus once and for all put an end to the idea of the 'abhorred vacuum', Otto von Guericke must confirm and reinforce in practice this new and revolutionary theory.

The idea that Nature abhors a vacuum was swept away, and the way opened to a radical transformation of the world by means of the machine.

"DOWN WITH THE FIRE ENGINE!"

The 'Kunsthaus' in Cassel, built in 1605 as the first permanent theatre in Germany, contains a memorial plaque bearing the following inscription:

> "Denis Papin, discoverer of the steam engine, successfully demonstrated the first large-scale application of steam on this spot, in June 1706, in the presence of Karl, Landgrave of Hesse."

This machine was the third built by the Huguenot refugee from Blois, then Professor of Mathematics at Marburg University. He had become familiar with the problems of the steam engine during his work with Huyghens, who had intended to build a gunpowder motor, but met with insuperable difficulties, because it was found impossible to produce an adequate vacuum. Moreover, the handling of the powder was very dangerous.

In 1690 Papin published his first design for a steam engine, based on evacuating the cylinder by condensation of the steam. "Since water has the property that it is changed by fire into vapour . . . and can then be condensed very readily by cooling, it should not be difficult to construct machines which would produce the complete vacuum which we tried unsuccessfully to attain by gunpowder, with a moderate heat and at low cost." These were the words in which Papin wrote to Count Philip Ludwig von Sinzendorff.

Papin's first two designs were no more than very simple heat-power machines, consisting essentially of a large steel-plate cylinder containing a movable piston. The steam raised in the vessel served to produce the desired vacuum, power being pro-

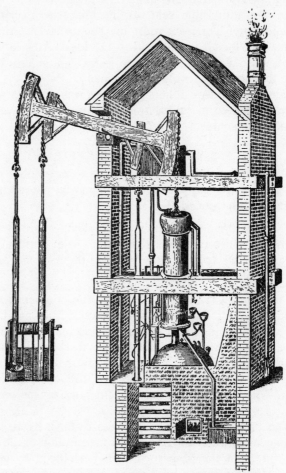

Newcomen's 1712 steam engine.

vided by the external air pressure, which thrust the piston down into the cylinder as the steam condensed. The laborious trials undertaken by Papin with these primitive designs were un-satisfactory. His friends and helpers were sceptical about these unpromising experiments. It is true that he had already become known as the discoverer of a method of softening and decomposing bones and sinews — which do not dissolve at normal boiling-point — by increasing the heat. This was Papin's 'digester', but would his machine work too?

On 25th July 1698 Captain Thomas Savery had been granted the first patent for the application of steam power to a number of machines, and a year later showed a working model to the Royal Society. In 1705 Leibniz gave Papin a sketch of Savery's steam pump, which enabled him to establish by 1707 a complete theory of the steam machine, to which he attached a drawing of his own design for such an apparatus. The British inventor had already used separate containers for raising the steam and for the useful power; in modern terms, he had a separate boiler and cylinder. The water to be pumped was drawn into the pear-shaped cylinder by condensation of the steam and then expelled — after the valve setting had been changed — by the injection of steam.

Savery's machine was very uneconomic, since the steam and cold water were in direct contact, but it did act as a pump. Papin — asked by the Landgrave of Hesse to make him a similar device for transporting water — applied the principles developed by Savery, but introduced marked improvements which eliminated the weaknesses of the Englishman's machine. He paid no heed to the mockery of his contemporaries, but worked away as though he had been an engineer all his life, till he succeeded, in spite of the gibe that he was a 'steam-pot mathematician'.

For the first time in the history of technology, mankind possessed — although without realising at first the tremendous advance made — a thermal power machine with a steam boiler and cylinder, containing a reciprocating piston; this was the first direct-acting piston steam engine. In tests begun in the summer of 1706, water was pumped to a height of more than 100 feet, although the pipe was not fully watertight.

However, although the French doctor and natural philosopher had succeeded in a bold and unprecedented venture, he had not reckoned with the pettiness of his critics, who spoke of the devil and quoted the still-remembered 'abhorred vacuum' to prove the impossibility and madness of the experiments made in Cassel. To make matters worse, the Landgrave's interest in Papin's work soon faded, so that after a few weeks he had to stop his trials of the first steam engine built in Germany.

*   *   *

Papin realised quite early that his machine could do more than pump water. In 1698 he wrote to Leibniz: "I am convinced that this discovery, if properly developed, can be of very great service . . . I firmly believe that it can be used for many other purposes than only to lift water. I have built a small model of a cart which can be driven by this power."

Think of it, a steam-driven vehicle in those days! Papin himself was well aware of the difficulties in the way of its realisation: ". . . I believe that the irregularities and curves of the main roads will make the successful application of this invention to vehicles very difficult, but I have hopes that I can succeed with a steam ship fairly soon . . ."

Even before the experiments in Cassel were stopped, Papin told Leibniz: "The further I advance, the more I esteem this invention, which must in theory infinitely increase man's powers . . . I believe I can say without exaggeration that with this machine one man can do the work of a hundred . . ."

Since the Landgrave of Hesse made it quite clear to the indefatigable inventor that his games with a steam engine for lifting water were tiresome, Papin decided to go to Britain, particularly as he hoped to find a works better able to manufacture the cylinders for his machine. He intended to travel in his paddle-driven ship, his most precious possession and the repository of all his hopes. Many historians have supposed that Papin wished to drive this ship by steam; he himself denied this, declaring that he did not wish to mix his experiments, but only to study the action of the hand-operated paddles as a beginning.

This decision to go to England was a decisive step in Papin's life. With all his family, and his goods, he left Cassel, but the Rivermen's Guild at Minden had the right to stop the passage of any foreign ship. To avoid difficulties, Papin arranged for a tug from Minden to tow his ship past the town as 'freight'. An excited crowd lined the banks, to see the devilish fire engine, belonging to the mad French doctor, who, having no homeland, was forced to keep on the move. This new thing, which was

Erecting the Obelisk in St. Peter's Square, Rome, in 1586.

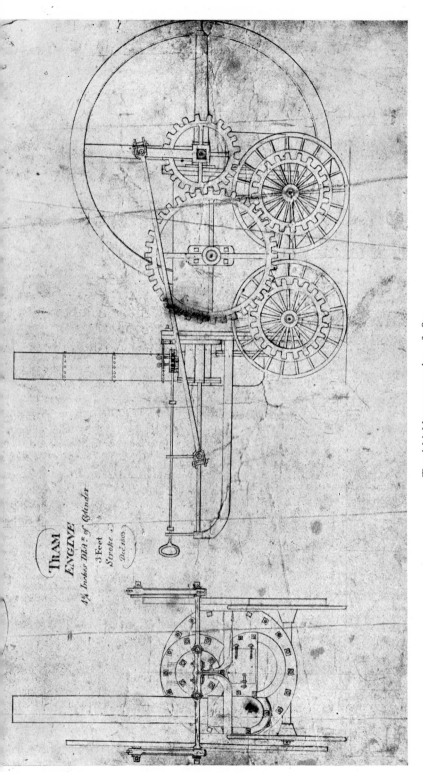

TRAM
ENGINE

1¾ Inches Dia.ʳ of Cylinder

3 Feet

Stroke

Dec. 1803.

Trevithick's tram engine of 1803.

evading their ban, threatened their traditional methods. And then there occurred what had often happened before in man's history; the crowd, egged on by the rivermen, dragged the ship to land and smashed it in pieces.

Papin, having lost ship and possessions, continued his journey. He was coolly received in London, and was not given an opportunity to compare his machine with Savery's. After 1712 no more was heard of him, though some say that in 1714 he died in poverty.

The time was ripe for the new machine, but the men of that time were not ready. No one knows when the discoverer of the steam engine died, or where he was buried.

A VERY IMPORTANT DOCUMENT

Half a century after Papin's miserable death, James Watt received his first patent for a steam engine; this document, one of the most important in the history of invention, cannot be omitted from such a survey as this, and is therefore reproduced in full.

WHEREAS His most Excellent Majesty King George the Third, by His Letters Patent under the Great Seal of Great Britain, bearing date the Fifth day of January, in the ninth year of His reign, did give and grant unto James Watt, of the City of Glasgow, Merchant, his executors, administrators, and assigns, the sole benefit and advantage of making and vending certain engines by him invented for lessening the consumption of steam and fuel in fire engines, within that part of His Majesty's Kingdom of Great Britain called England, the Dominion of Wales and the Town of Berwick-upon-Tweed, and also in His Majesty's Colonies and Plantations abroad, for the term of fourteen years, with a proviso, obliging the said James Watt, by writing under his hand and seal, to cause a particular description of the nature of the said Invention to be inrolled in His Majesty's High Court of Chancery within four months after the date of the said recited Letters Patent: And whereas the said James Watt did, in pursuance of the said proviso, cause a particular description of the said engine to be inrolled in the said High Court of Chancery upon the Twenty-ninth day of April, in the year of our Lord One thousand seven hundred and sixty-nine, which description is in the words and form or to the effect following; that is to say, my method of lessening the consumption of steam, and consequently fuel, in fire engines, consists of the following principles:—First, that vessel in which the powers of steam are to be employed to work the engine, which is called the cylinder in common fire engines, and which I call the steam vessel, must during the whole time the engine is at

C

work be kept as hot as the steam that enters it, first, by enclosing it in a case of wood, or any other materials that transmit heat slowly; secondly, by surrounding it with steam or other heated bodies; and thirdly, by suffering neither water or any other substance colder than the steam to enter or touch it during that time. Secondly, in engines that are to be worked wholly or partially by condensation of steam, the steam is to be condensed in vessels distinct from the steam vessels or cylinders, although occasionally communicating with them; these vessels I call condensers, and whilst the engines are working these condensers ought at least to be kept as cold as the air in the neighbourhood of the engines, by application of water or other cold bodies. Thirdly, whatever air or other elastick vapour is not condensed by the cold of the condenser, and may impede the working of the engine, is to be drawn out of the steam vessels or the condensers by means of pumps wrought by the engines themselves or otherwise. Fourthly, I intend in many cases to employ the expansive force of steam to press on the pistons, or whatever may be used instead of them, in the same manner as the pressure of the atmosphere is now employed in common fire engines; in cases where cold water cannot be had in plenty, the engines may be wrought by this force of steam only, by discharging the steam into the open air after it has done its office (which fourth article the said James Watt declares in a note affixed to the Specification of the said engine should not be understood to extend to any engine where the water to be raised enters the steam vessel itself, or any vessel having an open communication with it). Fifthly, where motions round an axis are required, I make the steam vessels in form of hollow rings or circular channels, with proper inlets and outlets for the steam, mounted on horizontal axles, like the wheels of a water mill; within them are placed a number of valves that suffer any body to go round the channel in one direction only; in these steam vessels are placed weights, so fitted to them as entirely to fill up a part or portion of their channels, yet rendered capable of moving freely in them by means hereinafter mentioned or specified. When the steam is admitted in these engines between these weights and the valves, it acts equally on both, so as to raise the weight to one side of the wheel, and by the reaction on the valves successively to give a circular motion to the wheel, the valves opening in the direction in which the weights are pressed, but not in the contrary; as the steam vessel moves round, it is supplied with steam from the boiler, and that which has performed its office may either be discharged by means of condensers or into the open air. Sixthly, I intend in some cases to apply a degree of cold not capable of reducing the steam to water, but of contracting it considerably, so that the engines shall be worked by the alternate expansion and contraction of the steam. Lastly, instead of using water to render the piston or other parts of the engines air and steam-tight, I employ oils, wax, rosinous bodies, fat of animals, quicksilver, and other metals in their fluid state.

WATT BEGINS TO MAKE MONEY

Legend has it that the idea of the steam engine came to the young Watt as he watched a kettle boiling on the hob, as though it were such a simple matter to invent and construct machines at a time when engineering was in its infancy and the inventor met with nothing but mistrust. Perhaps intuition did help him, but this can very rarely have been the case in his inventive life. Watt had first to master all the knowledge then available regarding the use of steam; moreover, the day of rough-and-ready experiments had passed. The progressive inventor had to be a skilled mechanic before he could successfully construct a machine.

Watt's difficulties began almost on the first day. In London, he had learned to make mathematical instruments and hoped to open a workshop in Glasgow, but the 'Smith's Guild' barred him, because he was not the son of a Glasgow citizen. Fortunately, Watt was able to work in the University laboratories without offending the Guild's rules and regulations so much. The persevering young man lived in the poorest conditions, and his future can scarcely have seemed very bright. He constructed apparatus for the University and for an odd private client or two, meanwhile instructing himself by reading every book he could obtain. In spite of the legendary kettle, he cannot at that time have been thinking of steam engines, but one day chance brought the decisive turning-point in his life.

Glasgow University possessed a steam engine made by Thomas Newcomen, who had been building such machines — then still called 'fire engines' — since 1711. Something was wrong with it and Watt was asked to carry out the repairs. Not only did he discover the fault, he also found the problem which was thenceforth to fill his whole life — steam power.

*   *   *

In 1755 the Colonial War between France and England broke out, while the Seven Years War between Austria and Prussia already threatened. The French social theorist Morelly was calling for the abolition of private property. Ivan Shuvalof was occupied in founding the first Russian University in Moscow, Rousseau was teaching in Paris, Kant in Germany and

Lomonossov in Russia. It was the era of Frederick II, Catherine the Great and Maria Theresa, while Goethe and Schiller, Pestalozzi, Mozart and Beethoven were all unknown.

Children from four to seven years of age were working in the coal and iron mines of Britain, to bring the loosened material to the horse-tramway or to the main shaft. The time when human muscles would gradually be replaced by machines seemed overdue, but no one dreamed what effects these machines would have on their life and work.

Watt soon realised that Newcomen's machine was inefficient.

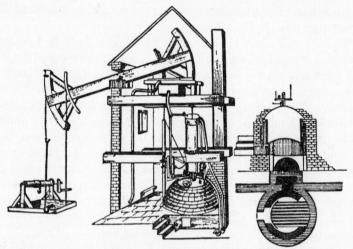

Newcomen's atmospheric machine, 1722.

He began to think about the physical bases of the problem, until he finally discovered the main weakness of the design. When cold water entered the cylinder, the machine was chilled too much; Watt set himself to maintain the cylinder as hot as the injected steam, and to reduce the temperature of the steam on condensation as nearly as possible to the temperature of the surrounding air.

Watt's thoughts and actions during this period impress upon us the creative activity of the human mind. None of his contemporaries had realised what was needed to perfect the steam engine; Watt himself took some five years before he solved the problem by separating the cylinder from the condenser. He

had other difficulties too. A new engine would have cost a great deal, but a bigger, modified machine had to be constructed to confirm his theory. Bad workmanship led to early failures, and when the new steam engine did eventually function, it was badly damaged by unskilful helpers.

On his thirty-fourth birthday, less than a year after receiving the first patent, Watt wrote despairingly to a friend: "Today I enter my thirty-fifth year, and I have not yet done thirty-five pence worth of good in the world."

Worse was to come, for the patron he did at last find, Dr. Roebuck, had to suspend payments, leaving the inventor up to his ears in debt, and with his machine unfinished. Harassed by his creditors and mocked by his friends, Watt was ready to throw his drawings in the fire and give in to those who had pronounced his project impossible. However, he remembered that, years before, he had met Matthew Boulton, the famous machine manufacturer from Birmingham. Boulton was one of the few men, perhaps at that time the only one, with enough vision to recognise the true importance of Watt's patent. In 1843 the *Brockhaus Encyclopædia* said of him: "His long life was devoted to furthering the useful arts and the trade of his homeland; he had much charm and was a man of noble mind."

Whilst still young Boulton had taken over his father's steel works and considerably enlarged it. Now he repaid Dr. Roebuck the money he had advanced and brought Watt to his works in Birmingham. The way now seemed open to transform a design into a machine. But there were still great difficulties to be overcome. The machines used until then could not be simply modified, and Watt and Boulton had to design and build new ones and sell them to the mine owners.

In 1774 the collaborators set up their first new machine at Soho, near Birmingham. The tests and demonstrations were successful and clearly showed the value of the improved machine and very soon the first examples were installed in the Cornish mines. Watt became a partner in Boulton's steam engine works, the first in the world and for many years the best. Although the sceptics were still not silenced, Watt's machines paid him well. He received the equivalent of one third of the coal saved every year by his machines.

For about six years steam engines were used for pumping

water out of mines, and their great advantages remained unknown. The idea of putting them, for example, to driving mills was fairly obvious, but when the water was fed to an ordinary water-wheel after being pumped up, a good deal of its energy was naturally lost. The efficiency of such combinations was very bad. A further big improvement was necessary and Watt introduced it. He first tried out a movement resembling that of the crank on a lathe, but his design was filched and subsequently patented. New experiments gave him the proper solution to the problem. He replaced the beam by a gear system and thus obtained the rotary motion required. After this he devised the regulator, the pressure gauge and many other important accessories. Pierer recorded in his *Dictionary of Sciences*, published in 1836: "This invention made the steam engine suitable for driving ships, spinning and weaving machines, mills and trucks; Watt will be famous in the future for the impulse he gave to steam engineering, undreamed of 50 years ago and whose limits are still unknown."

*   *   *

In all, 134 patents are known to have been taken out in Britain between 1784 and 1880, all dealing with the rotary motion of steam-driven machines. They prepared the way, as it were, for the steam engine's younger relation, the steam turbine. These developments were only beginning towards the end of the 18th century, and Watt's task was to turn the see-saw motion into a rotary motion. It is his success in doing so that has largely been responsible for the sobriquet 'father of the steam engine', although he had only improved the imperfect old 'fire engine' and given it a promising field of application in industry.

While Watt had become a rich and respected man, and his partner Boulton and his friend William Murdoch worked, successfully, to introduce the steam engine, he was still far from being famous. The hindrances, not only from the problem itself, but even more from human opponents, were still considerable.

By 1800, some 500 machines from their factory had already been installed, but on the Continent the resistance of the conservatives was even greater. It is true that since 1785 a Watt

steam engine had been pumping water from a colliery at Mans-
feld, and that the — for those days — remarkable technical
achievements of British factories were much admired in Germany; yet it was only at the beginning of the 19th century that
this machine, which replaced so many men, gradually began to
gain entry into Germany.

Early in that century, Georg Reichenbach — a young Ger-

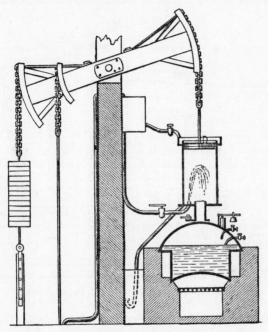

A later model of Newcomen's steam engine.

man engineer — visited Birmingham to study British machine
manufacture. Nowadays he would be called an industrial spy,
and we can easily understand that Boulton and Watt were
friendly, but not particularly pleased with the interest shown by
their guest. Reichenbach was able to see some of the famed
steam engines, before going to Soho. His diary for 1791, most
amusingly written, is in the manuscript collection of the library
at the Deutsches Museum in Munich; he writes: "When I at
last found it and went to my lodging, I was much troubled that
my position was not the best for obtaining information, and that

I was quite alone; nevertheless, I tried to reconcile myself quickly to the situation. Soon I regarded things in a better light, for, unbeknown to Messrs. Boulton and Watt, I managed by a little bribery to get a good opportunity to study the mechanism of the Watt steam engine. For six weeks I worked at my drawings, for I had to hide not only from Boulton but also from all his workmen; for this cause my work gave me in-

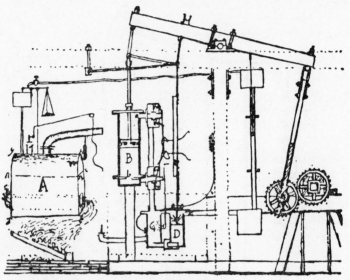

Reichenbach's sketch of Watt's steam engine.

describable trouble; not only could I not question anyone, but dared not even see the machines without permission, to excite no suspicion."

In this somewhat laborious manner Reichenbach completed his famous sketch of the double-acting Watt steam engine with rotary movement. In his diary he recorded: "The machine made 24 strokes a minute. Steam consumption per second without losses 5·04 cu. feet. Valve area 7 sq. inches. Speed of steam entering through valve 104 feet per second . . . Mr. Watt gives the steam enough pressure to balance the atmosphere, plus a water column of 8 feet. That is, the pressure of this steam against a complete vacuum would be equal to the pressure of a column of water of 41 feet, English measure."

Such reports about the new machines must have sounded to the Continentals of the time like the announcements in the 20th century of American and Russian space rockets, or the launching of the first artificial satellites.

* * *

Slowly the steam engine became a widely-used source of power, and a symbol of the machine age which had just begun.

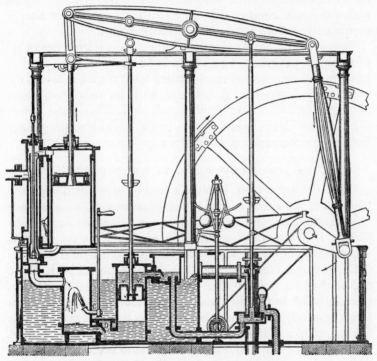

Watt's low-pressure steam engine.

It replaced not only human muscle power but the horse capstan too; in fact, when Watt introduced the term 'horse-power', it was a monument to the horse, which had till then so often been ill-used.

However, one horse-power does not exactly represent the performance of a horse, because the English brewer who, wishing to obtain one of Watt's first steam engines, and attempting to compare the machine with the horse, drove his poor creature to exhaustion. He actually succeeded in carrying 440,000 gallons of water in eight hours; Watt, in turn, defined one horsepower as the work needed to lift 33,000 pounds by one foot in one minute.

In the latter half of his life, Watt was free from financial worries. He lived through the tremendous changes brought about by the new machines, and considerably assisted the training of many mechanics, who travelled throughout the world with the steam engines. He died in 1819; eight years later a monument was erected to him in Birmingham.

Thus it was from England that the steam engine began its triumphant progress. The machine-breakers tried to hold it back, but as time passed man learned what it means to replace muscles by machines. A machine with an output of 1,000 horse-power does the work of 36,000 men. Today the power delivered by all the prime movers in the world is much greater than the performance of the entire population.

"HE MULTIPLIED THE POWER OF MEN"

With the success of Boulton's and Watt's ideas and the triumph of the steam engine in the 19th century, we can leave this branch of engineering in which so dramatic a struggle took place. This was the beginning of mechanical developments which have continued unchecked down to our own day.

Boulton and Watt were hardly able to keep pace with all the orders they received; within fifty years, 10,000 steam engines were installed in Britain alone. But several decades passed before it was fully realised in other countries that this machine was freeing mankind from the heavy burden of physical labour. France bought only 300 of Watt's engines to begin with, and for a long time the machine installed at the Berlin Porcelain factory was the only one in Germany. Again and again the objectors were able to delay or prevent the introduction of the steam engine. One of their arguments ran: "The steam engine produces noises which hinder reflection and greatly damages human health by poisoning the air." The Prussian Minister for Internal Affairs tried, at the King's wish, to disarm all protests by means of a circular, but even the offer to give 'fire engines' to the Berlin manufacturers was refused, as they were convinced that "this cast-iron monster makes manufactures dearer and interferes with trade". It was fifteen years later that the owner of a spinning mill accepted the gift of a second steam engine, because British competition was causing him difficulty

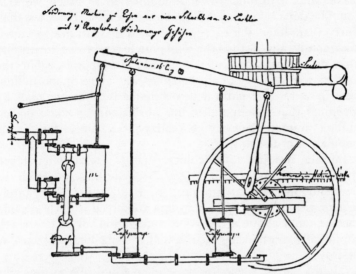

Dinnendahl's sketch of his reciprocating steam engine
as used in a colliery near Essen in 1807.

and forcing him to rationalise production. Eventually, in 1817 Borsig set up his factory in Berlin; from this time onward the resistance in Germany began to weaken gradually.

The term 'iron angels' was coined in England when it was realised that the steam engine was not only capable of preserving collieries from flooding, but could also — if properly used — eliminate want. When Watt died, the British Prime Minister declared that without the inventor and his work Britain would probably have been unable to sustain the war against Napoleon.

Such a view strikes us today as completely logical, but it was certainly not so for many people at the time.

*   *   *

The steam engine did not long remain the only machine to replace muscle power; other inventions, including the motor, followed it, multiplying production a hundredfold, even a thousandfold. In 1933 the first exact calculation of power from mechanical sources was made at Harvard, and showed that the energy provided by coal, wood, petroleum, natural gas, wind-power and hydraulic power amounted to as much work as could be done by 10,000 million human beings. Now, less than thirty years later, the energy consumed by man has increased enormously, and in 1950 the total muscle power of all men and animals was estimated at 150 million horse-power, while the total power delivery of all machines was about 3,000 million horse-power. The natural forces made available to man by machines thus correspond to the work done by some 90,000 million human beings, i.e. thirty-three times the whole population of the world.

But the hostility to machines persists. It has often taken strange forms, and the sermons of the Reformation — with the frequently misused catch-phrase, 'back to Nature' — are rarely taken seriously now. The objectors are forced to turn to other themes, such as atomic energy, automation, or space travel, continually emphasising the risk that our machines will one day destroy us.

That is why it is good to remember, from time to time, the words engraved on Watt's monument:

"He multiplied the power of men and therefore rose to a prominent place among the most famous men of science and the true benefactors of the world."

"This is the most absurd plan ever invented by a human being."

Report on the railway engine, 19th century.

CHAPTER II

REVOLUTION ON WHEELS

Captain Dick gets up steam — Early experiments — The steam carriage — Mr. Stephenson's absurd plan — The beginning of worldwide transport — Gloomy prophecies — The locomotive race at Rainhill — The railway becomes accepted — The end of the struggle — The internal combustion engine — The four-stroke engine — Petroleum — From the velocipede to Benz's patent coach — The petrol carriage

CAPTAIN DICK GETS UP STEAM

WHEN he was thirty, Richard Trevithick, a Cornish engineer, drove a steam carriage through the narrow streets of Camborne, accompanied by a few friends, on Christmas Eve, 1801. The steam coach was of his building, and he had invited his bravest friends to a trial run, which one participant described as follows: "Captain Dick got up steam . . . When we see'd that Captain Dick was agoing to turn on steam, we jumped up as many as could; may be seven or eight of us. 'Twas a stiffish hill going from the Weith up to Camborne Beacon, but she went off like a little bird." Horseless travel was a reality at last!

From earliest times man had only animals, especially horses, at his disposal to drive wheels and carts, but for centuries he was unable to increase the speed of his vehicles appreciably. Ten horses would draw a bigger carriage than one or two, but no faster. A journey was still a major undertaking, for travelling had hardly changed over the ages, and the average speed remained almost constant. Now came a sudden transformation, but mankind showed no interest in it. Had they not been travelling fast enough for centuries? Most people thought that the place for steam engines was in the factory, not on the road. Nevertheless, the time had come for the conquest of distance and the earth's surface to begin. It advanced with the first industrial revolution, which had already brought mass production,

27

and could not have taken place without the development of means to carry men and goods.

Improved possibilities of transport in turn necessitated the construction of new and better roads, the building of bridges and canals, the enlargement of the merchant fleet and the design of more powerful vehicles. In Great Britain as early as 1662 the law allowed private persons to build roads and to levy a toll. This arrangement gradually began to operate in the 18th century, but it was only by the middle 1650s that there was

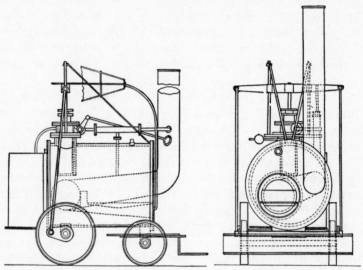

Trevithick's Camborne road carriage, 1802.

an adequate road system, connecting London with the growing industrial areas of the Midlands and the North. In France, too, scientific road-building began about the middle of the 18th century. The young professional engineers trained at the École des Ponts et Chaussées in Paris developed new methods of road-making, so that by the end of the century France possessed a good system of roads.

Nevertheless, for a long time the highways in Britain and on the Continent remained inadequate. A contemporary print shows a seaman with a wooden leg, refusing a ride in a mail coach, "because he was in a hurry". Road construction was not keeping pace with the growing requirements of industry and commerce, both of which were in full development. On many journeys the coaches travelled at barely five miles an hour, even towards the end of the 18th century.

Gradually, however, the highway companies became richer and more enterprising, so that they could even employ prominent road-building engineers. Ways were found of providing well-drained foundations, measures introduced to counter the damage caused by water and ice, and various road-surfacing materials employed.

Then McAdam, the pioneer British road-builder, introduced 'Macadamized' roads, which consisted of small broken stones covered with tar. His object had been to find a new use for the coal-tar produced in the gas industry, but he was also aware of the urgent necessity of building new roads. His bold proposal was that the traffic itself should, so to say, contribute to settling the road-metal. The vehicles crushed the small stones, which were lightly held together by the tar, thus forming a binder for the surface. The horse-drawn vehicles of those days, having iron tyres, compacted the material even more. Macadamizing was officially introduced in Britain in 1815, and continued to be used until horse traffic was replaced by motor-cars, which dragged the fine stones out of the road-metal, damaging the surface. At that time no one dreamed of this immense additional load on the highways.

The disappointment and failure of McAdam were, nevertheless, due to other causes. The railways, now developing gradually, began to compete with the roads. Parliament decided to compensate McAdam for his great financial sacrifice in developing the modern method of road-building, but told him plainly that roads would soon be completely replaced by railways for all land traffic. On the Continent things were even worse, for while anyone could study the excellent text books on road-building, all the European Governments refused to spend money on a scheme in which they had no faith.

At times military or political objectives favoured road construction, as, for instance, when Maria Theresa of Austria ordered the construction of a road from Cracov to Bohemia, so that the peasants would not need to drive their cattle through hostile Silesia. Generally the mail-coaches followed old, unsurfaced cart-tracks, while travelling was hazardous and frequently called for extensive preparations. Travelling princes not only took a courier with them, but a whole staff of travelling attendants. It is not surprising that journeys were not undertaken for pleasure, the only reason "to cover a considerable distance being to fulfil a specific purpose in some distant place".

Notwithstanding this, it was essential for a rich and cultured man of the 18th century to have done 'the grand tour'. Generally, for travellers from England, the route began in Holland, passing through Belgium and Paris to south-west France and thence to Seville via Madrid and Lisbon; it continued through southern France and Switzerland to Italy and Greece. The last leg of the journey followed the Danube from Vienna up to Munich, passing through Germany along the Rhine, the return to England being via Bremen and Hamburg. All this, be it noted, in horse-driven coaches, and in conditions very little changed from the time of the Cæsars. For months the voyager would be moving through the various European countries, large and small, according to the attractions included in the itinerary.

In 1832 Pierer described a journey of this kind in the following words: "The introduction of steamships, the improvement of the posts, and better roads and inns have now made travelling easier and more agreeable, so that an Englishman who would once have considered his education completed by the grand tour, now feels out of fashion if he has not at least passed through America and the West Indies, the Levant, Greece and Egypt, or visited the North African ports. If he has been to Rio de Janeiro or at the Cape, so much the better, for the time is past when a man could attract attention in company because he had been to the East Indies. Moreover, the time cannot be far hence when the British consider it essential to have made a journey round the world."

But it was not only the British who were taken with the 'wanderlust'. "Next after the British it is the Germans who most enjoy travelling, which has become 'à la mode'. Almost every educated young man has been to Italy, France, or England, or further afield; even the poorest, moved only by ambition, seeks by hook or by crook to find a way of visiting Switzerland or the Rhine on foot."

George Stephenson driving 'Locomotion No. 1' at the opening of the Stockton and Darlington Railway, 27th September 1825. This was the first passenger-carrying railway open to the public.

The 'Puffing Billy' at work at
a colliery in 1813.

The Alweg Monorail, an experimental installation near Cologne.

The time was ripe for a great change in the world, and enterprising men devised steam carriages, even before the steamship and the railway train.

EARLY EXPERIMENTS

Watt was fully aware that, in addition to being used as a stationary machine, his steam engine could be used to drive carriages; in fact, he patented the idea, but did not make use of it.

It was still not very easy to imagine a steam engine which would move in a vehicle and drive it at the same time. Newcomen's old 'fire engine' and Watt's low-pressure engine were not suitable for the purpose. They required too much space for the power supplied and would have been too big for any vehicle. Furthermore, they would have been unable to move their own weight, let alone provide spare power to carry loads. Indeed, every clear-thinking man was forced to admit that a mechanical vehicle was impossible. Even the steamship was unthinkable at the time, and the sceptics found it easy to ridicule the 'foolish' inventors' plans. But the inventors were indefatigable and could not be deterred from their one object of making their machines succeed.

John Fitch was one such man, who, dogged by ill-fortune, spent his life toiling as a watch-maker, metal-worker, silversmith and coppersmith, hawker and tinker until, prematurely old at forty-two, he began to build models of steamships in Pennsylvania. A prosperous citizen of Philadelphia, impressed with his demonstrations, supported the construction of a steamship some 40 feet long, which finally covered forty-odd miles on the Delaware River in 1787. After this Fitch was able to build a second, slightly larger boat, for thirty passengers. The general public was, however, indifferent to his experiments, considering that steamboats were unnecessary, since sails and oars had existed for centuries.

Fitch ruined himself and made himself ill in the pursuit of his consuming passion, and eventually committed suicide in 1798, shortly after writing the following words: "We shall not live to see the day, but the time will come when the steamboat will be preferred above all other means of travel. Steamboats will sail up the Western rivers from New Orleans to Wheeling and cross

D

the ocean. More powerful men than I will win fame and fortune through my discoveries, but no one will remember that
poor John Fitch did anything worth speaking of."

In 1791 Clarke demonstrated the steamboat in Scotland, but
the problem was virtually disregarded in Britain — and elsewhere — until the turn of the century. It was only in 1807 that
Fulton launched his steamship in New York, and three years
later started a regular service on the Hudson between New York
and Albany.

Both in the Old World and the New, steamships began to ply
in coastal waters, and several experiments were made to link
North America to England and England to India. But in 1830
experts still thought that steamships were principally suitable
for river traffic, especially as they could easily travel upstream.
As might have been expected, they were also sceptical. "Steamships can indeed be used, but are of little use for long sea journeys, needing to take so much coal with them that they can
carry little freight. They will be even less suitable as warships
since they manœuvre slowly, and can only be used singly with
the fleet, so as to fall on the enemy when the wind drops
entirely."

Another American, Oliver Evans, was rather more successful;
he was a builder of steam engines and even received official permission to construct steam wagons. It is true that all the States
were not so far-sighted; the Pennsylvania legislature considered
steam carriages to be a dream and only gave Evans permission
to use his steam engines to drive mills. Maryland was rather
more generous, and the authorities declared, somewhat apologetically, that they could well afford to let him build steam
wagons since they would, after all, harm no one. Many of his
contemporaries thought him mad, because he also wanted to
build steamships and railway trains; yet his proposals were
undoubtedly sober and he was only a little ahead of his critics.

"If we think of the stubborn opposition of the majority to
every step forward — from earth roads to surfaced highways,
from highways to canals, from canals to horse-driven railways —
then we are expecting too much if we try to make the tremendous jump from bad roads to steam-drawn railways in one
stage. A step in each generation is the best that we can hope
for. If we today accept canals, the next generation will try

horse-drawn trains, while the third will develop the steam wagon."

That was written early in the 19th century. In 1801 Evans perfected the non-condensing steam engine, for installation in a carriage, but he lacked the money to carry out his proposal. First of all he used it to drive a plaster mill, and soon after built a steamship for the Philadelphia Health Department to use as a harbour dredger. The transport of his flat-bottomed, heavy vessel to the harbour raised a difficulty, which nearly brought failure to Evans's project, but his solution was as brilliant as it was simple. He simply fitted wheels to the boat, transforming it into a steam wagon for the short journey to the harbour.

Thus it came about that the Philadelphians were awakened one morning by a heavy rumbling noise, as the strangest vehicle they had ever seen rolled through the streets. Evans had shown that vehicles could be driven on land by steam at almost the same time as Trevithick did so in England. But the mockery of his contemporaries continued, so that he felt constrained to prophesy against them in the following terms: "The time will come when people will travel in stages moved by steam engines . . . fifteen or twenty miles in an hour . . . A carriage will set out from Washington in the morning, the passengers will breakfast at Baltimore, dine at Philadelphia, and sup at New York, the same day."

But they answered him: "Who wants to get to New York so quickly? Anyhow the wind will blow your fire out!!"

THE STEAM CARRIAGE

As early as 1769 a French artillery officer named Cugnot had driven a steam-propelled carriage around Paris. On one of the first journeys he ran into a wall and thereafter abandoned his experiments.

Since Watt did not follow up his idea of using steam to drive coaches, Murdoch, his assistant, set to work. To begin with, Murdoch built small models which ran about in his workshop. After this he constructed a full-sized carriage; on its first trial it ran away from him. This experiment caused a great deal of unrest; the surprised spectators took the unfamiliar 'monster', which bore down upon them roaring in a cloud of smoke, for the devil, and demanded its destruction. But it was the fact that

Boulton and Watt did not welcome his interest in devices which were covered by the patent of one of the partners that brought Murdoch's experiments to an end. Consequently, his friend Trevithick, with whom he had once worked in the same mine, gained the distinction of driving the first steam carriage successfully on the roads. Trevithick used high-pressure steam, and achieved a speed of eight to nine miles an hour.

A series of experimental carriages, made by Evans in 1804 and by other constructors in later years, was followed by the

Trevithick's road locomotive, 1808.

successful steam-coach service introduced in 1831 by Gurney and Hancock. This steam carriage was called the 'automaton', thus emphasising an obvious fact, namely, that it moved 'automatically', i.e., without horse-power. Gradually there developed on British roads a fairly active system of steam carriages and steam omnibuses. These vehicles were hotly opposed by coachmen and carriers, who feared that they would be thrown out of work. Moreover, they were expensive to run, because of the heavy tolls levied towards the maintenance of the roads, which were damaged by the excessive weight of the steam carriages.

To crown these difficulties, there came the introduction in Britain of the law which required that a man with a red flag, or a red lamp, must precede the vehicle to warn pedestrians of its approach. This law was still in force in 1896.

An English steam-coach, early 19th century.

But it did not really need the resistance of the public and such remarkable restrictive laws to hinder the development of the steam engine. The inventors had got into a blind alley, from which they would only be released by the invention of the internal-combustion engine.

Steam was not to conquer the roads but was destined to be supreme in the railway system which was to come.

THE BEGINNING OF WORLD-WIDE TRANSPORT

It would not have been extraordinary or unexpected for people to discuss the railway in the 1820s. An enquirer would have been told that this was a system of iron rails serving as a track on which there ran carriages driven by steam or drawn by stationary steam engines. It might have been added that these rail tracks were particularly to be found in England and that the results obtained were remarkable, since they might one day render canals quite unnecessary. There was, certainly, no question as yet of steam locomotives and passenger carriages. Nevertheless, the prerequisite for this means of transportation, which was finally to give mankind freedom of movement over long distances, was already there in the shape of the rail.

The idea of a fixed track — the basic feature of the railway —

is not as new as it seemed to people in the era of steam engines and steam coaches, and can actually be traced back as far as the Greeks and Romans. Vestiges of rails on which carriages ran have been discovered in the ruins of the Temple of Ceres at Eleusis. The Romans also knew the advantage of having a level road with fixed tracks for vehicles, as can be seen in the remains of the Appian Way.

For centuries fixed rails on wooden blocks had been common in German mines. When Queen Elizabeth brought skilled miners from Germany to help develop the British mines, they introduced the system into Britain. In the 19th century the combination of fixed rails and the steam locomotive produced the railway as we know it. Originally, the rails were made of wood, but in the 18th century cast iron, and later forged iron, was used, the latter until 1860. Since that time, railways all over the world have used steel rails.

Trevithick's first steam coach had attracted a great deal of attention, but had not brought in any money. He therefore tried to sell his efficient high-pressure steam engine at a profit; this brought him in contact with the mine owner Hill, of Pennydarran, in 1803. Hill was using a horse-drawn train be-

Trevithick's improved rail locomotive, 1803–4.

tween his iron works and the town of Cardiff; his 'railway' could carry as much as a whole string of ordinary road vehicles.

Having already succeeded with horseless carriages, Trevithick felt that he could achieve far better results using his steam engine to draw the load, and claimed that he could move a payload of ten tons. Hill, while thinking it not impossible, thought Trevithick mad in offering to prove it, and wagered £500 that it was impossible to build a steam railway with this performance. Notwithstanding this, Trevithick set to work and produced the forerunner of all locomotives, known as the Tram Wagon; this ugly, bulky machine had an enormous — and unnecessary — flywheel which was intended to ensure a smooth rotary movement. This high-wheeled and curious construction was finally completed; in Trevithick's first trial, his Tram Wagon successfully drew five trucks containing ten tons of iron and seventy passengers over ten miles of rail track. The total load was more than twenty-five tons. Trevithick won the £500 wagered by Hill, although the primitive train took over four hours to cover its ten-mile stretch.

Thus Trevithick almost became the creator of the railway, but he was dogged by ill-fortune. His first locomotive finished up as a stationary steam engine in a colliery, because its excessive weight broke the cast-iron rails on which it ran. Moreover, there was still very little interest in the steam railway. Trevithick instituted a sort of 'railway circus', realising that his problem was not only technical but a matter of publicity. In 1808 he built an improved locomotive with the amazing speed — for that time — of nearly twenty miles an hour; he laid a circular track some sixty yards across for his locomotive, fenced it in and charged an entrance fee, so that the braver spirits could ride in carriages behind the snorting engine, while the others looked on from a safe distance. But public interest soon waned, and the rails rapidly deteriorated; Trevithick had to abandon his exhibition. Filled with disappointment he abandoned all his work on the development of the railway. The rest of his life was marked by alternating successes and failures. He emigrated to Peru, to sell his high-pressure pumps for use in the mines, and after winning a great deal of respect, was finally deported a ruined man. He died in 1833 at Dartford, forgotten and alone, and local workers and manufacturers, who still remembered his earlier successes, collected sufficient money to pay for his burial.

Although Trevithick failed, his idea of the locomotive on rails continued. Some of the designers who followed in his foot-steps did, it is true, consider some of his proposals impossible; they thought that the wheels of locomotives would not grip the

Trevithick's business card — and a customer's comments.

rails and their trains therefore somewhat resembled a modern rack railway. One especially cautious man fitted his engine with wooden stilts which were intended to push it along. The first true locomotive, with smooth wheels running on a smooth track, was built by Hedley in 1813; this was the 'Puffing Billy', which ran for fifty years, eventually going to a museum in 1862.

Hedley's locomotive was intended exclusively for hauling

coal, but the railway pioneers were turning more and more to passenger transport. This was a problem that needed more than enterprise; it was no longer sufficient to build the engines and lay the tracks — exhaustive investigations had to be made; the moment had come to introduce a concept of railways based on sound scientific principles. The problem was plain to see; and yet the solution did not come from one of the prominent men of the steam-engine era, but from a man who could not write until he was nineteen; his name was George Stephenson.

MR. STEPHENSON'S ABSURD PLAN

We would today consider young Stephenson a successful railway engineer, but his contemporaries thought him mad, because he was not deterred by the dirt and noise of the engines, but cherished the iron horrors as though they were living creatures.

Stephenson was the son of a poor mine worker and learned to read and write in night school. During his work as a machine-minder at Killingworth, a new pump could not be started, and was to be scrapped. Stephenson obtained permission to see whether he could repair it, and was completely successful after four days.

This remarkable machine-boy, who worked during the evening at tailoring or watch-making to earn a few shillings, and studied at night, was rewarded; the respect his achievement brought him gave him the opportunity to tell the mine owner of his dream to build a locomotive for use on a track. His employer was very dubious, but placed a few workmen at his mechanic's disposal; however, they were only unskilled men, as the trained mechanics would not work under the one-time herd-boy.

The construction of the locomotive was begun in 1812 and two years later it ran. Unfortunately it was far from efficient, and Stephenson had to spend years in improving its performance. Firstly, he replaced the conventional cast-iron wheels by wrought-iron ones. He also carried out continual improvements in the shape and mounting of the rails, and made thorough studies of the friction and pressure of the wheels on the smooth tracks. In addition, he improved the cylinder of the steam engine, made close-fitting pistons and, finally, increased the performance of the engine by connecting the piston directly to the driving-wheels.

The mechanics completely mistrusted Stephenson — saying that he was not an engineer — but, notwithstanding this, hard work by unskilled men gave the locomotive its basic form; it was not yet the fully-perfected design we now know, but was nevertheless already capable of efficient operation.

Finally, after eight years of hard research, Stephenson and his seventeen-year-old son Robert succeeded in obtaining an order to supply a colliery with five locomotives and sets of track for carrying coal.

An event of decisive importance in Stephenson's life was the plan to build a passenger railway between Stockton and Darlington. Stockton, a market town of 4,000 inhabitants, had a flourishing trade in sail-cloth, lead, corn and fish, as well as workshops building ships and equipment for them. Darlington, with a population of 5,000, was equally prosperous, producing straps, leather and optical apparatus, and selling large quantities of water from the local mineral springs. These rising communities were, however, cut off from the new transport system; lying in a part of Durham where there were no canals, they were unable to carry their wares by water. After long discussions, with frequent allusions to the 'dangers' of this new means of transport, the progressive manufacturers and far-sighted councillors decided to build a railway track between the two towns.

The responsibility of construction was entrusted to an engineer named Pease. He was a conservative man, who moved slowly but surely; his original idea was to use a horse-drawn train, and he was not at first very taken with Stephenson's proposal to provide a locomotive with the power of fifty horses. In the end, Pease was won over by Stephenson and, since there was nowhere in the world a firm which could build or supply a locomotive for their purpose, the two men decided to set up their own works. Initially, they built three locomotives for the new railway, but as time went on their factory became a centre of steam-locomotive development.

It is quite amusing to see how railway trains were built at that time. The new transport system had not yet developed its own style, so the builder of 'passenger carriages' thought of the

familiar mail coach, which had served so faithfully for generations. It was not possible to set such coaches on rails as they
stood, but a certain amount of experience had already been
gained with horse-drawn rail carriages. Stephenson and Pease
had therefore only to combine the two ideas; they built special
chassis to run on rails and fitted the bodies of old mail coaches to
them.

On 27th September 1825 a considerable crowd gathered to
celebrate the opening of the railway between Darlington and
Stockton.

Stephenson's steam-engine, the 'Active', drew a train of
thirty-four converted mail coaches; six were loaded with coal
and flour, one carriage was occupied by the Directors, a further
twenty-one carriages by almost 450 guests of honour, while another six coaches of coal brought up the rear. The distance was
almost ten miles and was covered in sixty-five minutes. Even a
band came on the return journey, to enliven the occasion.

Thus, while the experts all over the world were declaring that
the locomotive wheels would slip hopelessly on the smooth rails,
and the trains therefore would be unable to surmount any rise
in the track, the foundation stone of the modern system of
world-wide transport was laid, on a ten-mile stretch of line
between Stockton and Darlington.

GLOOMY PROPHECIES

Stephenson was convinced that the railway had a great
future, and declared that one day "railways will supersede almost every other method of conveyance in this country, when
mail coaches will go by railway, and railroads will become the
great highway for the King and all his subjects. The time is
coming when it will be cheaper for a working man to travel
upon a railway than to walk on foot."

However, this was far from the general view. Even when
Stephenson's Darlington railway proved so successful, capable
experts were saying that this kind of technical game with steam
engines on rails would soon disappear. Resistance to this new
method of travel arose from very different grounds and sometimes took very curious forms. The panel of experts from
the Royal Society decided that it was dangerous for trains to
exceed thirty miles an hour, because the air would enter the

compartments and the passengers would be suffocated. For years such sinister prophecies disturbed the population. The farming community feared that cows grazing peacefully near the railway lines would be so frightened that they would give less milk, or even none at all.

The introduction of the railway shows clearly how difficult it is for everyone to accept a new development and to realise its utility. There exists a kind of mental inertia, an incomprehensible conservatism, which leads men to cling to what is traditional, sometimes even with fanaticism. Almost a century passed before the public at large realised that the railway brought with it a rise in the standard of living, since many more people were able to enjoy the riches of the earth than previously.

The fact that the railway eventually triumphed in spite of all opposition is principally due to economic causes. The old system of conveying goods by river or canal was no longer able to keep pace with the increasing production. The canal companies were in bitter competition, while the locks were of varying sizes, making it difficult to pass from one canal system to another. The dues were too high and, particularly in winter, barge traffic was too slow, and often halted by ice. New ways of carrying goods were therefore essential.

THE LOCOMOTIVE RACE AT RAINHILL

Four years before the Darlington line was opened, the merchants of Liverpool and Manchester decided to link the two towns by a railroad. These progressive citizens invited Stephenson to prepare a project; he proposed that, in addition to building a rail track, they should also purchase a steam locomotive. With this was coupled a bold and surprising promise, namely, that the journey which required nearly forty hours by water would by this means be reduced to some four to five hours.

The big landowners and the Canal Boards had already opposed the plan, but now open war broke out. Angry farmers chased the surveyors off their land, and the villagers beat Stephenson's employees. The canal owners circulated reports claiming, for example, that sparks from the locomotives would set the houses on fire, that clouds of smoke would poison the air and kill the animals, that horse-breeding would rapidly be stopped, and that the trains would frighten the hens and stop their egg-laying. Preachers inveighed against the devilish machines, and protest meetings were held by the landlords.

In spite of all this, the work of surveying was successfully completed, but the struggle now moved to higher circles; Stephenson had to obtain the permission of Parliament. He was subjected to a very searching cross-examination, during which his opponents brought many expert views against the railways:

> The rain would put out the locomotive fire.
> The locomotive would therefore have to be wrapped in sheets, but the wind would tear them away.
> The rushing air would blow the boiler fire out.
> The rushing air would fan the boiler fire so strongly that the boiler would burst.
> The break-neck speed of ten miles an hour (mail coaches usually averaged five miles an hour) would make the passengers lose their reason.

One member of Parliament asked Stephenson what would happen if a cow were to run in front of the train at this great speed. Did he not think this would be most disagreeable? It would, replied Stephenson with a smile — it would be most disagreeable — for the cow! This answer was, of course, not welcomed by the countryfolk, who were always fearful for the life and limb of their beasts.

Another member attacked Stephenson in the following words: "The proposals show unbelievable ignorance. The entire project is absolute madness . . . The plan shows that Stephenson has no idea of what he is about. Carriages rushing along at ten miles an hour, drawn by the devil in the shape of a locomotive . . . Beelzebub himself at the controls, and behind him his assistant fanning the fire . . . What a crazy scheme! I can prove to you that the machine will never achieve five miles an hour, that it is governed by the weather — in short, that it cannot compete with the canal."

One expert declared: "This is the most absurd plan ever conceived by a human being!"

The influence of the canal owners carried the day and Parliament refused the necessary permission; nevertheless the struggle went on.

The success of the Stockton–Darlington railway proved that

Stephenson's calculations were sound. A year after the opening of this line, he asked an old friend, William Huskisson, to renew the request to Parliament for permission to construct a railway from Liverpool to Manchester. Again considerable protests were made against the railway, and its opponents marshalled new arguments. They prophesied that the workers would suffer from spreading unemployment, and that the railway builders would soon exhaust the deposits of iron ore. They called the railroad a mischievous thing, said it would disturb

First passenger carriage on the Stockton–Darlington line, 1825.

peace and quiet, and warned people that the smoke, noise and speed of the train would ruin their health.

This time, however, Stephenson was successful; after a dramatic session, Parliament authorised the construction of the railway.

Then began what was, for those days, a gigantic undertaking. It was necessary to build 63 bridges and drive a quarter-mile tunnel; a mile and a half of cuttings had to be made, and three miles of marshland had to be filled in. Stephenson's assistants had to design and construct rails, points and signals, while he himself concentrated on constructing the locomotive to meet his purpose. After three years he produced his masterpiece, an entirely new design.

To select the best locomotive for the new line, it was decided to hold a race, which took place in the autumn of 1829, near Rainhill, on a stretch of the thirty-mile line joining Manchester and Liverpool; the various new steam locomotives were brought together, presenting a unique sight. Five locomotives were entered. Two of them had to be disallowed by the umpires; one contained a horse hidden in its interior — completely against the rules of the race — while the other could not attain the required minimum speed. Two other engines soon dropped out because of technical faults. On the other hand, Stephen-

Robert Stephenson's 'Rocket', which won the race at Rainhill.

son's new engine, which he had named the 'Rocket' to show his scorn for the critical articles in the Press, fulfilled all the conditions, covering the trial stretch twenty times without any failure and achieving the — for those days — unbelievable top speed of twenty-six miles an hour, drawing thirty passengers in a coach behind it.

Stephenson was sure of the prize, but drove the 'Rocket' once more without a coach behind it. He achieved the first world record speed, as the locomotive rushed at thirty-five miles an hour over the rails. The spectators feared that the driver would be killed by the air pressure, but nothing of the kind happened.

A year later the Manchester–Liverpool line was operated by eight trains drawn by steam locomotives. On this occasion the first fatal railways accident occurred. Huskisson, who had championed the steam railway in Parliament, fell on the rails and was run over.

*   *   *

From this time onwards the development of the railroads was rapid, and they soon became the arteries of the new industrial systems. Stephenson was called upon to build more and more locomotives, while in other countries interest was growing in this new means of transport.

As early as 1814 the Bavarian mining engineer Josef von Bader had suggested building a rail track between Nüremberg and Fürth; this was not to be a steam railway of the type developed by Stephenson — who was still unknown on the Continent — but a horse-drawn railway. His suggestion was, however, soon forgotten.

From 1825 onwards great efforts were made by Friedrich Wilhelm Harkort, one of the biggest Ruhr industrialists, to introduce the railroad into Germany. In the following words he described the revolution in commerce which they would bring about: "The rapid and safe transport of goods will still considerably raise the standard of living of a country which is maintained at a tolerable level by canals, navigable waterways and good roads. Railways seem to offer greater advantages than the means of transport used hitherto. A machine of eight horse-power will carry a thousand bushels of coal from Steele to the Rhine and will completely do away with water transport. All the collieries of the Ruhr would find rapid and regular market for their coal at low freight rates if a railway were available to them. If Elberfeld, Cologne, and Duisburg were linked to Bremen or Emden, Dutch Custom duties would no longer trouble us. What a tremendous impulse this would give to the industrial development of the Rhineland-Westphalia region as a result of such a link with the sea! May the time soon come when, in Germany too, the railway carries the product of our industry, encouraged by a spirit of co-operation!"

A year later Harkort wrote: "In drawing the attention of the public to the railways, we do not feel bound to re-open the old question as to whether machines have, by reason of their great development, brought good or ill to the community. For us, it suffices to remember the warning that if we do not progress, we must go back, and everyone is therefore responsible for making every effort he can to achieve technical advances useful to all ... One thing is certain, namely, that an efficient transport system, both within a country and beyond its boundaries, considerably raises its standard of living."

The fact that an industrialist should consider it necessary to write in such terms clearly shows us how strong was the resistance to steam railways in Germany at that time.

THE RAILWAY BECOMES ACCEPTED

Harkort's proposals fell on deaf ears. A further ten years passed before the new invention gained sufficient favour for the first railway to be constructed on German soil.

Work on the line from Nüremberg to Fürth began in 1833, and two years later it was completed. Agreement had not yet been reached as to the means of propelling the trains. Early in 1835 a Nüremberg paper suggested that the points of departure at the two ends should be at the level of the first floor of the houses, and that the line should have a steady downward gradient to the terminus, so as to eliminate altogether the necessity for a means of propulsion! In spite of all this the first German railway was drawn by steam locomotives. The Company bought an engine from Stephenson for 10,200 florins, as well as 11 horses which were to draw single carriages at intervals between the journeys of the steam trains.

On 7th December 1835 everything was ready for the opening of the line. Some 200 braved the dangers of the first trip in the train; the medical faculty at Munich had stated a little earlier that the great speed would cause the passengers to suffer from a new form of mental illness, called *delirium furiosum*. Moreover, it was seriously declared that travel at such a speed would give

E

the passengers fits of headache and dizziness and impair their vision.

In addition to the locomotive, the engine-driver — a Mr. Wilson — was also imported from England, and paid a salary almost twice that of the railway company's Director. In top-hat and frock-coat he attracted a good deal of attention, and a newspaper report said of him: "How can one refrain from see-ing personified in such a man the whole difference between the old and the new? Every shovel of coal is measured after due reflection, taken at the right time and distributed appro-priately on the fire."

On the first journey the train covered the three and a quarter miles to Fürth in fifteen minutes; this speed almost took away the breath of many of the passengers. One of them, impressed by his headlong progress, exclaimed: "It carries us faster than Apollo's sun chariot could do!"

This new experience of 'travelling at speed' soon became a question of personal taste; in 1837 the journey on the Nürem-berg–Fürth Railway was still a kind of Bank Holiday outing. The excitement produced by travelling at fifteen miles per hour was great. A year later, however, a Berliner wrote angrily to the newspapers after the opening of the Berlin–Potsdam service, demanding that measures be taken to protect the passengers from the importunities of wooden-legged beggars, who might run alongside the trains.

Nüremberg at last had its railway, and the journey took fifteen minutes by steam locomotive against twenty-five minutes by horse-drawn carriage. The 'commissioner', later known as the inspector, was responsible for the punctual departure of the trains, and for turning the carriages at the terminus as well as for orderly behaviour during the journey. In its first year this 'dangerous' thing, the railroad, carried 450,000 passengers.

*   *   *

This first passenger railway on German soil was still partly operated with horse-drawn carriages. It was only the second German railroad, joining Leipzig and Dresden, which relied entirely on steam. The history of this line is associated with the name of the economist Friedrich List, who on his return from the New World in 1883 promulgated his doctrine of a national economy, closely linked with the idea of a national railway system. List published a number of works on this subject, among them one entitled: *A Saxon Railway System Considered as the Foundation of a Railroad System for All Germany.* In his opinion, a united German economic system called for an extensive transport network, which would help to overcome separatism.

The line from Leipzig to Dresden was roughly seventy miles long; other lines were built, but although he had championed the railroads, List was not allowed to co-operate. He sacrificed both health and wealth, and finally, bitter and disappointed, committed suicide. But the railroads continued to grow and began to change the face of the world; everywhere new links were made, tracks cut through woodland, carried on bridges over ravines and rushing streams, through tunnels and over mountains.

The history of the railway epitomises the struggle between the past and the present, to which we have already referred. Stephenson had named the locomotive with which he won the Rainhill competition the 'Rocket', because a British engineering journal had written in 1825: "Nothing is more ridiculous than the claim to build a locomotive which will travel at twice the speed of the mail coaches. It would be as easy to believe that the burgesses of Woolwich should allow themselves to be

The American locomotive 'De Witt Clinton', which inaugurated the Mohawk–Hudson Railway on 9th August 1831.

shot off in a Congreve rocket, as that they should trust themselves to such a machine."

In 1828 the first two railroads in the United States were built, one from Baltimore to Ohio and the other from Charleston to Hamburg. Initially little faith was placed in the wood-fired locomotives, and auxiliary sails were tried out experi-

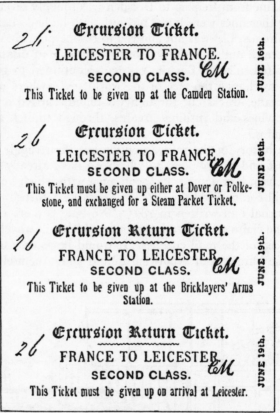

26   **Excursion Ticket.**

LEICESTER TO FRANCE.

SECOND CLASS. *CM*   JUNE 16th.

This Ticket to be given up at the Camden Station.

---

26   **Excursion Ticket.**

LEICESTER TO FRANCE *CM*

SECOND CLASS.   JUNE 16th.

This Ticket must be given up either at Dover or Folkestone, and exchanged for a Steam Packet Ticket.

---

26   **Excursion Return Ticket.**

FRANCE TO LEICESTER *CM*

SECOND CLASS.   JUNE 19th.

This Ticket to be given up at the Bricklayers' Arms Station.

---

26   **Excursion Return Ticket.**

FRANCE TO LEICESTER *CM*

SECOND CLASS.   JUNE 19th.

This Ticket must be given up on arrival at Leicester.

Thomas Cook's first excursion ticket to the Continent.

mentally! In 1836 the first sleeping car was put into service in Pennsylvania. The vast virgin territories of North America were very suitable for railroads, and from 1830 onwards American locomotive and rail manufacture had developed actively.

One of the first engines exploded, because the driver, unable to bear the hissing of the steam discharged from the safety valve, had plugged the valve! Such foolish mistakes were readily seized upon by opponents of the railway in their wild attacks, but even this could not hinder the progress of the railroads which soon covered long stretches of the wide prairies.

The year 1841 found the Austrians planning to connect Vienna with Trieste. Once again architects and engineers produced careful reports; stating that the project was impracticable; once more doctors gave their warnings, asserting that the passengers would not survive the crossing of the Semmering Pass. The opposition even incited people to attack the construction gangs, so that at times armed guards had to be posted to protect the workmen.

By the end of 1843 the railways of Britain were carrying eighteen million passengers a year, and those of Germany eight million.

The first Pullman coach was built in America by George M. Pullman in 1858. Railway carriages had already taken on a characteristic form very different from that of the days when they were exact copies of mail coaches. Several European countries, including Britain, soon copied the Pullman design.

In 1860 the German railway system had a total length of some 7,300 miles; the first sleeper coach was introduced in Britain in 1873, the first restaurant car in 1879, and the first express coach in 1890. That year Germany built 1,800 locomotives. It was estimated that the total number of locomotives built in the world up to that time was a little over 100,000, at least 50,000 of which were in service, with an aggregate rating of approximately ten million horse-power.

THE END OF THE STRUGGLE

Had it been possible to observe the earth from outer space during the 19th century, and supposing the railway lines to have been marked by a red line, it would have been a fascinating sight, as the tracks spread in all directions over the continents, eventually covering all land areas like a net.

The rapid development of the railroads in densely-populated regions, such as Western Europe, was a consequence of the increasing traffic which the roads and canals could no longer carry. In North America the railway fulfilled a different

purpose; it transformed that enormous continent — inhabited by
Red Indians and wild animals — into a huge agricultural and
industrial country. This was the foundation on which America
rose to be a world power. It was only when the Eastern States
were covered by a close railway network that the westward
advance of the settlers really began. The Mississippi was
crossed by rail in 1854, and by 1890 the railroad had traversed
the broad plains and high mountains of the West.

"Can't catch me, Daddy!" A caricature from *Fliegender Blätter*, on
the early days of railways.

Thus the net spread across the earth, in spite of the mis-
apprehensions and prejudices of successive generations. By
1956 the total length of railroad in the world was estimated at
some 810,000 miles.

The age of the mail coach, the one-time 'bone-shaker', was
soon lost sight of; if people were reminded of it, in books or
newspapers, it was in romantic fashion. No one paid any attention to this old style of travelling, which was frequently dangerous and always uncomfortable. Moreover, men forgot the

resistance of their forbears to the 'devilish' railway, a resistance often couched in the strangest terms.

One personal experience in 1955 showed me how much most people now take the railway for granted. During a lecture I mentioned an aeroplane accident which was referred to again in the subsequent discussion. Judge of my extreme surprise when a charming but energetic old lady suddenly cried: "People shouldn't fly they should go by train, as God meant them to"!

*   *   *

The transformation of the solar energy stored in wood, peat and coal to produce mechanical work by the agency of the steam engine was a remarkable human invention. Without steam power, our engineering and manufacturing industry — always calling out for more energy — would be inconceivable. Even today steam locomotives form the backbone of most of the world's railways. The steam engine was, however, unable to conquer the roads, in spite of many laborious experiments with steam omnibuses and noisy steam coaches. Nor could it rise into the air, although attempts were made to achieve steam-driven aircraft, and there was even a 'steam-engine' period at the beginning of the development of flight.

The French aircraft pioneer Clément Ader installed in his first aircraft a steam engine weighing one cwt., much to the amusement of his contemporaries; this was in 1890 and his steam engine had a rating of twenty horse-power. Some years before, Golightly had patented in England an aircraft which was to be driven by the reaction of a jet of steam, but only a caricature of this curious craft has come down to us.

These experiments did however show the tremendous new impetus given to man's desire for rapid travel by the great success of the steam engine in the 19th century. Fire, long since tamed by man, and now controlled steam power, turned the chemical energy locked up in natural fuels into motive power. The steam locomotive had demonstrated that the step from motion to locomotion was not so very large. But machine power needed to be much more highly concentrated before man could undertake mechanical locomotion on roads or in the air.

*   *   *

If we liken technology to a mountain which mankind is climbing in order to reach the summit, it is astonishing to see how long man has remained in the valley. Creatures to which the name 'man' has been applied may have been living on the earth for 500,000 years, or even for more than a million years in the view of some scientists. But during the greater part of this period man relied on the power of his feeble arms, on the speed of his legs, and, later, on the strength of the beasts he tamed and bred. So long as workmen remained undemanding and could therefore work 'cheaply', it was not worth while to envisage mechanical aids. It may be that *homo sapiens* was capable of discovering and using machines very much earlier. Because he did not so use them, the path from Hero's steam turbine to the high-speed car and the rocket aircraft was long and marked by many ups and downs.

Machines and motors were invented and built in a matter of just 200 years, from the steam engine and petrol motor to the jet engine and the rocket; what is more, the steam engine reigned unchallenged for almost 100 years until the coming of the internal combustion engine.

Man's machines not only helped him to travel faster, they also made him stronger, which was more important. He was provided with a very large number of mechanical helpers. About the middle of the 20th century the machines of America were performing the work of nearly 25,000 million human beings. This means that, at this period, each American worker had on average about 400 'mechanical' helpers, and the number was increasing year by year. Consequently any man could manufacture 400 times as much as his ancestors, who worked with unaided hands, and he could therefore produce and make use of a correspondingly greater quantity of goods.

However, although a few thousand men working together could do as much work as a large steam engine, how inefficient by comparison would this concentration of energy be, if a serious attempt were made to replace the machine by so many human beings! This calculation may be quite accurate, and yet the 'exchange' of power would be completely impossible, unless the task were spread over many decades, as was for instance the case in the building of the Pyramids. But if the object is to provide electricity for a town, to drive a ship across the ocean in a few days, to carry by rail hundreds of tons for thousands of miles or to fly an aircraft round the earth faster than sound, the energy available must be concentrated.

The power delivered by the propulsive unit of a single large rocket in the 1950s exceeded the power from all the machines in existence on the earth 150 years before! Moreover, those machines would fill hundreds of great workshops, while the rocket unit could be carried on a lorry. That is a measure of the concentration of power which man has today achieved as a result of taming fire.

THE INTERNAL COMBUSTION ENGINE

The steam engine had made both rail and sea transport its own, but it was too heavy for road vehicles, let alone for aircraft, and its power–weight ratio was too high. For such purposes it was necessary to combine combustion chamber, boiler and cylinder in a single, lighter and more compact unit. The combustion process must take place in the cylinder, thus eliminating indirect stages utilising water and steam, and achieving a better power delivery per unit of weight. Such were, in outline, the considerations which led to the development of the internal combustion engine, and to the gas engine.

A few general remarks will show the superiority of the gas-pressure engine over the steam engine. Since in the gas engine the combustion process occurs in the cylinder, dispensing with the entire boiler unit, water supply, etc., the combustion losses are smaller, and a simpler and better thermal balance is achieved; consequently, fuel combustion is also lower. Furthermore, the power–weight ratio is lower, and, not least, the engine is always ready for operation, as against the steam engine, which must be heated up first. If cars were driven by oil-fired or coal-fired boilers the rapid starting we are now accustomed to would not be possible.

With these great advantages in mind, it may be asked why steam engines are still used today, together with large numbers of gas engines. Leaving aside the fact that the large number of existing machines must be written off gradually, and not scrapped overnight, the principal reason must be economic. The steam engine is better placed with regard to fuel costs, and often this outweighs the disadvantage of its larger size and the need for constant attention, especially if there is plenty of room and operators are easy to obtain. As a result, the steam engine and the internal combustion engine can continue to exist side by side, since one or the other will be preferred according to conditions. However, there may, of course, be surprises in store in future technical development.

*   *   *

In these general remarks we have spoken of internal combustion engines or gas-pressure engines. The first term means that power is produced by combustion inside the cylinder, the second that the piston movement is caused by gas pressure, in contrast to the steam pressure in the steam engine. Furthermore, we must distinguish between gas-burning motors and those which use liquid fuel; in the gas engine the fuel is actually in gaseous form. Hot-air engines, fire-air machines and gas engines began as low-power drives.

The large steam engines of the early and middle 1900s were almost exclusively for the use of "wealthy private persons and big manufacturers", as Reichenbach put it. They were too expensive for the small craftsmen and involved too much labour; a joiner or a mechanic could not afford one, much though he might wish for a small and cheap engine to drive his machines. It was therefore inevitable that the inventors should turn their attention to a suitable apparatus.

The gas motor was developed relatively early in the history of technology; for instance, such a motor was patented in 1784 by a man named Lebon, who also tried to produce the gas required for fuel. A better design was built by Rivaz in 1807, while Reichenbach made attempts — largely unsuccessful — to bring out a small, cheap and movable high-pressure steam engine for use in light industry.

Numerous inventors studied the hot-air engine in the first half of the 19th century; many of them believed that they had already developed the small, handy power machine for the craftsman, but none of the designs proposed was really satisfactory. It is only in 1860 that we hear of the first of the four great names in the history of the internal combustion engine; this was Lenoir, the other three being Nikolaus Otto, Gottlieb Daimler and Rudolf Diesel.

Lenoir, a French mechanical engineer, was thirty-eight when he patented his gas engine with electric-coil ignition; it was most successful and aroused great interest in industry. The engine was gas-driven, and was soundly designed, but it was only an intermediate solution; its consumption of gas was too high, and gas was dear. In his memoirs Carl Benz gives this somewhat facetious description: "It was the first engine with the praiseworthy characteristic of working for ten minutes, with a bit of luck, but it swallowed oil and lubricating grease at such a rate that it was jokingly called a 'rotary oil-ball'."

As with the much-maligned steam engine, this new power-supplier stirred up much opposition to its constructors. The steam engine was no longer a novelty, but was almost traditional, handed down from the previous generation, and was therefore vigorously defended against the new machine, which constituted a competitor. These defenders mockingly said that Lenoir's gas machine did not need a heating unit, but only an oil can. Nevertheless, the criticisms proved unnecessary, since the steam engine maintained its position for some time.

In spite of this, the attack on the steam engine had already begun, although its champions were not yet alive to the fact. Professor Reuleaux, of the Industrial Institute in Berlin, published in 1875 a book on theoretical kinematics; speaking of the need for a small power unit for the use of the craftsman, he said: "The idea of distributing prime energy to small consumers is gaining ground in several forms and in various places. One form is the provision of energy on a contract basis; this has been tried successfully in large towns. One consequence is to bring many families of workers together in one building, so that the people are crowded together in unhealthy conditions, thus reviving an old evil in a new form. However, this is far behind the method of providing the light industries with small power units. Several very successful devices in this class exist already, from the gas engine to the hot-air machine, the small water-column machine, and the petrol engine, which is shown by tests to be most promising . . . These must therefore be considered among the most important of all new machines; they can completely change one section of industry . . . Gas and air engines can be used almost anywhere and are constantly being improved. These little motors are the true power unit for the people."

THE FOUR-STROKE ENGINE

Newspaper reports drew the attention of a young merchant's assistant in Cologne to Lenoir's gas engine; Nikolaus August Otto, self-educated son of an inn-keeper, was twenty-eight years old. He first tried, unsuccessfully, to ignite electrically the gas/air mixture in a model engine. The Prussian Ministry of Commerce considered this a far-fetched idea and flatly refused the support for which he had asked. Otto therefore moderated his plans somewhat and began to study the 'free-piston' gas engine, which operated on the principle of Watt's steam engine. His faithful friend and helper Eugen Langen carried out the patenting of the design, and in 1867 the engine was awarded a gold medal at the Paris Exhibition. Lenoir had found his master; he was only awarded a silver medal, because the gas consumption of his engine was five times that of Otto's. Five years later Otto and Langen established their gas engine factory in Deutz; the technical manager was Gottlieb Daimler from Würtemberg, who was thirty-eight.

Although his gas engine was now selling well, Otto continued his experiments with his earlier invention, the direct-acting engine, from which came the internal combustion engine — known in Germany as the Otto Motor — or four-stroke compression gas engine, the basic principles of which have remained unchanged from 1877 until today.

Four separate operations go to make up the four-stroke cycle: suction, compression, combustion and exhaust; the first stroke of the piston closed the exhaust valves while a mixture of finely-divided fuel and air entered through the inlet valves. The second stroke reduced the size of the cylinder chamber and compressed the mixture, the valves being shut. At the beginning of the third stroke the mixture was ignited by an electric spark and the piston thrust outwards by the exploding fuel. The fourth and final stroke opened the inlet and the exhaust valves, and the combustion products were expelled by the piston.

In the four-stroke motor the work was only done on the third stroke. Several cylinders — Otto started with four — go together to make up the motor, and do not all function on the same stroke, the ignition taking place in successive cylinders at predetermined intervals. This ensures that, in spite of the unbalance of one power-stroke to three power-consuming strokes, the motor runs smoothly.

PETROLEUM

The Reich patent for the four-stroke motor was issued in 1877. The new machine was already being manufactured in Deutz; it was, unlike the steam engine, not directly dependent on coal, but only indirectly, since it ran on coal gas. The designers therefore turned to the problem of finding some other fuel than gas.

The new source of power which offered itself was petroleum, together with its distillation products. Petroleum originated from the remains of very small organisms, deposited millions of years ago over long periods in quiet coastal bays, and subsequently covered by thick beds of sand. The resulting pressure, coupled with the absence of oxygen, favoured the transformation of the organic material, firstly into sapropel, then into oil shale, and finally, in a series of complicated changes which were probably assisted by fermentive bacteria, into what we now know as petroleum.

Petroleum was one of the many products from the growing United States of America. It floated on the surface of the lakes and pools of Pennsylvania in an iridescent oily film, and the Red Indians had for years known it under the name of 'Medicine'. Quacks sold it at high prices; moreover, it was known that this oily substance burned well and could be used for lighting purposes.

'Colonel' Edwin Drake demonstrated at Titusville in 1859, by methodical drilling, that petroleum could be obtained from deep rock strata. At a depth of sixty-odd feet he struck oil, the initial production being roughly 330 gallons a day. By the middle of the 20th century drilling was carried out to 18,000 feet or more and the world production of petroleum in 1957 was over 913 million tons.

The constitution of crude oil varies, and it contains various hydrocarbons. According to its asphalt content, the oil is lighter or heavier than water, and light or dark in colour. Fractional distillation separates the various components of the crude oil, giving petrol, light oils, heavy oils and asphalt. Originally, the refineries only produced paraffin. Grandmother's paraffin

lamp and the 'Lamps of China' were at one time the most important large-scale consumers of paraffin, the lighter fractions—
including petrol — being thrown away because there was no
use for them. Petrol, too, was already known as being easy to
ignite and forming a very explosive mixture with air. Initially,
its rôle in daily life and in business was quite subordinate. It
was used to preserve small creatures, to drive away moths and
insect pests and to remove grease from bones, wool and cleaning
rags.

*   *   *

Otto's four-stroke engine was not a petrol engine. From 1875
experiments were carried out in Deutz with petrol as a new
fuel, although many engineers were sceptical about the utility
of this 'explosive waste' from petroleum refining. The inventors nevertheless studied the possibilities of this remarkable
liquid, as well as those of petroleum. Only the boldest among
them dared to think that it could become the fuel for a new type
of motor, and they were not taken altogether seriously by the
mechanical engineers.

About this time Carl Friedrich Benz began to build gas
engines in Mannheim. His father had been one of the first
engine-drivers in Germany; he himself was a student of the
Polytechnic College of Karlsruhe and had also worked as a
practical designer. With no knowledge of Daimler's successes
in Cologne, Benz built a gas engine of his own design.

In 1883, after much litigation, the German High Court freed
Otto's patent, thus opening the field to the inventors whose designs were based on the four-stroke principle. Although for
several years it looked as though the gas engine would break the
supremacy of the steam engine, the latter held its ground and
finally took on a new lease of life as the driving power for the
generation of electricity, which had just been discovered. The
gas engine — our modern motor — only came into its own
when it was applied to the 'horseless carriage' — the car. Its
history might be said to go back to the day when Otto discharged Daimler, his trusted technical manager, because nothing could be done with so "indescribably thick-headed" a man.
Daimler settled in Cannstatt; thus began a new chapter of
technical development.

FROM THE VELOCIPEDE TO BENZ'S PATENT COACH

The railway had provided rapid connections between towns without greatly assisting local traffic. Trials of steam coaches or steam buses were not successful over long periods, but the desire for more rapid means of travel persisted. Meanwhile, the quality of steel had been improved, and road-springs invented, so that it was possible to increase both the speed and safety of road vehicles. Coaches were more comfortable and quicker, and even the roads improved.

Between 1820 and 1840 new vehicles appeared on the roads: cabriolets and hansoms, and lastly the horse bus. The first tram service started in France in 1855; it ran on raised rails, which were a considerable hindrance to other traffic. Not until 1870 was it realised that the rails could be sunk below the road surface. Horse-drawn trams were found to be more economical than buses; electrification did not begin until 1890. However, one other, most curious, conveyance was seen on the road in the 19th century; this was the bicycle. It had had many 'forerunners' and even Greek gravestones bore pictures of a sort of

The Draisine, built in 1817.

roller cycle. In the 17th century a mechanically-driven device was produced, rather like a wheel-chair. Towards the end of the 18th century there was in France a kind of four-wheeled cycle which was pedalled about by two footmen.

About the end of the 19th century Carl Friedrich von Drais was beginning to make a name for himself; in the first place, he had built a four-wheeled truck running on rails, now known as the 'Draisine', and then set about improving the velocipede.

This peculiar vehicle consisted of a clumsy wooden framework supported on two flat wheels set in line, bearing a hard saddle, and fitted with the steering bar invented by Drais. The rider propelled his mount by pushing on the ground with his feet. Although this was not a particularly easy or efficient method of propulsion, it was possible to move quite fast. This style of travel, which demanded a good deal of effort, looked most comical, so that it is not surprising that wherever he went the inventor aroused laughter which soon turned into mockery. However, Drais felt himself above the spectators' scorn, since his vehicle moved faster than a pedestrian. He distributed pamphlets and journeyed to Paris to give demonstrations. Soon he became involved in difficulties with the authorities, who banned him from many places, and he even fought with those who would not take his remarkable machine seriously. He lost his money and became an eccentric, wearing curious clothes as a sign of defiance as he stamped his way through the streets. This primitive cycle did achieve some temporary recognition here and there, but by 1840 it was forgotten, and some fifteen years later its discoverer died, impoverished and alone.

Very soon afterwards this curious machine was improved and slowly developed to the bicycle. As early as 1840 a machine driven by pedals which were connected by shafts to the rear wheel had been built in Scotland. Twenty-five years later a French designer built a more modern type of bicycle, with a pedal-operated front wheel; this was more efficient but less comfortable to ride. This crank-driven cycle later became well known under the name of the 'Bone-shaker'. The larger the pedal-operated wheel, the faster the bicycle could move; consequently large, high wheels were soon fitted. Thus there gradually developed the velocipede, generally a two-wheeled vehicle, "which was kept in equilibrium by the rotation of the wheels and the skill of the rider".

A report issued in 1890 described the 'penny-farthing' cycle as follows: "The driving wheel is as much as five feet tall, and is rapidly rotated by the rider, perched high up on his little saddle, by means of the pedal crank, and a small guiding-wheel set at the back and controlled by the steering bar, which the driver turns to left or right. The principal difficulty in bicycling is not the maintenance of the vehicle's balance, at least as long

Top left: The first Benz car of 1885–6, based on the patent of 29th January 1886.

Bottom left: The first Daimler car of 1885–6.

Right: The car of the future; T.3, the third Rover prototype of a gas-turbine powered car.

A Scottish motor rally, held at Selkirk in 1901.

as a certain speed is reached, since the tendency to tip sideways
begins only when the rider slows down; consequently, he is
forced to descend when an obstacle is encountered. The main
difficulty lies much more in avoiding falling on one's head,
which easily happens if the front wheel runs over even a small
obstacle."

Attempts were made to meet this shortcoming by the introduction of the so-called safety bicycle and of the 'bicyclette',

A typical 'penny-farthing' bicycle, late 19th century.

both of which closely resembled the later familiar bicycle. In
addition, a tricycle was suggested. These improved bicycles, of
which there were many types, were very successful. In 1883
the *Handbook of Bicycle Sport* recorded: "In one of the latest
struggles for the championship of Germany, bicycles covered a
kilometre in an average time of 117 seconds. The speed therefore corresponds approximately to that of a Berlin suburban
train or of a large steamer. A fair average speed when cycling
on a good country road would be 11 m.p.h., with a maximum
of 15 m.p.h. True, speeds of 20 and even 22 m.p.h. have been
reached, but only for a short time."

Once again success had come to a machine first considered a
'ridiculous invention', whose builders and pioneers had been
mocked. But it was still a long time before cyclists could venture

F

on to the roads without being followed by crowds of laughing children.

In 1878 R. H. Thurston wrote in his *History of the Steam Engine*: "An invention is not a creation, but a formation, and every great discovery is either a combination of smaller discoveries or the last step in a chain of development." A long series of discoveries and modifications proposed by many clever men eventually transformed both bicycle and tricycle into the favourite means of conveyance of millions at the end of the 19th century.

Several discoveries prompted by the bicycle contributed substantially to the development of automobile transport, such as the steel spoke, the roller bearing and, above all else, the pneumatic tyre, made possible by Goodyear's discovery in 1839 of the vulcanisation of rubber. Six years after Goodyear's proposal an inventor suggested the use of a hollow air-filled rubber pipe to cushion the shocks. But he was laughed at, since his idea could not then be realised. It was only in 1889 that Dunlop successfully introduced the combination of tube and tyre.

This broke down all barriers and innumerable crowds of cyclists invaded the countryside. It was now no longer possible to delay the construction of a new and greatly improved road system in all civilised countries, which soon became covered as new road-building methods were developed. This gave new impetus to business and traffic and the way was thus opened to the development of the motor-car.

THE PETROL CARRIAGE

The wish to have a horseless carriage is quite likely as old as the invention of the carriage. Ancient monuments of the Pharaohs show vehicles which appear to be driven by the thrust of a jet of steam. Of course for thousands of years man's imagination exceeded his capacity to perform, and it was only in the 19th century that this wish could be fulfilled. Even in the 17th century and the beginning of the 18th, clever and curious-looking vehicles were proposed. Their designers certainly had imagination, but their skill and the technical knowledge of the time were incapable of producing a horseless carriage. Almost always the appearance of such vehicles caused riots, in which the enraged mob often smashed the curious contrivances, before they collapsed of themselves. For instance, a French inventor demonstrated in 1740 a coach driven by a huge clockspring. The spectators were neither pleased nor amused, but gave the good man a thorough drubbing, saying that "he could do much harm on the roads".

This was followed by the era of the steam vehicle; steam coaches ran quite frequently, especially on the roads of England. But opposition was soon shown. The counter-propaganda of the supporters and owners of mail coaches grew, and finally led to the Act that every horseless carriage must be preceded by a man bearing a red flag sixty yards in front of the coach, to give warning of the approaching danger. Moreover, a speed limit was imposed, of four miles an hour in the country and two miles an hour in the town. Steam carriage traffic did not suffer greatly from this Act, since it was, for technical reasons, doomed to failure. Nevertheless, it was to hinder the development of the automobile in Britain for a long time.

In France ideas were more practical and less conservative, and the visitors to the 1865 Paris Exhibition greatly admired the 'Lotz automobile'. This was an easily-steered steam tractor, which pushed a number of carriages before it. It is even recorded that one or two steam-driven velocipedes existed for a short time.

The steam carriages were still too heavy, but by now the first light gas engines were available, and it was not long before Lenoir installed one of his petroleum engines in a carriage and with it covered a distance of some ten miles.

In 1875 the German engineer Marcus introduced a car with a short-running four-stroke engine in Vienna. The vehicle was fitted with wheels from a horse carriage and the driver sat without protection on a hard wooden bench. Marcus was unlucky, for the spectators could not stand the noise made by his machine and the authorities immediately forbade further trials. The inventor might have been able to try again elsewhere in the Austro-Hungarian Empire, but he was so poor that he could not undertake further experiments. His car was placed in a museum. When it was taken out in 1950 for a demonstration, it moved quite easily under its own power.

In the early 1880s the first battery-driven electric automobiles were running in Paris. Several inventors tried to apply electricity to driving vehicles and many contemporary observers thought that the development of the automobile would follow a radically new line. But these vehicles disappeared so quickly from the scene that the critics did not even have time for their usual jeremiads.

Nonetheless, they were to have plenty of opportunity to oppose innovation — in the form of the 'petrol carriage' — in the years which followed. The petrol-driven car was born in Cannstatt, where Gottlieb Daimler had settled with his old colleague Maybach, who had left Deutz with him. It was here that he developed the Otto engine to a motor whose importance in the history of technology is equal to that of the first steam engine.

The gas engine was still bound, as it were, to the gas main, and must be freed if it was to drive carriages or ships. In fact, a new fuel was required; Daimler chose petroleum and, soon after, petrol, because it is easily ignited. He had already built petrol motors for Otto and Langen in Deutz, but they weighed 13 cwt. per horse-power and turned at only 180 r.p.m. If they were run any faster, ignition did not occur. Daimler improved the ignition system and brought the engine speed to 900 r.p.m. His new motor ran on petrol, weighed only 88 lb. per horse-power and had an efficient ignition system.

In the autumn of 1883 and during the following winter Daimler built three engines of this type, and he and the indefatigable Maybach continued to experiment in his summer-house. Neighbours who heard the banging and the explosion of the engine became nervous and called the police. "It was a long business," wrote Daimler in his memoirs, "for endless trials were needed together with the untiring work of a practical engineer."

Naturally, Daimler now wished to travel by means of his motor, since this was the real object of all his work. Having no suitable carriage, he fitted the engine to a wooden cycle. And so it came about that the era of motor travel began with a motor-cycle, although the significance of this combination was certainly not realised at the time.

In the following autumn there was great excitement on the road near Stuttgart, for Daimler and Maybach were driving the four-wheel horseless carriage from Cannstatt to Esslingen. Apart from the motor equipment, this vehicle looked very like a

horse-drawn carriage and the absence of horses was very striking. The pioneers reached the 'enormous speed' of nearly
eleven miles an hour.

In the same year Daimler received the first French patent for
his motor, and in Paris he saw for the first time Carl Benz's
motor-car. The final German patent was awarded to Daimler

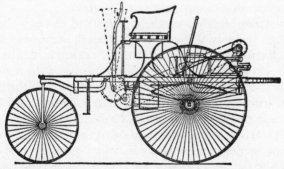

The 'Benz' Patent; the title-page of the patent for a gas-engined
vehicle, granted to the Benz Co. in Mannheim on 29th January 1886.

for a "vehicle with a gas or petroleum engine" on 29th August
1885. Exactly five months later, on 29th January 1886, the
Imperial Patent Office in Berlin granted Benz patent number
37435, for "a vehicle with gas-engine drive". Daimler's high-
speed engine and Benz's motor-car provided the final impulse
for the 'motorisation' of world transport.

*   *   *

Carl Benz had founded his gas-engine works in 1883 and had begun making a type of two-stroke motor; he was also busy with his car. The inventor — whose moustache and bushy hair make his portraits show a resemblance to Albert Schweitzer — aroused a good deal of interest and unrest in the town as he drove his motor-car through the streets at the tremendous speed of two German miles, about nine English miles, per hour. He was able to do this only after much trouble, for a law of the kingdom of Baden forbade "conveyances driven by prime energy". His first automobile was soon put on the market; Benz's designs were to show the automobile industry the way for years to come.

The famous Daimler Motor Co. was established in Cannstatt in 1890, and in 1900 — the year Daimler died — produced the first modern motor-car. As the gleaming new car stood in the factory, someone remembered that the owner's daughter had a Spanish name, and so the car was christened 'Mercedes'.

The firms of Daimler and Benz amalgamated in 1926. Their founders had created the motor-car, which had now developed to such a point that its influence on the civilised world was greater than that of any previous invention.

At first the horseless carriage, propelled through the streets 'as though by invisible forces', was obliged, like everything new, to fight for recognition and to struggle against criticism. Man's love of sport was very helpful in this respect, and the new adventure of a race between machines destroyed much of the mockery and mistrust. The first international 'race for horseless carriages' was run in 1894 between Paris and Rouen. A total of 102 cars started; many were petrol-driven, but others were propelled by steam, compressed air, water pressure and electric motors, for the petrol engine had not yet overcome the scepticism of the engineers. Only fifteen cars — all those with petrol engines — finished the race. But the winning cars had attained the astonishing average speed of twelve miles an hour; every one was powered with a Daimler motor.

Between 1907 and 1909 a Benz car crossed Africa from Dar-es-Salaam to Swakopmund. A Protos car from Berlin crossed the American Continent from East to West in 1908; it then crossed Russia from Vladivostok to St. Petersburg and finally, for good measure, continued across Europe to Paris. It was a fantastic and quite incredible reliability test, at a time when many people had never seen a car at all.

This sealed the victory of the automobile, although the 'experts' still said that motoring was as unhealthy as alcohol or nicotine, although critics declared that the automobile — having no brain — was inferior to the horse, in spite of angry country folk who stoned the rattling vehicles, threatened the motorists with flails, or strewed the roads with broken glass — convinced that they were right.

In time, the wrath of the non-motoring public died down, but the hidden resistance, the hostility to the motor-car, continued well into the 20th century. The pedestrian raged against the motor vehicles, not only because they bothered him, but also because he believed that the drivers were likely to destroy his peace of mind. This was the feeling that could be sensed between the two wars. Those who stood to lose by the progress of the automobile were particularly obstinate, such as the blacksmiths, saddlers, coachmen and ostlers. In America alone there were in 1890 more than three million people earning a good living by providing transport with eighteen million horses and mules.

Even in the 1930s and 1940s books were written containing scathing condemnations of motors and machines; for instance, Josef Popp wrote in 1929: "The Titan spirit of Prometheus threatens to become a Frankenstein's monster which will turn against its creator, Man himself. We must begin a counter-offensive against the Machine . . ."

The Italian Nobel Prizewinner Pirandello wrote in 1934 in his novel *Cranks*: "This is the triumph of folly. So much genius and so much zeal is devoted to the creation of this monstrous thing, which ought to remain a tool, but instead becomes our master. The machine, which knows no rest, will swallow up our life and soul."

*   *   *

In a few decades the motor-car spread over the whole world. A young farmer's son from Dearborn, named Henry Ford, put his first automobile on the road in 1893, after three years' work. After a short journey it stopped; and yet — this was the forerunner of many million Ford cars.

Sixteen years later, the famous Model T Ford was produced

in the Ford Works in Detroit; it was ugly and noisy, but cheap, reliable and indestructible. It was the first car for the little man, who had long since given up mocking the motor-car. When the Model T was finally abandoned in 1927, outdated in every respect by the newer models, the Ford Works had built and sold, over a period of twenty-eight years, fifteen million cars of this one type!

The development of the engine is always bound up with that of the automobile and the aeroplane; the first designs were both bulky and heavy. When Wilbur and Orville Wright began their experiments with powered aircraft they had to construct their own engine. It had four cylinders and drove a single propeller.

As time went on, motors became more powerful and since aircraft engineers — and automobile designers — were continuously pressing for more power, several cylinders were arranged in line. Aircraft engines were made with not only four, but six, eight and finally even twenty-four cylinders, growing longer and longer in the process. This led to setting two rows of cylinders side by side, to form the shorter V engine. Then two Vs together formed the radial engine, which could accommodate more cylinders still, so that eventually a multiple radial engine had thirty-six cylinders! In the whole process of development the designers eliminated every excess ounce of weight, with a care which might have been copied from a watch designer, producing engines that were miracles of precision. A single radial engine of this kind delivered as much power as two modern express locomotives, and yet weighed less than a single wheel from one of them.

Engineering development had travelled far, and with what results!

The steam engine had been 'an invention of the devil' and therefore opposed. The bicycle was laughable and its inventor reduced to poverty. Steam coaches, steam locomotives and railways were all attacked in word and in deed. Soft soap had been spread on the rails to halt the trains. For years car designers and drivers had been considered fools, had been abandoned by their families and by their friends.

Neither the courageous innovators nor the obstinate and narrow-minded conservatives had any idea where the path that was being followed would lead. But followed it was.

> "But I think it most unlikely that aeronautics will ever
> be able to exercise a decisive influence on travel. Man is
> not an albatross . . ."
>
> H. G. Wells, 1901.

WINGS FOR ADAM

*A dream come true — The hazards of flying — Prophecies false and
true — Man-made wings — By-paths of fancy — "The most wonderful things in the world" — The balloon — Adventurous balloonists —
The dirigible airship — The Heroic Era — First steps in aeronautics —
The beginnings of aerial travel — The last laugh*

NOT very long ago, in a typical travel bureau with modern
furnishings and decorated with attractive posters, where the
present-day traveller books his aeroplane ticket, I saw on the
wall an indicator, taller than a man, showing the total number
of passengers carried by all airlines in a year. The broad blue
line, like the rising mercury in a clinical thermometer, would
obviously soon pass the red pointer against the hundred million
mark.

Just think, a hundred million air passengers in one year! The
head of the travel bureau did not seem very impressed. It was
only a chance reference to a film of Lindbergh's life, then showing in the town, which brought any reaction from him at all.
He said that he often wondered what the pioneer pilot of thirty
years before would have said about the tremendous increase in
civil air travel.

I, too, had similar thoughts on seeing the illuminated sign of
one of the foremost airlines of the world which proudly displays
the total number of Atlantic crossings by their planes. When
these lines were written the neon-tube figures, which sometimes
change every hour, showed more than 65,000 flights.

Is it really only thirty years since Lindbergh flew his 'Spirit
of St. Louis' single-handed across the Atlantic? He later wrote
about it: "Bill MacCracken, Under-Secretary of State for Air,
flew in from Washington. I asked him about riding lights for
the 'Spirit of St. Louis'. New regulations require that every

71

plane flying at night should have lights; I had left them off to avoid trouble and save weight.

" 'Could I have permission to fly without lights for this special flight?' I asked.

"MacCracken smiled. 'Well now, there won't be much night traffic where you're going,' he replied. 'I think we can let you go without.' "

A DREAM COME TRUE

Often there peeps out from behind the colourful, peaceable operations of air traffic another, darker picture: the military airfield with high-speed jet fighters, inter-continental jet bombers and capacious transports for airborne troops and equipment.

It was in 1903 that the Wright Brothers, Orville and Wilbur, successfully made the first, short flight with a controlled powered aircraft. Forty years later, hundreds of European towns were laid in ruins by the aerial bombardments of the Second World War, while in 1945 the 'Enola Gay' dropped the first atomic bomb on Hiroshima.

Is that the other end of the path which began at the turn of the century? Have science and technology given us in air travel a gift of the Danae? No one can answer this dreadful question, without first examining the first fifty years of powered flight from a different angle.

On 17th December 1903 the following telegram from Kitty Hawk was received by the Wright family in Dayton, Ohio:

"Successful — four flights on Thursday morning — took off with motors from level ground — average speed thirty miles an hour — longest flight fifty-nine seconds — inform Press — home for Christmas — Orville."

By 1939 air traffic had registered 4½ million passengers, while in 1955 alone nearly 68 million people flew on the air routes of the world. In that year a single airline carried nearly 700,000 passengers across the Atlantic. In the same year another company — one of several — clocked up more than 30 million air-miles; the airlines of the world together had nearly 3,000 aircraft in operation, logging a total of 1,250 million miles. All the American airlines alone ran 1,100 flights every twenty-four hours, carrying 150,000 persons, with a total fuel consumption of 2,640,000 gallons — in a single day.

Shortly before the outbreak of the Second World War, almost all the Atlantic traffic was carried by ships. In 1957 the situation was entirely different. At any hour of the night in the spring of 1957 — shortly after sunset in Western Europe and shortly before midnight in New York — there would have been some 120 aircraft over the sea, bearing about 3,500 passengers agreeably engaged in filling in the time between take-off and landing by eating, reading or sleeping.

Flight is changing our world much more than we realise. The technique of flight itself has also been changing very rapidly since the middle of the 20th century. The speed of flight is increasing by leaps and bounds. The Lockheed 'Starfighter' reaches 1,800 miles an hour in operational flight. From 1960 there will be civil aircraft available, for the man in a hurry, travelling at more than 600 miles an hour.

Aircraft are growing in size. The four-jet airliners of 1960 — of which well over 300 have been ordered — carry up to 150 passengers on each flight, and each aircraft can replace one of the largest 'Blue Riband' liners. Twenty-five such aircraft are expected to carry approximately a million passengers a year across the Atlantic by 1960.

Aircraft are flying higher and higher. A rocket research aircraft still on the secret list in 1957 reached a height of at least ninety miles.

No one can foresee where this development will end.

True, these are cold, sober figures which tell us nothing of the human stories hidden behind the bare statistics. But so often technical developments have very great effects on the lives of human beings. The speed of an aircraft has often been the means of saving a sick man's life, and we have little idea how often this has happened. Only occasionally do we read in the papers of incidents which throw light on the importance of air travel. An eight-year-old boy, a sufferer from hæmophilia, was bleeding to death in Vienna. The new drug which would save his life was only available in America. A consignment was ordered by cable and the next scheduled Atlantic flight carried a package, which reached Vienna twenty-two hours later. The boy's life was saved.

There is no denying that two world wars have served to accelerate the development of flying. Perhaps air travel would not have reached its present achievements in the easy-going days of peace. It is an open secret that the development of military aircraft subsidises that of civil planes. No aircraft factory could develop a new airliner without a parallel order for military machines. Thus military transports are developed from bombers, and airliners from transports.

The aeroplane has made possible the discovery of the earth from a new angle. The first discovery began hardly 5,000 years ago, with the birth of astronomy and sailing, and reached its peak in the era of the great voyages of discovery, as explorers pieced together their knowledge of oceans and continents to obtain the map of the earth's surface as we know it today. The new discovery of the earth opened when the dream of Icarus, the age-old human desire to conquer distance and the unknown, was realised and the era of land and sea exploration gave way to the air age.

Judging by the successes achieved in so few years, the pioneers of air travel would seem to have had a triumphal progress. In fact, it was a hard road, marked by many mistakes and much opposition. The development of aeronautics proves anew that it is sometimes more stimulating and helpful to make mistakes and to struggle against opposition, than to be lucky and to succeed without effort.

THE HAZARDS OF FLYING

"If you want to know about the future of air travel you'd better see a clairvoyant," once wrote the American airline expert William P. Lear. "But don't ask an engineer. He can only tell you about the technical possibilities and not what will really happen."

We shall not discuss whether air travel is not, after all, rather a problem for engineers than an exercise for soothsayers, but there is this much truth in Lear's remark — that man's longing to fly and his efforts to conquer the air cannot be understood only from a rational and technical viewpoint. We only need to remember that, if we examine the various species of animals on the earth, three out of four land creatures can fly; in other words, out of a total of some one and a half million known species of animal, roughly one million can move through the air.

The first unassisted flights must have occurred millions of years ago, long before man or creatures like him occurred on earth. It may have been some 300 million years ago that an early species of insect developed wings, during the Palæozoic period; the era when insects began to reach the land and to fly is known as the Carboniferous Era. The first means of flying developed by Nature were very strange; the earliest flying creatures had large dorsal plates which moved like screws, but after a few million years, a short time in the earth's history, Nature gave the flying insects a much more efficient flying device, the reticulate wing. Gigantic dragonflies flew through the humid jungles and primitive Equisetum forests, huge creatures with a wing span of almost a yard. It seems difficult to imagine dragonflies whose transparent wings spread nearly as wide as those of a goose!

Hundreds of millions of years later the Saurians dominated the earth, first in the water and later on land. Here again Nature opened a new dimension to the animal kingdom and some of the great reptiles took to the air; great flying dragons developed, with a wing-spread of more than twenty feet, soaring like living gliders over the oceans and forests of the Mesozoic Age. For a long time the flying reptiles shared the air with the insects and it was fifty million years later that the first of all birds, the Archæopteryx, appeared.

Even the animals did not find flying an easy matter to begin with, and the 'living aeroplanes' had considerable difficulties in taking off and landing, while the first birds were far from being as elegant in flight as the swallows. Constantly striving after perfection, Nature developed during further millions of years better means of flying, streamlined bodies, 'retractable under-carriages', wings of remarkable structure made of thousands of feathers, and even translucent membrane wings.

It is therefore not surprising that earthbound man should have stared enviously into the air, as he tried to discover the secret of bird flight. The early Greeks and Romans already knew that birds used their tails to control their height and that they took off into the wind. Dædalus and Icarus are said to have made wings of feathers and wax for their flight from Crete, but Icarus "passed too near the sun" so that his wings melted and he fell. Almost all races have similar legends of early flights.

The most experienced aircraft constructors once thought that man's best means of imitating the birds would be to copy their manner of flight. This idea was for decades a hindrance to the development of effective aircraft and sometimes led designers astray. It is a fact that most of the early inventors failed with their frail birdlike craft because of their movable wings. Moreover, since much of the knowledge assembled by the Greeks and Romans had been lost, man's imagination was for centuries dominated by very strange theories of the flight of birds.

It was only towards the end of the 18th century that Sir George Cayley, who has been called the father of air travel, gave his classical definition of powered flight as "the problem of making a surface support a given weight by the application of power to the resistance of the air".

Nearly a hundred years later Otto Lilienthal published his epoch-making book *Bird Flight as the Basis of the Art of Flying*, based on twenty-five years of studying the flight of storks with his brother Gustav.

PROPHECIES FALSE AND TRUE

As far back as we can look man has made attempts to fly, but often the achievements of those pioneer inventors became legendary, and it is now no longer possible to distinguish the poetic element from the facts. And as we have already seen with other human inventions, the idea of flight has always met with scepticism, hostility or ridicule.

For instance, towards the end of the 17th century a learned writer issued a warning: "All the newspapers would record deaths caused here and there by falling out of the air, with the fliers having to be lifted out of the hedges and buried half-eaten; if every rascal could fly, how they would insult everybody below them or bestrew them with dirt and stones, and leave the marks of their mischievous passage everywhere, even on the roofs of churches and town halls." Almost equally prophetic is another view expressed shortly before flying became a reality by Zeidler in his book *The Flying Traveller or The Philosophical Art of Flying*: "It is enough to make one's hair stand on end to think of all the damage, danger and injury which aeronautics will inevitably bring to the human race once it spreads."

It is amusing to read such opinions from earlier days, but it is easy to forget how such opinions checked the inventiveness of progressive and thinking men. As late as 1908, when powered flight was beginning to develop, the *Engineering News* prophesied in a leading article: "Aerial transport of passengers or goods will never be able to compete with land transport. Consequently, flying will be restricted to military and sporting uses; although military possibilities seem rather doubtful, the sporting uses, on the contrary, are fairly certain."

The great pioneer flier Louis Paulhan was undoubtedly right, when, two years after this leading article appeared, he said: "One of the most dangerous occupations in flying is prophecy. Most of the prophets have bitterly regretted their flashes of intuition."

Nonetheless, these 'flashes of intuition' continued to be poured out on the early aviators, and even today they still distort the latest reports from the laboratories and design offices. It is a fact that mankind can more easily believe in the existence of mysterious and inexplicable phenomena than in the possibility of certain definite technical developments. Consequently, hardly anyone believes the well-founded idea that aircraft will be flying at about 1,800 miles an hour by the turn of the century, even though this assumption is very conservative and likely to be considerably exceeded in fact.

*   *   *

If we for a moment shorten the time scale of historical development, we shall see how short is the period in which man has made himself wings. The era of fossil *homo sapiens* goes back some 60,000 years, and that of modern man 30,000 years. If we compress this whole period within the space of twelve months, then the discovery of the wheel occurred on 20th October. Man's first use of bronze occurred on 7th November and the Iron Age began on the 23rd. Archytas demonstrated the 'wooden dove' — driven by reaction — on 3rd December. Christ was born on 8th December. And it was only on 29th December at ten o'clock in the evening that James Watt perfected the steam engine! Aeronautics — or at least what we nowadays understand by aeronautics — would have begun on the last day of the year, at 11.42 a.m., with the first successful powered flight by the Wright Brothers. The First World War started at five minutes to three and the first atom bomb fell on Hiroshima at about midnight on the last day. At that rate, we are now in the first day of the New Year and it is seven minutes past three in the morning. Only fifteen hours and twenty-five minutes have passed since the Wright Brothers' flight.

Philosophers and poets have depicted man's longing to fly. Goethe wrote: "It is innate in all of us, and our feelings carry us upward and forward," while Schiller exclaimed: "Ah, had I but pinions, had I but wings!"

And now we have them — Adam has taken himself wings.

MAN-MADE WINGS

My friend Arthur C. Clarke, the English author, once described in one of his fascinating stories a race of intelligent beings from another planet who possessed highly-developed brains but no hands; they could solve the most complex mathematical problems, without ever being able to dissect a flower to examine its structure or build ships to link the continents of their planet. A closer examination shows that this imaginary situation is not at all far-fetched. Man does indeed possess very skilful tools — his hands — in addition to his brain, which gives him the power of thought and of learning from the past; he was able to travel on land and on water very early, but with regard to the air he was in much the same position as Clarke's imagined handless creatures. Like them, man was able to do something which was forbidden to the earthbound creatures around him, for he was able to fly in thought, to travel in imagination through space to the planets, which in his early days he held to be the home of his gods, who were already able to fly. Perhaps when we see rockets nowadays, climbing heavenwards on their incandescent jets of gas, we are reminded a little of the chariot of the Sun God of the Ancient Greeks.

Tradition records that in a moment of weakness Helios allowed his mortal son Phæton to drive his sun chariot for a single day; but the young man soon allowed the winged horses to leave their normal course, and to set heaven and earth ablaze. The clouds began to smoke and mountains and forests burst

A poster from the early days of ballooning.

R.101, Britain's last dirigible airship which crashed at Beauvais, France, on her way to India in 1930.

The end of the German airship 'Hindenburg' which

into flame. Earth herself appealed urgently to Zeus to destroy the clumsy charioteer with his thunderbolt. This he did, and Phæton fell like a meteor into the Eridanus. On his tombstone were graven the words: "He was great, for great was his daring."

The Bible, too, has its references to flight, and the fiery chariot is mentioned in the book of Kings: "And it came to pass, as they still went on, and talked, that, behold, there appeared a chariot of fire, and horses of fire, and parted them both asunder, and Elijah went up into heaven by a whirlwind" (II Kings 2: 11).

A Persian legend, some 2,500 years old, depicts the dramatic flight of Kai Kawus, King of Persia, who had discovered that the earth was "tiny, as nothing beneath the arch of heaven". This led him to build an aerial carriage of thin wood and spear hafts, to which he tethered young male eagles. Large lumps of meat were suspended above them, out of their reach, so that they took to their wings in an attempt to enjoy the proffered meal. It would seem that the King had some idea of the needs of modern air travel, in that he took with him plentiful supplies of food and rare wines. The eagles did carry him upwards with his carriage, as they strained after the meat, but they soon tired and the King had to come down. Although everything had really gone as planned, one of the King's counsellors told him that he belonged in a mad-house. Inasmuch as he was a 'pioneer of flight', the King — normally respected by his subjects — could hardly have expected anything else.

Even the tactical Air Force appears in legend. An Indian tradition tells how Vishnu, who was accustomed to fly on his giant bird, the Garuda, one day found himself imitated by a presumptious weaver, who built a wooden aircraft with the bird's shape. The weaver flew to the King's palace and landed in the Princess's quarters, which were clearly quite large! The Princess seemed highly delighted — not so much with the aviator, as with the supposed god — and shortly afterwards married him, whereupon the King decided to exploit his good fortune to the full by waging war on his neighbours. After all, with a god for a son-in-law and an Air Force in reserve, he could scarcely lose. The weaver, forced to make the best of a bad situation, had to fly his craft over the battlefield, but fortunately for him, Vishnu, feeling his own reputation at stake,

G

took a hand and routed the enemy. Overcome by terror, the weaver confessed his deception, but, although the King was by no means pleased, he was much more frightened of the consequences if the truth came out. He therefore ratified the marriage of his daughter and raised his son-in-law to high office, instead of having him beheaded as a swindler.

Even the ancient Greek myths are full of stories of flying gods and their human imitators. The best known is the legend of Dædalus and Icarus, who had taken refuge in Crete, but, falling foul of King Minos, had been thrown into prisoñ. The sentries were very generous to them, for Dædalus was able to fabricate for himself and his son wings of feathers stuck together with wax and to try them out. Before they started Icarus was given theoretical instruction by his father, with the final warning not to fly too near the sea or the sun. They both started well but Icarus, enchanted with his flight, forgot the instructions and flew so near the sun that the wax of his wings melted and he fell into the sea which still bears his name.

Many generations have come under the influence of the legends of flight handed down from antiquity; the fact that they were legends has been quite unimportant, for it is not bare facts alone which assist progress. The energy of the human spirit and the curiosity and intuition of genius played an equal part. Repeatedly men have sacrificed strength, health and life to the dream of flight. Their story is a unique romance of ardent enquiry, and it would need a complete encyclopædia to record all the incidents and ideas, whether born of magic or of pure research, which this objective has called forth.

Professor Berthold Laufer, Curator of the Chicago Field Museum for Natural History till his death in 1934, wrote that: "The progress of aeronautics is not due to our generation alone, for it is the result of a long and gradual development, the result of creative planning, tireless efforts, unceasing research and a chain of successes and failures spread over many years."

BY-PATHS OF FANCY

Winged horses, mechanical airships, carriages drawn by birds, sails, genii and gigantic magnets, to name only a few of the possibilities named in legend, were not the only means proposed at different times to achieve flight.

The ancient Chinese used large box kites for aerial recon-
naissances over towns they were about to attack, and Japanese
records tell of similar applications. In fact, on one occasion
enterprising robbers are said to have used a kite to steal gold
from a castle, which led to a ban on large kites of this kind.

In the Middle Ages flying was for a long time regarded as of
the devil. Witches flew on broomsticks to the Blocksberg Mountain in the Harz, and tricksters claimed to have made successful
flights; as a result, when genuine inventors tried to put their
theories into action, they ran the risk of being thought to have a
pact with the devil.

Nonetheless, over and over again bold men tried to copy
Icarus. Fact and fancy are so inextricably mixed in the accounts handed down to us that we can hardly distinguish
between the dreams and the deeds of pioneers.

Simon, the Magus, who is mentioned in the Book of Acts, is
said to have been "borne upwards by demons", in the presence
of the third Pope, Petrus Romanus; the Magus announced that
he intended to return to the heavens, and the people therefore
hailed him as a god. Petrus Romanus reported that his prayers
caused the magician to fall.

In the beginning of the 16th century, Damian, an Italian in
the service of the King of Scotland, essayed a flight, using
feathers, to overtake a diplomatic mission on its way to France.
Like all imitators of Icarus, Damian knew it to be impossible
to rise from the ground by means of artificial wings; unfortunately, instead of drawing the only correct conclusion and aban-
doning the experiment, he tried to take off from a roof, fell into
the courtyard and broke his legs. The only novelty about the
whole affair was the explanation — that, unhappily, a few
chicken feathers had been included in the artificial wings and
their natural tendency to return to the fowl-yard brought the
flier down.

In Germany Berblinger, the 'Tailor of Ulm', who made an
unsuccessful flight before a large crowd, is still sometimes remembered. He was clever enough to begin his flight above the
Danube, and although almost drowned, did not break any
bones. Most of the crowd laughed heartily, except those who
tried to beat the dripping aviator, who they considered had
deceived them.

The idea of flying with artificial wings was gradually abandoned during the 17th century, and yet, even in the middle of
the 20th century, we find now and then 'bird men' who claim
to be able to fly with the aid of home-made wings, using their
own strength to drive them. One of them offered to demonstrate his skill to the Civil Aviation official of the Government

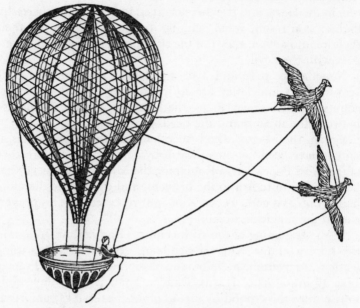

A suggested method of 'guiding a balloon at will', 1801.

of one German province, intending to fly several times around
the tower of Frankfurt Cathedral under his own power. The
official representative refused the demonstration offered and
thus saved the discoverer from becoming a second 'Tailor of
Ulm'.

Since man-made pinions were unsuccessful, other means were
sought. Cyrano de Bergerac, the French author who worked in
Paris in the first half of the 17th century, hit upon the idea of
using the dew, which obviously drops from the stars at night to
the earth and returns to heaven when the sun rises. What more
natural than to use this 'uplift'? De Bergerac provided one of
his fictional heroes with bottles filled with dew and attached to

a belt so that (in his romance) the man was borne upwards. Unfortunately, fearing that he would be carried too high, he broke too many bottles and was forced to land. On the same page there appears the suggestion that balls should be filled with the smoke of sacrifices which "as is well known, rises to heaven in accordance with its purpose". Another suggestion with a very learned ring was to lift an iron carriage with a "ball of extracted magnetic attractive force", the ball being naturally fastened to the carriage. This was indeed like a man trying to lift himself by his own boot straps.

Many inventors in the 19th century could count themselves fortunate that their proposals were never put into practice, for there is no knowing what might have happened if all those fragile structures of wood and paper had really flown! The *Leipziger Illustrierte*, published in 1847, shows pictures of an aircraft driven by gun-cotton. Explosions in a combustion chamber were to give a reciprocal motion to a series of levers which operated the wings of the aircraft. The inventor thought that gun-cotton would be lighter than a contemporary steam engine with all its gear. The artist depicted the worthy aviator standing upright in the aircraft in his top hat and morning coat. Everything was very simple except the raising of the money to build the machine, a fact which undoubtedly saved the inventor a great deal of trouble.

Inevitably, the almost inexhaustible imagination of Jules Verne brought forth a flying machine. His 'aeronef' resembled a thirty-seven-masted ship; the masts bore seventy-six horizontal airscrews, with a total of 230 blades. Many years later a historian wrote rather sardonically that it was strange that the manufacturers of airscrews should have let this tremendous outlet for their products go almost unnoticed.

But by the time that Verne's Utopian story was published, flying was gradually nearing realisation. We must not forget Hermann Ganswindt, the 'Edison of Schöneberg', who is normally quoted as one of the pioneers of space flight. Among numerous machines he designed was a type of helicopter which actually flew a few yards. Like all innovators Ganswindt stoutly defended his idea. "I am convinced that within a few years every household will have one or several flying machines, once my invention has brought aerial travel into being." That was written in 1891. Ganswindt had tried thoughtlessly to anticipate the development of half a century. But the public behaved as it always does in such cases: it laughed.

We shall meet Hermann Ganswindt again as the real discoverer of the dirigible airship.

"THE MOST WONDERFUL THINGS IN THE WORLD"

The achievement of dynamic flight with heavier-than-air machines proved unrealisable for the early pioneers of air travel; suitable power units were not available to them. They therefore followed another line which, while simpler and easier, ultimately turned out to be a by-road; this was the use of balloons and airships.

The 17th century research workers, led by Galileo and his pupil Torricelli, physicist and mathematician, were studying the weight and pressure of the air and associated problems. According to current ideas the atmosphere was a sea of air in which ships could sail as in the ocean, once the 'thin layer of heavy air' surrounding the earth had been penetrated.

As early as 1770 this idea fascinated an Italian, Francesco de Lana. He already knew of the air pump discovered by Otto von Guericke, demonstrated for the first time in Regensburg in 1654, and was also familiar with the properties of the vacuum which had been studied by Galileo and Torricelli. He developed the idea of evacuating four hollow copper spheres to make them lighter than air, so that they could carry an aerial boat. He calculated quite correctly the lift of the evacuated spheres, but overlooked the fact that they would be crushed by the pressure of the air around them. Thick-walled spheres could naturally resist the external pressure, but their weight would far exceed their lift. From these basic ideas, which were only theoretically correct, he drew up the exact plan of an airship, together with a method of manufacturing the copper spheres; he even developed a sort of theory of navigation. Convinced of the correctness of his ideas, he envisaged the difficulties of his project as follows: "On the other hand a greater difficulty is to restrict the vessel's speed when the wind is strong, because of the danger of being wrecked by driving against the mountains, which form the reefs of our sea of ether. I admit that our airship may encounter great dangers, but the aerial sea has no coastline, although it offers the advantage that the vessels will not need harbours in which to take refuge, for if danger threatens they can always descend from the higher levels of the air and land upon the ground." Clearly, de Lana considered an emergency landing an easy matter, but 200 years later the

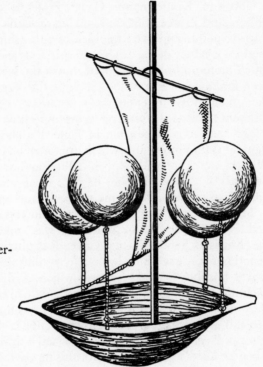

de Lana's lighter-than-air ship.

Wright Brothers were better informed. Wilbur Wright once said: "The only danger in flying is the ground."

Francesco de Lana, however, was very concerned about the possible consequences of building flying machines: "God would not suffer such an intention to take effect, by reason of the disturbance it would cause to the civil government of men. For who sees not that no city can be secure against attack, since our ship may at any time be placed directly over it, and descending down may discharge soldiers."

The German philosopher Leibniz, who studied physics and

technology in addition to mathematics, jurisprudence and politics, recognised the essential error in de Lana's proposed flying ship. Nevertheless he did not find the only correct and possible solution, but expressed himself with disarming logic: "God has set a limit upon mankind; if men could also ride through the air, their wickedness could no longer be checked."

Christian Kindermann, Court Professor to the King of Poland and Prince of Saxony, taking de Lana's proposal as his starting point, approved the idea of an airship, but forgot the vital importance of the evacuated spheres; he expressed himself much more optimistically, and, unlike the sceptics of his time, even foresaw space travel. "Airship: this might one day offer the opportunity to enter upon relations with occupants of different planets. If this now seems impossible to us, it does not follow that it is impossible in fact. Perhaps our forefathers thought things impossible which are today no longer surprising. Who knows what will happen a thousand years hence? Perhaps aerial ships will bring back to earth strange plants and animals as sailors today bring peacocks and apes from Asia!"

The achievement of flight with a balloon was drawing near, and the barrier spoken of by Leibniz was broken in 1766, when the English chemist Henry Cavendish obtained, after many experiments, a gas which he called 'combustible air'. With this it was possible to make spheres which, without the use of a vacuum, were lighter than air, although filled with gas, and were not crushed by the external air pressure. Nowadays we call this gas hydrogen. Sixteen years later Lichtenberg, a Professor of Physics at Göttingen, performed a thrilling experiment, when he filled soap bubbles with this newly-discovered gas and sent them sailing through the lecture hall. Curiously enough neither the little Professor of this new science of physics, nor his fascinated students, thought of replacing the soap bubble by a stronger envelope.

Only one little step, one little advance of ideas, was necessary before the discovery of the balloon.

THE BALLOON

In fact a new solution was tried without this step being taken.

On 5th June 1783 the news reached Paris that in Annonay, a little town in the South of France where the Assembly of the

District of Vivarais was meeting, a balloon had risen into the sky and landed again undamaged. The report said that the paper manufacturers Joseph and Etienne Montgolfier had made a long linen and paper bag, and filled it with a "vapour which they knew how to make", so that this air ball rose to the clouds. A few months later men flew for the first time like the ancient gods, high over Paris in a 'Montgolfière'; thousands kneeled and prayed as the frail craft crossed the sky, women fainted and men embraced each other for joy. The chains of gravity which had so long fettered man to earth seemed to be broken once and for all.

The name of Montgolfier was on everyone's lips, for the brothers had been highly successful; and yet the proper, final solution of the problem was not theirs. They wanted to fly and had sufficient knowledge of mathematics and natural science to realise their bold ambition. First of all they tried with 'artificial clouds', that is, steam, to raise a light envelope; but the steam rapidly condensed. One day Joseph Montgolfier read a new book by the English scientist, Priestly, on *Experiments and Observations with Various Kinds of Air*, which described the new gas discovered by Cavendish. This led them to try hydrogen to obtain lift. But the bag was not sufficiently gas-tight and the hydrogen escaped too quickly, so that the neighbours, who had shaken their heads for years at the mad behaviour of the brothers, seemed once more to be right: flying was something for birds, or perhaps for magicians in league with the devil, and not for honest Christian men.

Nevertheless, one day they succeeded. Historians have been unable to determine every detail of the discovery of the hot-air balloon, and consequently many stories have arisen. It is said that Joseph Montgolfier was in Avignon on business in the autumn of 1782 when Gibraltar was besieged by the French and Spanish. One evening he sat before the fire gazing at the mounting smoke; if only the defenders of the fortress could be overcome from the air! Suddenly Joseph had an idea; he called for some taffeta, made a simple balloon from it and held it over the fire so that, when the innkeeper's wife entered the room, she was astonished to see the tiny structure rise to the ceiling. Whether this is a tale or the truth, there exists a letter, sent at the time by Joseph to his brother, in which he says: "Make no delay in gathering taffeta and ropes and you shall see the most wonderful things."

This led to the famous first ascent of the hot-air balloon in Annonay. The bag consisted of a linen sack lined with paper. To begin with the crowd grumbled because there was nothing to see, but soon the shapeless contraption took on more and more the form of a tightly-stretched sphere, held by a hempen net from which hung eight ropes. Each rope was held by a strong man, and all eight of them had as much as they could do to hold the straining balloon down. At a command they let go the ropes and the balloon shot skywards, reaching within ten minutes an estimated height of 25,000 feet. The story of this 'miracle' spread like wild-fire, which in fact depended only on the burning of some ten lb. of straw and a little sheep's wool. The spectators thought the straw and wool were a trick of the Montgolfier brothers to hide the real magic of their device. The brothers themselves thought they had produced the gas with mysterious electrical properties which was believed at that time to keep the clouds in suspension.

Even though the Montgolfiers themselves did not know why their flight had been successful, the Diet of Vivarais did not need to bother their heads about this remarkable event. They therefore only sent a report to the Academy of Sciences in Paris, who established a Commission to investigate the case and also invited the brothers to make a new trial in Paris, at the Academy's expense. The first garbled story preceded the formal report and had reached the ears of Professor César Alexandre Charles, a Paris physicist. The Professor gave public lectures in the Louvre which were always attended because he illustrated his talks with striking experiments. Charles realised the importance of the balloon ascent, even from the confused information which reached him. He declared that this new combustible air (hydrogen) should give even better results.

The impatient Parisians decided that they would not wait for the arrival of Etienne Montgolfier, but would collect a sum of money and make their own balloon ascent. As a scientist the Professor took the responsibility for the preparations. He had a balloon envelope prepared from silk made airtight by painting it with rubber solution. The hydrogen was manufactured on the spot and fed into the balloon through a tube. Before daybreak the balloon was completely filled with gas and fastened to a strong stretcher. It was then found that it could not be got through the door; gas had to be released and the balloon compressed before it could be taken out. Slowly the 'machine' was borne through the town, accompanied by torch-bearers and a section of watchmen. The darkness, the strange, enormous shape of the balloon and the silence of the streets gave the night's undertaking a mysterious character and many people sank to their knees as the procession passed. The balloon was brought without difficulty to the Champ de Mars. It was set up in a prepared enclosure and refilled with gas. The entire area was lined with troops; curious spectators crowded the river banks, the slopes of Passy and the entire district around the Champ de Mars. Almost half the population of Paris, some 300,000 souls, were present.

An eye-witness described the spectacle later in the following words: "At five o'clock a cannon shot marked the beginning of the experiment and also warned the scientists, who waited on the Terrasse des Gard-Meuble, the towers of Notre Dame and the École Militaire, to observe the experiment, as they would for the passage of a comet. Freed from its bonds, the balloon shot upwards so quickly that it reached a height of 3,000 feet within two minutes." A second cannon shot announced the disappearance of the balloon into the clouds. It was later seen once more at a great height and then vanished again in the dark clouds.

This highly successful beginning was, however, soon followed by descent and a sad end. Professor Charles had ordered the balloon to be completely filled just before the start to give it a completely spherical form, but this proved a mistake. At a great height the gas burst the envelope and began to rush out; the balloon sank to earth, not in Paris, whose inhabitants knew of the experiment, but near the village of Gonesse, some fifteen miles from the capital. Two farmers, ignorant of the circumstances, took the balloon for a monster, a view in which they were strengthened when the balloon almost rose again before finally collapsing. They threw stones at it before they felt that it was safe to approach and peep cautiously into the gaping tear which, it was subsequently related in Paris, they thought to be the monster's throat. The hissing as the remainder of the gas

flowed out forced them to draw back quickly. After a short discussion, they dragged the balloon to the village behind a mule.
The village clergyman found the notice attached to the balloon
by Professor Charles and arranged for its return to Paris. The
two farmers were repaid for their excitement by the promised
reward, and were probably not disturbed that the newspapers
made merry at their expense; they were reported as saying "the
monster is dead and now only smells very badly".

Nevertheless, the balloon was so damaged that it could not
be used again. The incident prompted the Government to
issue its "Announcement to the People Regarding Balloon

Hot-air balloon trial ascent at Versailles, 19th September 1783.

Ascents", which declared: "A discovery has been made concerning which the Government thinks it necessary to make an announcement to guard against the fear which such happenings might otherwise cause among the people . . . This warning is to any who see from now on such a ball in the sky, in appearance like a darkened moon, that they be not affrighted as though by some terrible thing. For this is nothing but a machine made of silk or thin linen and covered with paper; it can do no ill, and it may be hoped that it will one day have useful applications for the needs of mankind."

Amazement and doubt, excitement and scepticism were now equally aroused. While Etienne Montgolfier prepared for a balloon ascent from the courtyard at Versailles, a newspaper correspondent wrote: "In the coming week another trial is to be made with the new machine. Time will tell whether this discovery will be as useful as Monsieur Montgolfier promises."

The ascent of the second 'Montgolfière' at Versailles was marked by a small sensation: to determine whether living creatures could safely bear the movement through the air, a large basket was fastened to the balloon as a carriage for a "a sheep, a cock and a duck". The balloon rose majestically into the air but, beginning to leak, it came down some ten minutes later in a thicket, about an hour's walk from Versailles. Two foresters saw the blue and gold 'aerostat' sinking slowly. The animals were also safe, but closer examination showed that the cock was slightly wounded in one wing.

Immediately warnings were uttered about the dangers of flying. There were learned discussions as to what could have caused the accident, until one of the foresters reported that the sheep had probably inadvertently trodden on the poor cockerel during the emergency landing.

ADVENTUROUS BALLOONISTS

Once animals had flown safely, men did not want to lag behind. Would not the air offer unknown adventures, as well as scientific knowledge of immeasurable importance? The first man to fly in a balloon was one of the eye-witnesses of the second 'Montgolfière' ascent, Pilâtre de Rozier of Metz. He lectured in Paris on the electrical phenomena recently discovered by Benjamin Franklin, and, prompted by a feverish interest in the recent revelations of natural science, was in the habit of performing the most risky experiments. It is said that one day he filled his mouth with hydrogen and lit it; his cheeks were literally torn open.

When Etienne Montgolfier made a new and bigger balloon to carry several men, it was Rozier who dared the first ascent; the balloon was tethered by cords and would only rise some eighty feet. Rozier realised that he could ascend whenever he wished by stirring the fire but, of course, was checked by the rope. This experiment also showed that the balloon did not drop abruptly when the fire was extinguished but sank gently to earth. In later tests the rope was lengthened and another passenger carried; the balloon rose to more than 300 feet, presenting a "spectacle unheard of in the world's history, when two men could be seen floating in the air, peacefully and safely at such a height". After these tests Rozier decided to be the first man to make a free flight; he would cut the rope and let the balloon be carried by the air currents.

But hardly four months had passed since the discovery of the aerostat. Would the fire not set the balloon alight and throw the aviator to earth? Was it not possible that burning straw might fall on houses, barns and fields and cause great damage? Even Montgolfier expressed such misgivings; they came to the ears of Louis XVI, who declared that he would only allow the flight to take place if the balloon were flown by a condemned criminal. If he broke his neck, it was one man less for the executioner.

Rozier was horrified by this royal order but finally managed to interest in his enterprise a Major d'Arlandes, who persuaded the King to change his mind by declaring his own readiness to participate in the flight. Thus the first air journey in the world took place from the Bois de Boulogne on 21st November 1783.

In spite of a strong wind the balloon rose quickly. The fear and excitement of the spectators gave way to admiration and rejoicing when, at a height of some 350 feet, the balloonists waved their hats. In giving this signal they almost forgot to feed the fire, and when they relit it with a bundle of straw they were carried upward so quickly that they could not draw breath. The spectators on the towers of Notre Dame experienced a 'solar eclipse' as the 'Montgolfière' slowly passed between them and the sun. After twenty-five minutes Rozier and d'Arlandes let the fire out and the balloon slowly sank, finally settling some five miles from its starting-point. Two men had survived the first aerial journey safely.

Among the spectators was the American scientist and statesman Benjamin Franklin, as though "the New World had sent him over to be a witness of this event". That day he uttered a saying so often quoted that it has become proverbial. A sceptical spectator near Franklin said with a smile: "What use can these air balls be? What purpose can they have?" With great wisdom, the American representative replied: "Of what use is a new-born baby?"

This saying again overcame doubt and opposition 170 years later, when Wernher von Braun quoted it in a discussion and thereby convinced a nation of 150 million people that rocket flight into space might also have some use.

* * *

Man could now fly. Men were long gripped with a fantastic desire to make first-hand acquaintance with the heavens; but they were not always as fortunate as those first aeronauts.

On 3rd May 1784 at Bordeaux a balloon would not rise and the spectators, enraged at being cheated of their spectacle, began to riot and throw stones at the watch. The two ringleaders from the crowd were arrested and hanged out of hand. When twelve days later a second attempt failed, the magistrate of the town "forbade the balloon-making gentlemen under pain of heavy punishment to make asses of honest people and cheat them of their money, since they were in any case excited, for two men had been hanged on account of these childish doings". But those, like the Montgolfier brothers and Professor Charles, who succeeded in building better balloons were honoured by the King and the Paris Academy of Sciences with titles and orders as well as a life pension. Goethe wrote in his diary at the time: "Those who have experienced the discovery of the aerial balloon will bear witness how much excitement it caused, how much interest followed the aviators, how many yearnings were raised in thousands of hearts."

These yearnings, together with many over-optimistic hopes, ran side by side with apparently unyielding scepticism in the

hearts and minds of men. Exaggerated panegyrics were printed
in the papers next to bitter satirical poems, depending on
whether the latest experiment had finished well or badly.

When Professor Charles described his balloon ascent in

Blanchard's flight.

December 1783, he opened his heart in the following words:
"Nothing can compare with the fascinating joy in my spirit as I
felt that we were leaving the earth. It was not a simple pleasure,
it was real joy. Lifted above the agonies of persecution and
slander, I felt fully justified; I rose above it all. This moral

The Lockheed 'Starfighter' F.104, an extremely fast, high-flying fighter of modern design.

Testing a Comet IV by the water-tank method; this aircraft has completed the equivalent of twenty-five years' airline flying.

The De Havilland Comet IV, a triumph of engineering skill after the early tragic setbacks with the Series II design.

emotion was quickly followed by an even more lively impression, that of wonder at the majestic spectacle which offered itself. If only I had had with me the last of our traducers, to say to him, 'See miserable man, how much is lost if the progress of science is hindered.' "

The Channel was crossed from Dover to France on 7th January 1785 by the Frenchman Blanchard, together with his American patron, Dr. J. Jeffries, despite the fact that Blanchard really wanted to go alone, fearing that the balloon would not be able to lift two persons. Everyone was fearful of the consequences of this foolhardy journey, and sought to dissuade the headstrong American who was determined to risk his money and his life to win undying fame or lose everything in the attempt. In the end they both started, aided by a favourable 'tail wind'. But halfway across the balloon lost height so quickly that Blanchard had to jettison not only all the ballast and the books they had taken, but — shortly before the coast of France — the provisions, anchor and ropes, and even part of their clothing. As the balloon continued to sink, Jeffries was on the point of jumping out of the basket so that Blanchard at least should be saved. Fortunately at the last moment the balloon rose again slightly. Next day Jeffries was able to write to a friend in London: "We landed in the Forest of Felmore, almost as naked as the trees . . . you would have laughed to see how feverishly we worked, stripped of almost all our clothes."

Blanchard was honoured by the King; his triumph was complete. But Pilâtre de Rozier, the first to fly a hot-air balloon, soon paid for his interest in flying with his life. He, too, intended to cross the Channel, but unhappily thought of combining the hot-air balloon with a hydrogen balloon. Although friends told him that he might as well fly in a burning powder cask, he began the ascent on 15th June 1785. Shortly afterwards the balloon exploded, and Rozier and his companions were killed on the rocks below.

This was the first fatal accident in air travel.

*   *   *

It should be recorded that, in those early days of flight, the police issued bans which were often ridiculous. For instance, in Paris, Garnier was forbidden to make a flight with a young

H

lady "because an aerial journey made by two persons of different sex was indecent and immoral, and it was by no means unlikely that the pressure of the air could be dangerous to the delicate organs of a young girl", as the *Vossische Zeitung* reported on 4th May 1798. Moreover, balloon ascents from many European capitals were forbidden by reason of "the danger of causing fire". It is significant that almost 200 years ago a man foresaw the benefits of air travel: "How much information these machines will enable us to gather about the formation, division, duration and disappearance of clouds, and about the origin of hail, of snow, and of other aerial phenomena! It will be possible to repair wrecked ships and to raise sunken ones from the sea with these machines."

As a counterpart to this, let us quote again from Zeidler's book *The Flying Traveller or The Philosophical Art of Flying*, written before the discovery of the balloon: "It is enough to make one's hair stand on end to think of all the damage, danger and injury which aeronautics will inevitably bring to the human race once it spreads; firstly the flyers (even supposing them to be pious people) will have no guardian angel to bear them up in the stormy air, because this is not their proper and natural path; on the contrary, many will fall and be miserably dashed to pieces, slaying other people too. Secondly, there will undoubtedly be robberies and wars in the air, which will be much worse than on land."

THE DIRIGIBLE AIRSHIP

The efforts of creative minds to achieve new things were, however, also successful here — one might almost think independently of all prophecies — in accordance with the law, characteristic of technical development in the last two centuries, that once an objective has been recognised it is ultimately reached, in spite of detours and false steps or heavy resistance.

Thus, even the first aeronauts realised that their struggle to make aerial traffic possible would be completely successful only if cheaper balloons could be made, and if it were possible to steer them. This clearly defined the objective, namely, mass production of steered balloons. Man could fly and was dissatisfied with his achievement; consequently, the dirigible airship had to be developed from the balloon.

As early as 1784 the Academy of Lyons organised a prize competition for the best suggestions for steering aerostats. Ninety-six 'solutions' were entered, and sails, rudders and movable paddles were proposed to control the flight.

In Vienna Joseph Kaiserer put forward the fantastic idea of training eagles to pull balloons. He published an article on his "discovery of how to steer a balloon by means of eagles", giving exact instructions for training the eagles and a calculation of how many were needed to draw a balloon of given size. However, he refrained from putting his suggestion to the test himself. His compatriot, Degen, built a balloon with wings, which started successfully on a still day, but was carried away by a

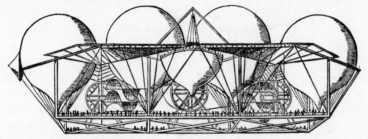

Petin's proposed dirigible airship.

strong wind during a test in Paris, to the mocking laughter of the spectators.

It soon became clear to the scientifically-minded pioneer aeronauts that the problem could not be solved by using artificial wings or human muscles, much less tame eagles. We now know that the development of the dirigible airship depended on the perfection of suitable motors, without which no efficient airship could be built.

The first power-driven, semi-rigid airship was built by Henri Giffard in 1852. He had seen steam omnibuses in England, and fitted his airship, which was 143 feet long, with a steam engine of his own construction, furnishing only three horse-power. Since his first flight was successful, he built a larger airship three years later, but this crashed. His opponents appeared once again to be right; the wind could do what it liked to an airship.

The German engineer Paul Haenlein experimented with a

gas engine in 1882, but this too was still imperfect and was
therefore abandoned.

Two Frenchmen, Renard and Krebs, studied air currents
closely, and decided to give their airship the form of a cigar;
this was in 1884 and they provided it with an electric motor.
The first trial flight was very promising, and after twenty-three
minutes the airship returned to its starting-point. However,
further trials showed that the craft was still at the mercy of the

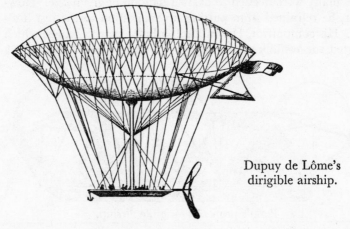

Dupuy de Lôme's
dirigible airship.

winds and would only unfailingly obey its helmsman on a still
day.

Failures, grave accidents with balloons and all his friends'
warnings were insufficient to deter Alberto Santos-Dumont, the
son of a wealthy Brazilian coffee planter, who came to Paris at
the age of twenty, from building small airships driven by petrol
engines of the type already being used in automobiles. The
motorists, who had themselves only just perfected their machine,
considered that the petrol engine was quite suitable for cars,
but doubted whether it would be so for an airship. Santos-
Dumont was not deterred, and the deficiencies of the motors
were made up for by enthusiasm. Shortly after the turn of the
century he was successful, and from then on the young man was
see in the air far more often than the sceptics had thought possible. Naturally he was risking his life, and crashed several
times. But in 1901 he received a prize for the first flight around
the Eiffel Tower.

For a very long time, in fact since 1883, there had been in existence a patent in which Hermann Ganswindt pointed the correct approach to the problem of the navigable airship. Ganswindt had studied this question early in his life and devoted a good deal of thought to determining why all the trials carried out up to that time had failed. He asked himself why the first strong wind had carried away Giffard's craft; after much reflection, he hit upon the answer. In order to be navigable, the airship must have a speed of at least thirty miles an hour; to achieve this speed it would require an estimated total drive power of 100 horse-power. If this power were to be provided by a steam engine — for there were then no internal combustion engines — the airship would have to be bigger than any yet proposed or built.

The young inventor abandoned his study of the law, which his parents had persuaded him to follow, and began to work on his project. His fate is typical of that of all seekers and farsighted inventors ahead of their time. He submitted his patent to the War Ministry with the plans of his airship, but Field-Marshal von Moltke gave him a short and sharp 'No'. He proposed an airship twice as long as a church tower is high. The military pundits pronounced that the Army did not need it. Science, said the experts, had long ago proved that the construction of such a craft was impossible.

Ganswindt was not discouraged, but published a brochure on the navigability of airships. He also founded a patriotic association for the encouragement of air travel and collected funds for the construction of suitable craft. He trounced his opponents in violent public addresses on the "most important problems facing mankind", and said: "Even such a man as Napoleon Bonaparte declared that Fulton, the inventor of the steamship, was mad, because he wanted to drive the fleet to England with boiling water — as Napoleon contemptuously described the steam engine. And, even when steamships had been running successfully for a long while the learned Dr. Lardner gave scientific proof that steamships would never succeed in crossing the ocean to America." He pronounced the words 'learned' and 'scientific proof' in a mocking tone and the public, taking his point, laughed and applauded loudly. How foolish and reactionary to say that the steamship was impossible!

But as the speaker continued, saying, "I am convinced that within a few years every household will have one or more flying machines once my invention has brought aerial travel into being," the audience no longer laughed at the foolish reactionaries, but at the speaker on the platform, defending his new idea.

Ganswindt never had the opportunity to build his airship, which was correct in principle. Instead of this he tried his hand at constructing a helicopter which actually rose several feet into the air. His opponents supposed, however, that it was raised by a rope, and claimed that Ganswindt had tricked his patrons and the public. The inventor took up the challenge but became involved in costly litigation. In addition he bombarded the Ministry of War in Berlin with petitions in an attempt to obtain his due as the "original inventor of the airship", after Graf Zeppelin had actually constructed his first dirigible machine. An embittered man, he wrote: "The prejudiced view that the flying machine is an impossibility has prevented its development, for I have now been struggling for many years for the realisation of my inventions. But this prejudice has pursued me everywhere, has destroyed my work, has gagged me, has made my heart bleed and has brought me into the most miserable necessity; I have already been very near to a slow and wretched death for the sake of this invention. This is a shameful thing in the century of discovery." When finally one of Ganswindt's last petitions reached the desk of the War Minister of the day, von Stein glanced through the first few lines, and then, with a shake of the head, scribbled in red ink, right across the first page: "Is this miserable croaker still alive then?" The miserable croaker had discovered the airship, but another, more fortunate man, Count Zeppelin, was to build and fly it.

Zeppelin too had considerable reverses, and he too had to fight for his idea, risk his reputation as a sane man and give his wealth. But he had not only an iron will, a good old family name and the support of the King of Würtemberg, he had also an inheritance of 400,000 marks. After ten years of hard struggles which often brought him very near despair, he was able to start his first airship, the L.Z.1, on 2nd July 1900. This was 530 feet long and fitted with two fifteen horse-power

Daimler engines, and made its first flight in the presence of nearly 20,000 spectators.

Even this impressive spectacle and the records set up by the airship were not enough to bring general recognition or support for the Count's ideas. For five years he and his few friends struggled against the inertia and hostility of the people 'who knew better'. Financial difficulties arose and the airship finally had to be scrapped and sold, to enable him at least to pay off the accumulated debts. Finally, in 1905, he was able to continue his work. Further successes attracted the attention of the German Government; the L.Z.3 was taken over by the Prussian Army. Three years later the L.Z.4 was completed; after a triumphantly successful flight, this airship was set accidentally on fire by an electric spark and burned out, at Echterdingen.

Zeppelin hardly hoped to be able to recover from this setback, but at this very moment his fortunes took a change for the better. The disaster at Echterdingen served as a dark background against which the earlier successful flights shone with greater brightness. Whereas before this people were very liable to poke fun at the 'mad Count', the accident served to silence the mockers. A national fund, subscribed by the German people, provided a firm financial foundation for further development and in the same year the Luftschiffbau-Zeppelin Company was founded at Friedrichshafen on Lake Constance.

The construction of airships progressed during the First World War. In 1917 the L.Z.120 remained in flight for 101 hours, the L.Z.55 attained a height of over 24,000 feet, and the L.Z.59 flew 4,000 miles, from Jamboli in Bulgaria to Khartoum and back. After a short break at the end of the war, the huge civil airships L.Z.127, the 'Graf Zeppelin', and L.Z.129, the 'Hindenburg', were built. The latter was a magnificent craft, 715 feet long and 150 feet high; she made fifty-six flights, ten of them to North America. On 6th May 1937 she crashed and was destroyed by fire at Lakehurst, U.S.A. This catastrophe closed the era of the large airships. The L.Z.130, which was already under construction, was dismantled shortly before completion.

Nevertheless, the silver giants of the air left an ineradicable impression on those who had seen them. In 1929 the 'Graf Zeppelin' flew around the world under the command of Dr.

Hugo Eckener. Zeppelin airships were blazing the trail for regular scheduled air traffic across the Atlantic and made the crossing between the Old and the New Worlds many times.

Although aerostatic flight, that is, flight with craft lighter than air, ultimately turned out to be a dead end, its pioneers undoubtedly smoothed the path of those who were later to provide man with wings.

Balloons continued to be used for sporting purposes and research. In the summer of 1957 Major Simons of the American Air Force ascended from Crosby, Minnesota, to a height of over 113,000 feet in a hermetically-sealed gondola suspended from a plastic balloon. His purpose was not to set up an altitude record, but to remain for as long as possible on the edge of space. He stayed up for thirty-two hours, making observations and measurements, thus assisting those who would one day travel further.

When the elderly father of the Montgolfier brothers was created a hereditary noble by Louis XVI, he took for his motto *Sic itur ad astra*: this is the way to the stars. The balloon was only the beginning of this path, but it had served to lift man off the earth for the first time, and perhaps he would one day really reach the stars.

Wherever this path may lead, those who follow it will always experience "the most wonderful things in the world".

*   *   *

Looking one day for quotations of the opinions of famous persons on the possibilities of human flight, I came upon a collection of sayings, dating from around the turn of the century, cited in the periodical *Interavia*, which is devoted to the subject of air travel. One saying recorded was that "it is more dangerous to prophesy than to walk a tight-rope"; it is said that Hemingway, when asked to forecast the next fifty years, replied disgustedly: "Half a century? I am always wondering — quite uselessly — what will happen to us next week"!

Nostradamus, who lived in the first half of the 16th century, was not so reticent. In his 'prophecies' we find an astonishingly clear forecast of modern air traffic: "At the three hundred and twenty-sixth passage of the planet Mars when the Northern Kingdom and the Southern Kingdom have twice been in bloody conflict, carriages will fly noisily through the air. Men will wait for these carriages, as they wait in harbours today for ships to arrive."

The most dangerous things about all these predictions are the glaring mistakes, the real bloomers, which can arise in the forecasts of even the cleverest men. H. G. Wells, who described in his novels, written at the beginning of the 20th century, what the men of the latter half of that century would do and live through, was no exception. Apart from his imaginative novels Wells also wrote very sober technical treatises. In 1901 he published a brochure dealing with the effects of technical and scientific progress on human thought. The first chapter deals with the various means of transport in the future, air travel being given the following rather sceptical footnote: "I did not mention the discovery of flight in the foregoing chapter on transport. I doubt very much whether flying will be a practical proposition, or will have important effects on human existence. I therefore consider it most unlikely that aeronautics will ever be able to exercise a decisive influence on travel. Man is not an albatross, but a land biped." Later, when his error was clear, Wells himself admitted that: "No man can go beyond his own knowledge, and one can hardly even escape from the limited field of contemporary thought. We can neither divine nor prophesy."

If an imaginative writer like Wells, who was very alive to potential technical developments, was unable to visualise in 1901 the important influence that flying would exercise on travel, it is not surprising that, fifty years earlier, an American bishop should have declared emphatically during a discussion: "Men will never fly, because flying is reserved for the angels." The bishop's name was Wright and he had two sons Orville and Wilbur, who were to prove the contrary during his lifetime.

THE HEROIC ERA

The brothers Otto and Gustav Lilienthal had already begun, early in the 19th century, to study the dominant idea which was later to govern their entire lives. Although very enthusiastic they were prudent and modest. A professor had once said to Lilienthal when he was a student that there was no reason why he should not occupy his spare time in making aircraft calculations, as long as he did not spend money on pipe-dreams of that sort.

At this time a State Commission in Berlin, under the chairmanship of Hermann Ludwig von Helmholtz, had established that muscle-powered flight was impossible. The imitators of Icarus had already proved this fact on their own bodies. Unhappily, the Commission's findings gave rise to the impression that Helmholtz had also proved by his calculations that any kind of flying machine was impossible. This was a severe blow to the aeronauts, as scientific and technical experts were now all too ready to rank flight as a Utopian idea.

Despite this, Lilienthal began his investigations: "Nature proves daily to us that flying is not nearly so difficult; if we feel almost inclined to abandon the idea of flight, because our calculations show that we need to exert an impossible amount of energy, we are reminded by the bird flying above our heads with easy wing beats that the calculation must be wrong somewhere. The bird is clearly not exerting this tremendous force. There must be a hidden secret which will solve the problem in a moment." So Lilienthal set about studying bird flight. After years of observation, he discovered the secret. He had to apply the force of the wind and utilise the capacity of the air to carry a flying body, and he therefore had to discover suitable wing forms. Soon he realised that "research and experience are bringing nearer the moment when the first free-flying man will rise from the earth with wings. The moment is approaching which will usher in a new era."

In 1891, while Ganswindt was extolling the virtues of his flying machine, which still existed only on paper, Otto Lilienthal began gliding, with wings of coarse waxed cotton stretched on a light willow framework. One day he climbed to the roof of his house with his first pair of wings and sprang into the air. His wings checked his fall so that he did not break his legs. In point of fact those early wings were no more than an imperfect parachute, but in time he really flew with them.

Lilienthal's great merit was that he proceeded systematically, daring to turn knowledge into deeds. Others calculated and drew, gave lectures and were laughed at; Lilienthal observed, calculated and was also laughed at, but he went further and dared to fly. Near Berlin he had a small artificial hill thrown up, from the top of which he sprang into the air with his wings; he made hundreds of flights year after year, 100 feet, 150 feet and once nearly 400 feet. They were only gliding flights, but his French colleague Ferber later declared: "I consider the day on which Lilienthal covered the first fifty feet as the day on which man began to fly."

Ageing and tired, harassed by plans and ideas which could not be executed with the technical knowledge of the times, Lilienthal deplored that he found no one who would volunteer to continue his trials. He had also realised that sustained flight would be impossible without a motor. Although his gliding could progress no further, in the autumn of 1896 he once again dared a 'leap into the air' for the sheer pleasure of it. A sudden gust of wind brought him crashing to the ground and he died shortly afterwards.

It is said that his last words were: "Sacrifices must be made."

*   *   *

Lilienthal's gliding flights were made without a motor, but they had shown the way. In October 1897 the Frenchman Clément Ader attempted to demonstrate a stream-driven aircraft to a military commission. The start was unsuccessful. Eye-witnesses subsequently reported that the machine had already flown seven years earlier, but no one had seen it 'officially'. In spite of heavy damage Ader's aircraft was preserved. It had curved, bat-like wings, propellers like windmills and a ribbed tail. After this failure Ader destroyed his workshop; he died, almost forgotten, in 1925. Only twenty-five years later did France recognise him as one of her pioneers of flying.

There followed 1903, the famous year in the history of flight. On 17th December, a cold, windy day, the era of powered flight began in the sandhills of Kitty Hawk. The brothers Orville and Wilbur Wright had also been experimenting for several years with gliding. They now fitted to a light biplane a sixteen horse-power motor they had built themselves; it was just sufficiently powerful for the aircraft to start and to fly. The first powered flight lasted twelve seconds and covered 200 feet. The fourth and last flight of the day lasted fifty-nine seconds and reached 852 feet. How often the Wright Brothers had heard their father's deep-seated conviction that flying was reserved for the angels! But now they had flown after all.

Public recognition was only slight to begin with and the Press hardly noted the event at all. Man had a powered aircraft and did not know what to do with it. Later people criticised the Wrights' understandable reticence to press men, and uncharitably turned the 'flying brothers' into 'lying brothers', a nasty twist which provoked the reply that "parrots which talk a lot don't fly".

It may seem very strange today that two young men with no special aids should be the first to fly a powered aircraft; and one might also ask why this success should have occurred in 1903,

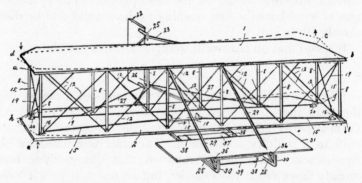

Sketch of the Wright Brothers' aircraft, which made the first successful powered sustained flight in 1903.

instead of falling to one of the many 19th-century pioneer aeronauts. The fact is that not even a clever idea can come to fruition at the wrong time, that is, if the requisite techniques have not been developed. Fifty years earlier even the Wright Brothers would not have achieved motorised flight. But it would be an over-simplification to say that in 1903 it was just that the time was ripe for powered flight. More was needed: patience, imagination, enthusiasm, energy, courage, determination and — last but not least — a little luck.

In the summer of 1902 the Wrights had already made a thousand gliding flights and had learned to fly in the process. They had discovered how to control the aircraft, and the relation between the controls and the aircraft's movements. Their simple motor-driven craft was completely under the pilot's control. This was the decisive new factor.

Perhaps the American Samuel P. Langley, who had attempted a powered flight ten weeks earlier than the Wright Brothers, might have succeeded. He had carried out thorough theoretical investigations, followed by exhaustive trials of model steam-driven and petrol-engined aircraft; he had himself developed a fifty-two horse-power motor for his first aircraft. This machine had neither undercarriage nor floats, since it was launched by a catapult. It was nearly fifty years later that this method of starting was to be successful. Moreover, unlike the Wright Brothers, Langley had never learned to fly. At the first trial the aircraft fell into the Potomac. At the second it broke up on the catapult.

Thus it came about that the Wrights succeeded nine days after Langley's failure and earned the place in history of the first men to fly a motor-driven aircraft.

*   *   *

While the Americans were slowly losing their disbelief in the flying brothers, they were still considered in many countries to be boasters. Only in France, where the ground had already been prepared, was there great interest in the experiments carried on in the New World. May 1903 saw the founding of an aeroplane section of the French Aero Club. In the same year Robert Esnault-Pelterie, a young chemist and physicist, began to carry out gliding flights. In 1905 the Aero Club organised a model aircraft race, and the French Government began negotiations for the purchase of their invention.

In 1906 Santos-Dumont, who had already flown an airship around the Eiffel Tower in 1901, succeeded in flying a 'kite aircraft', first 40 feet, then 200 feet, and finally 750 feet. This was still a long way behind the American achievements. But France hoped to become the leading aeronautic nation of the world.

FIRST STEPS IN AERONAUTICS

We do well to remind ourselves of these early days, for otherwise we are all too liable to forget the scale of the great advances made by the pioneers, and to label the revolutionary projects of aircraft engineers as 'impossible', a condemnation which has so often hindered all inventors and technical innovators, and still does so today. We have become accustomed to taking almost all the major technical advances for granted only a few years after their introduction. The heroic achievements of those early days of flying, between the beginning of the century and the 'twenties, clearly show how unjust this is.

The early aeronauts had no one to whom they might turn for lessons in flying. They were not in a position to buy their aircraft from a manufacturer, but were forced to build them themselves. Thus Blériot, for example, constructed between 1906 and 1909 the forerunner of the modern aeroplane; it was a low-wing monoplane with a metal propeller, control surfaces in the wings and a covered fuselage. In 1909 he crossed the Channel from France to England, winning the *Daily Mail* prize of £1,000. His aircraft weighed about 650 lb. and had a twenty-five horse-power motor — by modern standards a light aircraft. He only carried enough fuel for two hours, but his crossing from Calais to the Downs near Dover lasted thirty-seven minutes, for a distance of twenty-seven miles.

A few weeks later Hans Grade won the prize offered by the industrialist Karl Lanz by flying, near Berlin, just over a mile in an aircraft built entirely in Germany. The conditions of the contest laid down a figure-of-eight course around two markers. Grade practised at the Mars Airfield near Bork. On 11th October 1909 he told a reporter of the *Berliner Anzeiger* about his experiences with the public: "When I bring my aircraft out there is no one within sight. But as soon as the engine begins to splutter, a crowd appears in a moment. The local innkeeper — the only one for miles to supply us with food and drink — fears nothing so much as the rattle of my engine; the effect on his customers is like that of a cloudburst on a garden party, and in a twinkling they are all gone." Only nineteen days later Grade fulfilled all the conditions of the prize contest at the Johannisthal Airfield near Berlin, remaining exactly four minutes and four seconds in the air. Dr. Lanz personally handed him the cheque for 40,000 marks.

Roughly thirty years later the greying pioneer aeronaut dragged his old aircraft out of the shed to fly it once again, and filled up with oil and petrol. He took off from an airport lined with impressive giant airliners of modern aerodynamic design, machines of a type hardly dreamed of when Grade won the Lanz prize. The old aircraft circled safely and landed again. One of those who, in earlier days, had helped to fashion progress had been able to remind the young generation of airmen, to whom flying was an accepted thing, of those who had shown them the way.

The first long non-stop flight of more than $62\frac{1}{2}$ miles was made by Louis Paulhan, during a race from London to Manchester. He flew at night and covered a distance of 110 miles. A few weeks before the flight one critic of the undertaking was ready to bet a million pounds that an aeroplane would never cover such a distance.

The changes wrought in a few years had been tremendous. The absolute speed record for aircraft was a little more than 25 miles an hour in 1906, but in 1913 had already reached 125 miles an hour. An aeroplane with a fifty horse-power engine set a world height record of 1,500 feet in 1909, and four years later an eighty horse-power machine reached 19,900 feet. The public still remembered how they were not quite able to decide whether the Wright Brothers were impostors or genuine inventors. But by now the best designers and flyers were beginning to master the air. Technical developments in flying were moving at a truly breath-taking speed.

In the First World War flying grew from an adventure followed by a few enthusiasts to a state-supported organisation with official standing. The most significant event in flying during that war was the construction, by the German Hugo Junkers, of the first cantilever-wing aircraft, which dispensed with the usual bracing wires. This construction also enabled Junkers to reduce the number of lifting surfaces — which had actually reached a total of nine in one Caproni design — until ultimately there was only one. By the end of the war, Junkers had built his first all-metal aircraft. But he had to face many opponents who considered his plans "much too bold". "When one has eventually got through the jungle of error and confusion," he wrote later, "one still oftens feels bitterly disappointed. It is a well-known fact that no good invention ever introduces itself. In fact, the introduction of a new product is frequently the most difficult part of the job."

In the First World War flying not only attracted attention
and even respect, but many people believed that the experience
gained would be an adequate foundation for future development. "They wanted multi-planed aircraft and not mono-
planes," complained Junkers; "the prejudice against all-metal
construction was even worse, and no one would believe that the
'tin donkey' could fly. And when the curious contraption did
fly, it still had to stand a long time in its stable." A famous war
pilot asked a friend who was flying the Junkers metal aircraft:
"Are you then so tired of life that you have to fly a plane without bracing wires?"

Hugo Junkers knew that it is ultimately the mental powers of
the innovator which can win the struggle. They also govern
his success: "The thing is not to be frightened by hindrances,
but to overcome depression and follow the task with determination. It is this which makes the true pioneer or research worker.
The technical achievements are far less important for success
than the spiritual ones."

THE BEGINNINGS OF AERIAL TRAVEL

The Versailles Treaty compelled Germany to destroy some
17,000 aircraft; only the fliers remained and they did their best
to make use of their skill. The first scheduled air service between Berlin and Weimar was opened on 5th February 1919
using converted, open military two-seaters, in which the passengers were exposed to the wind. But it was passenger traffic
by air.

An airmail service was started in 1918 between New York
and Washington, and in 1920 the coast-to-coast mail service
began. Junkers' first all-metal cabin aeroplane, the famous
F.13, finished in 1919, exerted a considerable influence on the
further course of passenger-aircraft construction. Despite the
difficulties of the years of inflation, aerial travel prospered and
by 1925 there were thirty private airlines in Germany. The
Deutsche Lufthansa Company was founded in 1926.

After the war some fliers hazarded the first long-distance
flights. An American flying-boat flew the Atlantic in stages
under Captain Read, followed by Alcock and Brown, whose old
Vickers-Vimy bomber took them from Newfoundland to Ireland non-stop. In 1920 Ferrarin set out from Rome to Tokyo,

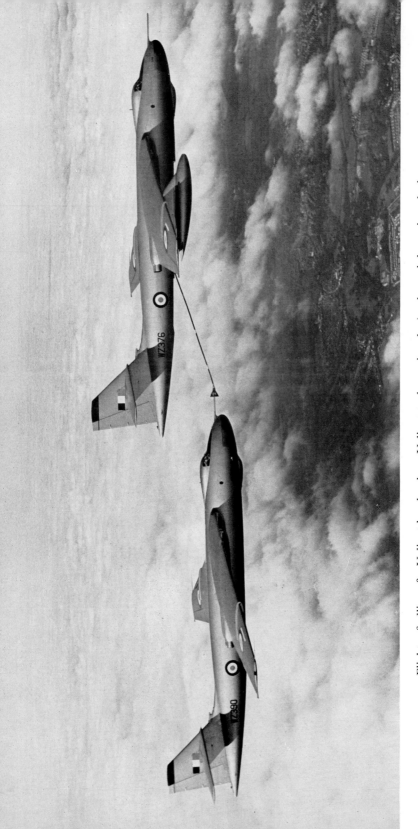

Flight refuelling of a Valiant bomber by a Valiant tanker, using the 'probe-and-drogue' method.

The De Havilland 'Spectre' rocket motor on test.

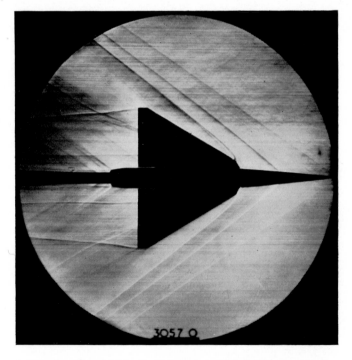

A plan-view photograph of a $\frac{1}{24}$th-scale model of the Fairey 'Delta-Wing' aircraft in a wind tunnel at the Royal Aircraft Establishment, Bedford. The photograph, taken by the Schlieren method, shows the shock waves produced in the air by the passage of the aircraft, in this case at a Mach number of 1·82, corresponding to a speed of 1·82 times the speed of sound at sea-level.

and in the same year Schroeder took off from Dayton (Ohio) to enter the stratosphere for the first time at a height of over 30,000 feet. Three young American pilots, named Smith, Wade and Nelson, made the first round-the-world trip in three triplanes in 1924, against the advice of all the experts. Byrd flew over the North Pole in 1926.

On 21st May 1927 the heroic age of air travel came to an end with the remarkable achievement of a bold lone flier. That evening Charles Lindbergh landed his 'Spirit of St. Louis' at Le Bourget after a non-stop solo flight from New York of thirty-three hours and thirty minutes. A year later Captain Köhl, a German, and Colonel Fitzmaurice, an Irishman, flew a Junkers W 33 'Bremen' from Ireland to America, carrying Baron Günther von Hünefeld as passenger.

Dornier flying boats were also making a name for themselves the world over, and Wolfgang von Gronau crossed to New York in a Dornier Wal flying boat in 1930. By 1928 the 'Superwal' had won twelve world records. The first aircraft to fly with 170 passengers — a tremendous achievement for those days — was the Do X, a twelve-engined flying-boat which created a great stir by flying round the world, with a total mileage of over 21,000 miles, in 1929.

The speed and height records were also being constantly raised. After the First World War the absolute speed record was raised to 196 miles an hour. The world speed record of 450 miles an hour set up in 1939 in a Messerschmitt, flown by Fritz Wendel, was destined never to be broken by a piston-engined propeller-driven machine, for after the Second World War the speed record was the province of the jet aircraft. The world altitude record for aircraft rose from some 33,000 feet in 1920 to nearly 57,000 feet by 1938.

The achievements of the first fifty years of flying would fill an entire encyclopædia, and the list of men and women who contributed to aeronautical progress is endless. Dr. E. E. Heiman, the publisher of *Interavia*, was right when he wrote: "The first fifty years of powered flight are not the special achievement of two energetic and courageous men, they are the common heritage of all civilised nations."

*   *   *

I

Is this development of flying a blessing or a curse to mankind? If we ask ourselves this question today, in a moment of sober retrospection, we might well hesitate before answering. It does, however, seem to me that a Dutch chronicle of the 17th century has already provided an indirect but telling hint in these words: "No man can halt the wind, but he can build wind-mills."

In my book *Wings of Our Century* — which first sketched the outline of this chapter — I pointed out that we need today a little more of the confidence which filled the aviator-poet Antoine de Saint-Exupéry, when he wrote: "The machine is not an object in itself, and this is also true of the aeroplane, which is no more than a tool or device, little different from a plough. What are the hundred years of the machine age compared with the two hundred thousand years of man's history? We have only just entered an unfinished house. Nevertheless, slowly our house will undoubtedly become more humanised."

THE LAST LAUGH

An American engineer once told me of an old foreman at the Boeing factory, who, together with his companions, was observing the take-off of the first B17 Flying Fortress. When the huge four-engined plane left the airstrip, the old man, who remembered the Wrights' first flights from his young days, turned and said pensively: "There goes the last light aircraft." This man had not only a sense of humour but also a sound judgment of the further possibilities of aeronautics. He was careful not to say that it was the largest and finest aircraft that was ever built, or to assert that larger and better planes would never be built. But then, he belonged to a country whose air traffic had undergone a tremendous industrial development.

In a study of the decline of Europe, Heiman referred to the tremendous changes which occurred in energy economy, automobile construction and air travel between 1920 and 1955. During the 19th century, the era of the steam engine, Europe possessed unchallenged supremacy. However, as industry gradually changed over from coal to oil, the energy monopoly fell to the United States. Henry Ford and petroleum notwithstanding, the British, French, Germans and Italians led the world in motor-car construction until the end of the First World

War, while, until 1930, the French, British, Italian, German
and Dutch aircraft factories dominated their field. Only about
the end of the 1920s were names such as Pratt and Whitney or
Curtiss-Wright heard outside the United States, without any
loss of prestige by such European factories as Rolls-Royce,
Hispano-Suiza or Gnome-Rhône. But as time went on the
picture changed. American aircraft engineers were not backward in making far-reaching and enlightened plans for the
future. And it is interesting to observe why.

The first multi-engined American high-speed aircraft came
on the market in the early 1930s. They differed considerably
from the types current in Europe, where designers had clung
for too long to out-dated forms. In America a radical change to
monoplane types with retractable undercarriages and variable-
pitch propellers occurred, and firms like Boeing, Douglas,
Lockheed and Glenn Martin began to determine the tempo of
development. Around 1935 aircraft in Europe were built at
State expense. Firms did not carry out their own programmes
of development, but still very largely relied on conventional
designs, built in large numbers. In America, however, the
private aircraft factories, still relatively unimportant, were
fighting for their existence. Although forced to apply revolutionary ideas, they had to curtail their manufacturing series because of inadequate support from the State.

However, the position soon changed, and the American aircraft industry suddenly began to receive its first large-scale support from three sources.

The Americans discovered their airway system, which had
hitherto lagged behind the subsidised European airlines. The
factories received funds from the United States Government
and were able to build rapid, modern aircraft and four-engined
flying boats for overseas services, and began, for the first time,
to compete with American railways. Moreover, a new flow of
capital reached the industry as the American Army placed considerable orders for aircraft.

Meanwhile, the rise of the German aircraft industry had
started an unrestricted armament race. Great Britain and
France began to envisage additional purchases in the United
States and American firms built large new workshops with all
the necessary machines. Deliveries of American aircraft to

Europe began in 1938 — a year of crisis. British and French contracts brought appreciable sums of money into the country. A constant stream of American aircraft, which has not been interrupted since, began to come into Europe.

Once the United States had entered the Second World War, Roosevelt announced the construction programme of 100,000 aircraft a year. In Europe, especially in Germany, this was reckoned to be bluff; but the programme was fulfilled on time. Since then the aeroplane industry of the New World has never lost its dominant position, in spite of numerous post-war crises.

On the other hand, the end of the war found the German aircraft industry entirely destroyed, the Italian practically non-existent and the French hardly alive after four years of occupation. Only the British aeroplane industry remained. Here great new advances were achieved. German engineers had built the first jet aircraft, but were unable to reach series production. Whittle pioneered jet engines in Britain, showing the way to companies like Rolls-Royce and de Havilland. While stagnation took hold of the aircraft industries in almost every European country, Britain suddenly dominated the world market with her new jet engines.

This, however, did not last long. American firms purchased British licences, developed jet engines still further and ultimately produced quantities of which no one in Europe dared dream. Other American firms designed their own jets, and by 1957 at least four had begun mass-production.

In ten years some 90,000 jet engines left the assembly halls of the American aircraft industry.

*   *   *

This transformation affected every branch of flying. In 1928 a Berlin newspaper said: "Let us hope that the mania for ocean flying, which has cost the world so much this year, is over. If we still see land planes over the ocean, then — as this year's frightful lessons have taught us — they must be piloted either by fools or romantic suicides." Two years later Wolfgang von Gronau, certainly not a 'romantic suicide', flew the Wal flying-boat to America, while in 1932 he piloted another Dornier flying-boat around the world, with several landings en route.

In 1957, almost exactly twenty-five years later, three B-52

Trends in the American aircraft industry. The proportion of expenditure devoted to guided missiles is rising, and will exceed that for manned aircraft from 1961. (After W. P. Lear.)

eight-jet Strato-Fortresses of Strategic Air Command landed in California. They had flown non-stop round the world, remaining in the air for forty-five hours and nineteen minutes; they covered one stage of 500 miles at an average speed of 540 miles an hour. These new aerial giants had flown almost twice as fast as the B-50 Super-Fortress, 'Lucky Lady II', which went round the world in ninety-four hours and one minute. The three bombers had no need to land, since they had been refuelled four times in the air by KC97 Strato-Tankers.

This idea of flying tankers was no dream. In the space of six years the aircraft of Strategic Air Command were refuelled in flight some 500,000 times with a total quantity of aviation spirit of 22 million imperial gallons. By the end of 1956 this Command was using more than 220 gallons of spirit a minute in its planes, while the aircrews averaged 750,000 flying hours per month.

During the entire round-the-world flight of the three Strato-Fortresses, airman Eugen Preiss did not once leave his place. This is worth mention, because he was the first man to fly round the world backwards.

*   *   *

We have seen earlier how Dr. Lardner, Ganswindt's opponent, had proved that it was impossible to cross the Atlantic with steamships, and that one might as well try to swim it. Serious competition by large passenger aircraft began to face ocean liners, so long taken for granted. By 1957 as many as 3,000 transatlantic flights were completed each month. This

meant that at any moment of the day or night thirty-five aircraft were in the air between Newfoundland and the English
coast. Invisible radio beams marked out their tracks high above
the sea. The horizontal intervals between routes and the vertical distance between aircraft on the same route were clearly
laid down. There was strict discipline in the air over the ocean,
and the aircraft had to maintain prescribed intervals of twenty
to thirty minutes.

Every twenty minutes a large passenger aircraft leaves each
side of the Atlantic carrying from fifty to eighty passengers!

*   *   *

Fifty years after the quotation from the *Engineering News* on
page 77, the American Air Transport Command despatches a
plane over the Atlantic or the Pacific every forty-eight minutes.
This Command alone carries almost a million passengers and
170,000 tons of freight per year. The total strength exceeds 500
four-engined transports and about 1,000 twin-engined aircraft.
Between 1948 and 1956 over 100,000 ocean flights were made,
more than 22,000 in 1956 alone.

The largest series-manufactured transport aircraft being built
in 1957 was the giant C-133A four-engined Douglas, which
weighs 130 tons and has a payload of 30 tons; the machine has
a wing span of 179 feet 8 inches and a range of 5,000 miles. But
by the spring of 1957 this mammoth aircraft was overshadowed
by the Douglas C-132, which was already in the prototype
stage. This new type was to be powered with four extra-
powerful turboprops of 15,000 horse-power each, with an
estimated take-off weight of 200 tons and a payload of up to 90
tons.

Ninety tons; that is about the weight of 900 fully-equipped
troops or 100 cars. To be able to assess these sober figures
rightly, one has to be able to see this gargantuan aircraft on the
ground, to walk through its enormous cargo compartments and
to see the 200-ton monster take to the air.

*   *   *

A few years before the beginning of the Second World War,
the American Navy set up a special committee to study the
potentialities of the gas turbine engine. The committee worded

its findings as follows: "The gas turbine is unsuitable as a means of propulsion for aircraft, by reason of its excessive weight."

In autumn 1955 the leading engineers of Lockheed's commented on the prospects of newer and more powerful jet transport aircraft as follows: "Now that the F104, the Lockheed Starfighter, is in series production, we are looking a long way ahead. The future will bring us out of the supersonic field into the hypersonic speed range. This is the zone from Mach 4 to Mach 20, with heights of up to 75 miles and speeds between 3,000 and 15,000 miles per hour. We do not know how pilots will fare at such heights. In fact the rocket experts say that at speeds of this order no pilot is needed. But when it is time to build such an aircraft, we shall build it!"

Such tremendous optimism is justified. From 1960 the transatlantic air passenger will board his aircraft at 7.30 a.m. local time in Paris or London, and land in New York at 9 a.m. local time on the same day. After dealing with his business, he can leave the United States that evening and be in his familiar office the next morning. The consequence is that any point on the earth can be reached in a day. The flying time from London to New York will be six hours, from Paris to Johannesburg just about eleven hours and from Stockholm to Los Angeles ten hours. The journey from London to Sydney, which once occupied several weeks, will shrink to twenty hours.

*   *   *

It is astonishing in how many fields the designers and airmen have disproved the scathing judgment which has been expressed by the word 'impossible'.

The French physicist Gay-Lussac, who was carrying out height soundings with balloons in the 19th century, considered the idea of heavier-than-air flying machines to belong to the realm of fantasy. But as early as 1907 the first motor-driven helicopter rose from the soil of France. Fifty years later the big twin-rotor helicopters manufactured in Britain, Russia and America were carrying up to forty-five passengers. The normal flying weight of the Piasecki H-16 transporter was sixteen tons and the payload more than five tons. At the beginning of the 1950s the Westland Aircraft Company of Great Britain were planning even bigger helicopters. The W85 was to carry 102

The British 'Fairey Ultra-light' helicopter with
tip-jet drive.

persons and the W90 as many as 450! The diameter of the
rotors for these giants was more than 200 feet and the craft
weighed 100 tons. The 'Flying Crane' proposed by Howard
Hughes, and principally intended to lift heavy loads, has two
jet turbines, plus two ram-jets at the tips of the rotor blades; the

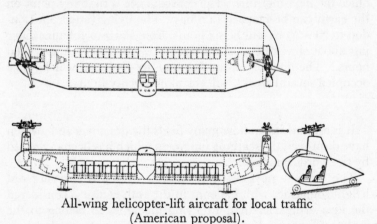

All-wing helicopter-lift aircraft for local traffic
(American proposal).

rotors are to be 130 feet in diameter and the aircraft could lift a
load of eleven tons.

*   *   *

Helicopters take off vertically. They can also land in a very
small area, but sacrifice a certain amount of speed, so that they
cannot compete with normal passenger aircraft for rapidity.

To find a way out of this difficulty the designers of new types of aircraft have proposed the construction of vertical take-off planes capable of high speeds. Helmut von Zborowski, a rocket engineer and aircraft designer working in France, took a bold, and perhaps revolutionary, step with his 'coleopter'; this is an entirely new type, designed after many years of co-operation, and introduces a new concept in aeronautics.

The coleopter is a 'ring-wing' aircraft; the extended wings of the normal aeroplane are replaced by a tubular construction forming both lifting surface and engine housing. The inner 'fuselage' of the aircraft consists of the cockpit and the cabin in the forepart, with a turbo-jet engine at the rear. The housing around this engine is surrounded by the 'ring-wing' and also serves as the housing of a further ram-jet engine. Air enters the annular space between the body and the ring-wing at the front, and assists the combustion of fuel injected into it, so that the 'exhaust' contains no air, but only combustion gases, which provide an additional reaction thrust. That is the basic principle of the coleopter. When the coleopter takes off, it is lifted by the jet from the engines or by the air-screw. The stationary thrust must therefore be somewhat greater than the take-off weight. The aircraft is brought into the normal position at the desired height by means of jet baffles. When landing, the coleopter approaches the ground at about 300 feet and at reduced speed. A further reduction in speed is brought about by using the jet baffles to turn the aircraft into a vertical position; the descent and landing are then carried out with the coleopter 'sitting' on the jet. This is the latest example of the struggle between progress and tradition.

I was present when von Zborowski described his coleopter for the first time to a large number of specialists at the Annual Conference of the Scientific Association for Air Travel in 1954. Old and experienced engineers had come with the idea of "giving Zborowski a piece of their mind during the discussion". I shall never forget how one of them, a highly-respected man in aeronautical research and once a disciple of progress, declared that it was absolute nonsense to use for the take-off such high engine thrusts, which had never been necessary for horizontal flight. For many years heavy aircraft had successfully taken off after an adequate run on a smooth runway so that engine

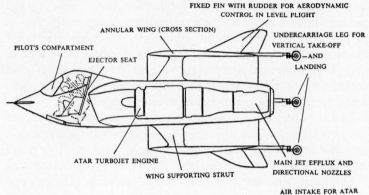

FIXED FIN WITH RUDDER FOR AERODYNAMIC
CONTROL IN LEVEL FLIGHT

ANNULAR WING (CROSS SECTION)

PILOT'S COMPARTMENT

UNDERCARRIAGE LEG FOR
VERTICAL TAKE-OFF

EJECTOR SEAT

—AND
LANDING

ATAR TURBOJET ENGINE

WING SUPPORTING STRUT

MAIN JET EFFLUX AND
DIRECTIONAL NOZZLES

AIR INTAKE FOR ATAR
TURBOJET ENGINE

A step towards manned vertical
flight. The revolutionary French
'Atar Volant' P.3 coleopter
based on a diagram by Helmut
von Zborowski.

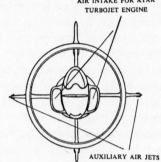

AUXILIARY AIR JETS

ratings were kept at an economic level. And now, he continued,
we were confronted with a self-opinionated engineer who
thought he could disregard the experience of half a century!
For months afterwards we were told: "That thing will never
fly. And if it did it would be scrapped; it is no use at all . . ."

Three years later I saw the forerunner of the coleopter —
now being steadily developed in practice — at Le Bourget,
when the test pilot Morel took off vertically in the 'Atar
Volant'. Elsewhere I saw the French rocket aircraft 'Trident'
rise like a projectile into the stratosphere at almost twice the
speed of sound. The coleopter and the vertical take-off aircraft
have become facts.

*   *   *

That was the situation shortly after the First World War
when Junkers' 'tin donkey' flew for the first time and the first
jet engines were used; it will be the same in the future, what-

ever direction man's creative skill will follow. The further potentialities of flight are undeniable, yet when a new type of aircraft appears in the sky, the old scepticism is aroused almost automatically. A man judges whatever is new in the light of what he has for years proved and applied. When Bernoulli proved by mathematics and with complete credibility that steam propulsion was a fanciful dream, he based his calculations on the efficiency of the cumbersome steam engines of his day; Werner von Siemens' criticisms of experiments in heavier-than-air flight were based solely on his knowledge of the unsuitable power units available at that time.

But what foundation have the sceptics who ruthlessly criticise the plans or achievements of the innovators, and caricature their projects, without taking the trouble to prove their criticisms?

The following little story is a warning to every over-hasty critic: the American airman Guy Murchie tells how an Australian aborigine expressed his doubts of the aeroplane by asking, "Can it see?" "No," replied the air mechanic, "it isn't an animal, it is a machine." "Well," said the aborigine, "if it is blind, it can't be much use, can it?"

CHAPTER IV

THE INVISIBLE NET

Rapid communications — The cabled word — The telephone — Opposition to the telephone — Patent disputes — The electric waves — Radio telephony — The spread of broadcasting — The face of the world — Seeing by radio — Waves from space — Fifty years of radio progress

As Heinz Mueller, head of the Rocket Research Department of the Bell Aircraft Co., left the first session of the 7th Astronautical Society, held in Rome in 1956, he suddenly remembered that he had omitted, either during his change of planes in Paris or his short stop in Frankfurt, to give his wife at home in Buffalo the promised news of his safe arrival in Europe. He looked at his watch and, not wishing to fetch the family out of bed, mentally subtracted six hours to allow for the difference of time and then put in a call to his home. Shortly afterwards his voice was heard in Lockport as clearly as if he were speaking from nearby Niagara Falls. Mueller had chosen the easiest way of communicating with his family in America, whilst he was discussing technical problems with his colleagues 4,000 miles away in Europe.

When Andrew Haley, the Chairman of the Committee for International Affairs of the International Astronautical Federation, was informed that he was expected on 13th April in Stuttgart to give a lecture, he was in Seattle on the Western Coast of America. He had assumed that he had much more time, since a meeting of his Committee was arranged for the very next day in the Unesco building in Paris. This was no problem to the energetic American lawyer; he immediately flew from Seattle to Washington, where his secretary was waiting with his airline ticket and passport, together with the papers he required for the meeting. Thence he flew to New York, changing directly to a

Super Constellation. As the plane left, the airport clocks showed 5.30 p.m. on Friday, 12 April.

Haley saw little of Gander or Shannon because of bad weather. When he left his plane in Frankfurt for a short talk with Welf Heinrich, Prince of Hanover, and Professor Dr. Alex Meyer (two international experts on aerial and space law), it was exactly three o'clock on Saturday, 13th April. Two hours later he met Dr. Eugen Sänger, Director of the Institute of Research into the Physics of Jet Engines, at Echterdingen near Stuttgart; there was ample time to carry out a number of test-bench demonstrations before the lecture which was to take place that evening in the Technical College. It was an interesting meeting and discussion continued into the early hours of Sunday. Punctually at twelve o'clock of the same day Haley was being driven along the Champs-Elysées by Dr. von Kármán's chauffeur. The meeting of the Committee began on time, for Dr. L. R. Shepherd had arrived from London, Dr. Sänger from Stuttgart, von Kármán from Brussels and Dr. Kosta Sivcev from Belgrade.

They had all chosen the second possible means of 'communication' — travel by air, sea or land — and Haley had covered not less than 8,000 miles in a few hours.

*   *   *

These two examples show that it is not the engineer's projects but man's real requirements which decide how quickly and how far people travel. Any new means of communication is likely to develop only if its existence can be justified in practice.

All man's technological advances have been based on his needs. The wheel was discovered when he had to carry heavy loads over long distances, steam was applied to replace muscles by machines, and nuclear research reached its first peak of development when energy demands threatened to exceed the supply from conventional sources such as water, coal and petroleum. Moreover, trains, cars and aircraft were not built to satisfy the whims of a few engineers, but because men and goods had to be transported on an ever-increasing scale. When the large supersonic airliners are introduced in the 1960s this will not be because they are technically possible, but because they will meet a new and urgent demand.

William P. Lear, who manufactures equipment for modern aircraft of ever-increasing speed, has this to say:

"At first glance it is a bit disillusioning to apply the yardstick of human needs to the future of aviation.

"If we think of airplanes as a convenient extension of the horse, the railroad, and steamship, we must admit that airplanes are already approaching the highest speeds and the longest ranges that have any clear purpose. If within the next twenty-five years you can reach the other side of the world in a restful overnight sleeper hop, why dream of going faster? Or, if you want to go farther than that, why not turn around and fly in the other direction?

"If you visualise having thousands of tons to transport regularly to some distant point, it soon will occur to you that rails and ships can land a big load every day at almost any point on earth. The pipeline result is faster than air transport and much cheaper.

"Finally, do you yourself foresee an actual need to travel faster in your daily activity than your auto permits?

"If not, where lies that gloriously unlimited aviation future that we all feel in our bones must be consonant with the ages that men have dreamed of magic carpets and swift flight through the blue yonder? All history assures us that there is more of the drama of man's most wonderful achievement yet to unfold — but in what direction? Can we identify any real need for thousands of civilians to travel many times faster than sound?"

We may perhaps get an answer to this question from the fact that more than 20,000 private aircraft were registered in the United States by the 1950s. In 1955 they totalled a million more flying hours than the 2,100 twin-engined or four-engined planes flown by all American airlines. Even so, the American airline companies carry between thirty and forty million passengers a year, on an average journey of 600 miles per passenger; most of them fly for business or professional reasons — business men, senior officials, pianists, boxers, scientists, specialists and diplomats among them. Lear calls them the 'Twentieth-Century Nomads', who travel faster and faster from continent to continent, so as to be present at even more conferences in a month than ever before.

One is tempted to challenge these restless travellers in the words of the pilot of a 'slow' aircraft, who radioed to his exhausted colleague in a supersonic aeroplane which had just broken the record: "What's the hurry?"

Here again Lear has an answer. In his view an adolescent requires two decades to learn at least the principles of a profession; only then is he in a position to busy himself with the special problems of his calling and to gather practical experience. This requires another ten to fifteen years, so that little time remains for him to utilise his full creative powers, and the saving of time becomes a most important factor. Anyone who wishes to keep pace with developments and to enjoy those indispensable discussions with professional colleagues must frequently participate in conferences. Lear's conclusion is that any form of isolation and, in particular, hindrances to travel mean stagnation. This forces us to the conclusion that only one 'transport container' is suitable for the rich stores of knowledge which have been — and will continue to be — assembled: namely, the human brain. Thus, in Lear's view, the frequent rapid transport of 'brains' from one town to another is the best means of aiding progress and reciprocal understanding.

According to Lear, "When the world has twice its present population and four times present requirements for food, goods and understanding, may we not need to 'materialise' specialised wisdom instantly wherever it is called for?

"If so, we can conceivably 'materialise' a man halfway around the world at 3,000 miles per hour in about the time required now to get a cablegram delivered. Once this new medium is recognized as a means of communication, rather than transportation, there will be no limit to the speed desirable, and as that speed is needed it will be made available."

*　　　*　　　*

What we have just said is true of the specialists — of the most highly-developed brains. But there is still the task of carrying information — i.e., words and pictures — as quickly as possible round the world to give even its most remote inhabitants the news — so often without any bearing on their lives, but often also of fateful import. Both possibilities of communication may overlap and complement each other, but both must exist. If you cannot personally be present, you can wire, cable or phone — either by wire or even by wireless telephone — as in the example quoted at the beginning of our chapter.

The telephone was a new experience to Heinz Mueller's grandparents and the transmission of speech or picture by wireless a dream. Not once would the people of that time, blindly trusting to progress, have dared to imagine the invisible network of modern communications, to say nothing of the radiations reaching out to the stars. And yet one or two men did picture what was to come. W. E. Ayrton wrote in 1896: "The day will come, when we are gone, when copper wires and rubber-covered cables will only exist in museums; the man who wishes to speak to a friend, not knowing where he is, will use an electric voice. He will ask: 'Where are you?' The only one to hear him will be his friend with the similarly-tuned electric ear. And the answer will come: 'I am down a mine at Newcastle.' 'I am flying over the ridge of the Andes.' 'I am crossing the Pacific Ocean.' Perhaps there will be no answer. In that case you may be sure his friend is dead."

Many hundreds of years of man's history were needed before this prophecy became possible. But at that moment its fulfilment was not twenty years away.

RAPID COMMUNICATIONS

Somewhere at the beginning of this long path there was the desire for information. News is so cheap nowadays that most people are liable to underestimate its worth, and yet they still pay cash for information. News agencies span the entire world, and news has become a merchandise which is priced, offered, bought and sold again.

In past days the messenger with good tidings expected a royal reward. But woe to the unlucky bringers of bad news; cruel-hearted princes often had them beheaded out of hand. "Those were the days!" Tom Agoston, the European representative of a large American news agency in Frankfurt, once said to me, as we sat discussing mediæval customs regarding the carrying of news. "But naturally no news at all is even worse than simply bad news. The marathon runner is said to have given his life to make sure that the news of victory reached Athens as soon as possible. That was 2,500 years ago, and yet in the same circumstances we might well do the same to-day."

Agoston did not however trust to the speed of his legs, but only to modern means of communications. He and his colleagues have an easier yet at the same time more difficult job; communication systems make it almost impossible to keep news to oneself, since they facilitate not only its transmission but its world-wide dissemination.

Before the establishment of the invisible net of communications the monopoly of information regarding an event could decide the success or failure of an undertaking and the happiness or otherwise of men. History has many examples, and we shall briefly quote two: When Napoleon was beaten at Waterloo by the British and Prussian Armies, an unknown person raced to Brussels and thence to the Channel. He did not divulge his news to anyone, but, sailing to London, arrived even before the official couriers. He hurried to the Exchange and was able to make a considerable fortune by reason of his knowledge. While on the Continent an Empire was crashing in ruins, Rothschild, boldly grasping opportunity, founded a new financial dynasty.

The other example is more recent; the attempted German revolt of 20th July 1944 failed before it was properly begun because Hitler not only had the power but, above all, the best means of communication.

*   *   *

At the very outset man's need for information prompted an astonishing degree of inventiveness in the transmission of news. Five hundred years before the birth of Christ, mounted messengers of Darius I and Xerxes I of Persia are recorded as having travelled over 200 miles in forty-eight hours. Important announcements were transmitted across the Persian Empire by a sort of 'wireless-telephone line' formed by a chain of watchmen on towers and hilltops, who shouted their message from one to another. In this way a command from the King or a report from one of his generals reached its objective thirty times faster than by horsemen.

Experiments with visual signalling followed the acoustic transmission of news very early in man's history. Over 2,000

K

years ago the Persians and Greeks used torches in arrangements which represented the letters of the alphabet. Fire signals were also used by the Romans and Carthaginians under Hannibal, and we all know that the Red Indians signalled over long distances with puffs of smoke, as do some primitive tribes today. Such relatively rapid means of communication were not used in Europe in the Middle Ages, runners or horsemen being preferred. Only at the beginning of modern times was the rapid transmission of news by bells, flags, lamps or megaphones attempted.

During the French Revolution the twenty-nine-year-old priest, Claude Chappe, who possessed considerable knowledge of mechanics and physics, discovered a simple optical telegraph system. Small bars, which could be moved by means of ropes, were suspended from high masts at suitable points on high buildings or hilltops; the various arrangements of the bars corresponded to letters and signs in the code which Chappe also developed. When the inventor demonstrated his telegraph to the National Convention in Paris in 1792 he was immediately granted the State support he had asked for to build an experimental installation with a range of fifty-odd miles. Two years later the 142 miles between Paris and Lille were covered by twenty-two Chappe telegraph stations. Links with other towns were soon built. Once the operators had learned the Chappe code, telegrams were transmitted at a surprising speed. From Paris to Strasbourg took only five minutes, from Paris to Toulon twenty. One disadvantage of the system was that anyone who knew the code could 'read' the telegrams.

The importance of rapid communications was particularly obvious in connection with military and political intelligence. When, in 1809, the Austrian troops marched into Bavaria and drove the Bavarian King out of his residence, Napoleon heard of it so quickly via the Chappe telegraph that he was able to enter Munich together with the King only four days later. Impressed by the success of this system, the two monarchs called upon the President of the Bavarian Academy of Sciences to improve it. The President, Doctor von Sömmering, was interested in electricity, which — known as 'galvanic' current — was then little understood.

Knowing that electric current decomposes water into hydrogen and oxygen, he utilised this fact to develop the first electric telegraph. The 'transmitter', a current source, was connected by thirty-five wires to a 'receiver', a water container; thus each letter had its own wire. The bubbles of gas rising through the water when a signal was given showed the wire in use, and since all the wires were suitably labelled, it was an easy matter to read off the message. It was a clever idea, but, unlike Chappe's wooden telegraph, was too complicated. Sömmering was able to telegraph with his bubble apparatus but this was a long way from a rapid means of communication. His invention finally failed because of the complicated network of thirty-five wires.

THE CABLED WORD

In 1820 the Danish physician Hans Christian Oersted discovered that a magnetic needle is deflected by an electric current. One day von Sömmering showed the German mathematician Gauss, Director of the Göttingen Observatory, his bubble telegraph.

Gauss quickly realised that the proper sequence of ideas was: electric current — magnetic needle — telegraph. He and his friend and colleague Professor Weber began experimenting on these lines, and in 1832 the 'needle telegraph' was completed. The experimenters stretched two copper wires high over the roofs of the houses from the Observatory to the Physical Institute. When they signalled by sending an electric current along the wires, the magnetic needle at the other end was deflected; the degree of movement of the needle showed which letter was being transmitted. Gauss and Weber were convinced that this method could be used to telegraph over long distances, e.g., from Göttingen to Bremen. They had neither the time nor the inclination to concern themselves with the practical introduction of the electric telegraph, and entrusted its further development to Carl August Steinheil, an astronomer and optician in Munich. He later discovered, when installing a telegraph line for the Nüremberg–Fürth railway, that it was not necessary to install two wires; one was replaced by the earth which also conducts current.

The world now possessed an electric telegraph, but did not immediately enter upon the new 'age of communication'. Further experiments with various systems were carried out and the experimenters gathered more and more information which they discussed and exchanged. A disappointed painter who gave up art and came to this new science of electricity as a novice was to exercise a decisive influence on telegraphy for many years to come.

*   *   *

Samuel F. B. Morse, the eldest son of a Charlestown clergy-man, first took up art and travelled to Europe in 1829 to study

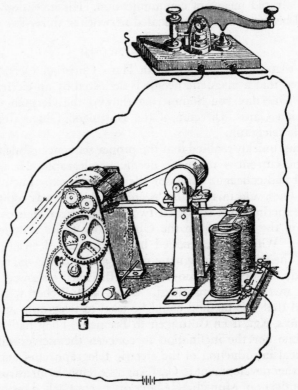

Apparatus used by Morse in 1837.

the various schools of painting in their countries of origin. Deeply impressed by the electro-magnetic experiments carried out by European research workers, he devised a new type of telegraph during his homeward journey in 1832. There was much discussion on board about the telegraph systems proposed by various European professors, but when Morse, known to be an American painter, declared with considerable excitement that it must be possible to transmit information directly by electricity, he was met with shakes of the head and disdainful smiles from his hearers.

This was no unusual treatment. Electric current was far from taken for granted until well into the second half of the 19th century, and its applications were frequently mysterious and highly controversial. Water could be seen flowing through pipes and gas could be heard but it was impossible to observe electricity in movement; no one believed that those wires could carry power and light over long distances. Even in the 1880s it was believed that electric lighting would disappear as quickly as it had come.

One example will show the technical difficulties encountered by Morse when in 1836 he constructed his first telegraph, using an old picture frame: there was no properly insulated wire. His solution was surprisingly simple: to avoid having to wrap the copper wires with silk, he obtained the only insulated wire available at the time — the wire used by New York milliners to make fashionable hats for elegant society ladies.

Morse did not use the magnetic needle; instead he employed an electro-magnet to press a pen against a paper strip which was unrolled slowly and uniformly. Short impulses on the transmitter resulted in a dot on the strip and long impulses in a dash. Combinations of dots and dashes represented letters, numbers and symbols; this was the Morse Code, patented in 1840. With this apparatus Morse telegraphed, in his first tests in 1837, over a distance of ten miles. For six years he worked to improve his technique and his code. Only then did Congress approve the installation of a line between Washington and Baltimore at a cost of 30,000 dollars.

Morse's work contributed to the final acceptance — first in America and then abroad — of the telegraph as a reliable means of rapid communication over long distances. The difficulties to be overcome were not purely technical; landlords refused the plots of ground for the erection of telegraph poles, farmers cut down the wires to mend their fences and boys delighted in shooting at the glass insulators. Southern farmers destroyed a whole line in 1849, claiming that it withdrew electricity from the air and spoiled the weather, as it had not rained properly since the line had been set up and one harvest after another had failed! Almost the same accusation was to be made again a century later, when man began to introduce nuclear energy into the structure of his civilisation.

When Werner von Siemens built a telegraph connection between Berlin and Frankfurt-am-Main he met with similar difficulties. The wires were to follow a projected railway line, but the land purchases had not been completed everywhere and the owners refused to permit the erection of the poles in advance. Nevertheless this, the first major telegraph line in Germany,

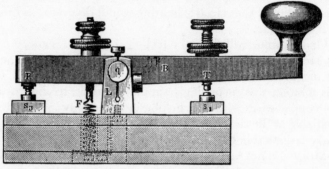

The symbol of an era — the 'Morse key'.

was put into operation in 1849. Von Siemens still used the needle telegraph which he had improved. Moreover, the Morse system became generally accepted, although many people flatly declared that no one could learn the Morse Code.

Morse, who left America as a painter and returned as a communications engineer, was appointed Professor of Natural History at Yale as a result of his tremendous successes, and received in 1857 a gift of 400,000 francs from ten European countries. Two memorials were erected to him in New York during his lifetime.

When he died in 1872, the telegraph had girdled the earth. Practical men developed the new means of rapid communication devised by the inventors, and constructed improved and more reliable equipment. Before long overland lines were no longer sufficient and intercontinental links were proposed. A few decades before, the Atlantic would have been considered the end of the known world, and it was still thought to be dangerous, only to be crossed by difficult sea journeys; yet now the communications experts intended, as it were, to reduce its width and send cabled messages like lightning from coast to coast. In 1850 the first experiment of this kind succeeded; after three laborious months, a cable was laid connecting Dover and Calais. A year later a fisherman encountered a 'sea serpent' in the Channel. His nets fouled and broke the cable which was soon repaired and restored to service.

This operation — successful in the Channel, which nowhere exceeds a depth of 200 feet — failed when it was first tried in the Mediterranean; during attempts to lay a cable between Sardinia and Algeria, places were encountered where the sea bed lay at considerable depths. The unwound section of cable was too heavy and the brakes on the cable drums failed; the engineers looked on helplessly while the entire length of expensive cable rapidly unrolled itself and sank to the bottom. Only in 1857 did an English firm — with Werner von Siemens as adviser — achieve success, and the first deep-sea cable was laid. The idea of a similar link between Europe and America no longer seemed unrealisable.

As early as 1854 Cyrus West Field, famous as the engineer who built the New York overhead railway, founded the New York, Newfoundland and London Telegraph Company; two years later he established — together with American and English industrialists — the Atlantic Telegraph Company in London. The sea journey between the Old World and the New still took several weeks, but the rapid growth of industry was making more rapid communications a necessity.

Although influential circles in London and Washington thought the proposal of a transatlantic cable fantastic, private citizens were willing to finance it; the manufacture of a deep-sea cable 2,500 miles long was begun in February 1857. Six months later the *Agamemnon* and *Niagara* sailed with their valuable cargo; the first reel of cable was unwound on 7th August. Everything seemed to be going satisfactorily, but three-quarters of an hour later the cable suddenly broke and disappeared. Next day it was recovered and repaired, but soon afterwards a storm sprang up and the cable broke again. This time the search was in vain, and the ships had to return. The approach of winter hindered the operations for a time.

Early in 1858 Field's fleet put to sea again. This time cable-laying was started from the middle of the Atlantic. The two ends of the cable were joined together and the two ships set off in opposite directions. The cable broke during an attempt to deal with a faulty connection, but was repaired; unfortunately when nearly 300 miles of it had been laid, it broke again and work had to be abandoned.

This great undertaking succeeded only at the third attempt. By 4th August 1858, 2,300 miles of cable had been laid, and Europe and America were linked. Queen Victoria and President Buchanan exchanged telegrams of congratulation. Three weeks later the connection was suddenly interrupted and the telegraph machines stopped — perhaps moisture had penetrated the insulation. The fault was never found; to this day the cable lies unusable at the bottom of the Atlantic, in places at a depth of 13,000 feet.

When the cable broke between Suez and India that same year, and was lost in the Indian Ocean, the company's losses were nearly £2,000,000. Field had to obtain more funds, test and improve the cables and revive the interest of business men in the new means of communication. He made use of the biggest ship then afloat — the *Great Eastern*. This paddle steamer, 650 feet long, had a complement of 500 men, including 120 engineers and technicians of the cable company. In the summer of 1865 she sailed from England. Four times the cable broke, and four times it was repaired, but the fifth time it sank where the crew were unable to recover it. Nevertheless the economic importance of the transatlantic cable justified a continuation of the effort.

A year after this failure the *Great Eastern* sailed again and this time the undertaking succeeded. Twenty days later the permanent telegraph link between England and America was completed. This time the engineers had a windfall; the cable lost in 1865 was found and repaired.

That was the beginning. More and more transcontinental and intercontinental cables were laid. In thirty years a world-wide network was established. By the end of the century there were 318 links, with a total of 250,000 miles of cable.

THE TELEPHONE

The dots and dashes of the Morse Code were only recognisable as letters and sentences to initiated or practised people. It was 'writing at a distance' not 'speaking at a distance'; news was 'wired', but it was not possible to converse with the correspondent at the other end. The realisation of this wish was the second great step in the development of communications. Professor Charles Wheatstone, the British physicist and inventor, had introduced the term 'telephone' in 1860, although he applied it not to an electric device for speaking over long distances, but to a non-electrical sound transmitter. The name was there, and the apparatus was soon to follow.

The very next year Philipp Reis, a physics teacher of Friedrichsdorf, succeeded in transmitting electrically the sound of a tuning-fork, using an apparatus invented and built by him. The receiver contained a kind of knitting needle vibrated by an electric current which reproduced the sound. There was still no question of transmitting the human voice. The experts actually said that this was impossible and the Reis apparatus aroused no interest, although the inventor spent several years trying to improve it.

The prize sought by inventors of so many countries fell to a young Scottish teacher who had emigrated to America; by day he taught, and by night — fascinated by the idea of transmitting speech over long distances — he experimented in spite of mockery and opposition, until he achieved one of the greatest successes in the history of technology. His name was Alexander Graham Bell.

Being Professor of Voice Physiology at Boston University, Bell was a specialist in voice and speech techniques. At the beginning of his career as an inventor he knew virtually nothing of electricity. Many of his contemporaries thought that Bell would never have become the inventor of the telephone had he had a good technical education. They were right. His success was not due to any skill as an electrical engineer but to his knowledge of the human voice. He had heard of Reis's experiments. He knew of the children's 'cocoa-tin' telephone, and he knew perfectly well what the experts carefully repeated over and over again — that sound and speech are two entirely different things.

'Impossible', said the electrical engineers when Bell began his experiments with the electric telephone in 1874. But the young Scot was undeterred, since he knew nothing of electricity. He was not worried by being told that intermittent electric current could be used to carry Morse's dots and dashes, but was completely unsuited for the vibrations of the human voice with its many overtones. The experts laughed when Bell replied that he would transform a direct current into vibrations — i.e., replace the vibrations of the air by electrical vibrations. The idea was thought to be completely ridiculous, so much so that he was not believed even when he had put his ideas into practice. But Bell had been right from the very beginning. His solution was simple and clever. In fact no one has yet found another way of making an electric telephone, let alone a better way. His unshakable confidence enabled him to follow his idea despite years of opposition, poverty and sickness.

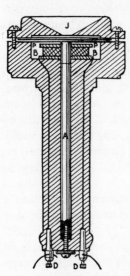

The earpiece of the Bell telephone.

In March 1875 Bell presented himself to Professor Joseph Henry, the Director of the Smithsonian Institution in Washington. This famous American physicist was almost at the end of his successful career as a scientist, while the young Scotsman with the sparkling dark eyes, thick black hair and fine, mobile hands was only at the beginning. Henry was not impressed when Bell told him that a spiral of insulated copper wire emits an audible sound when an intermittent current is passed through it. But next day Bell demonstrated his experimental apparatus in the Institute; this time Henry took Bell's 'mad idea' very seriously. He described the apparatus as the "germ of a great invention" and encouraged the hopeful teacher to continue his work.

Shortly afterwards Bell met Thomas A. Watson, a gifted young electrical engineer and later his collaborator. After many years of association Watson graphically described this first meeting as follows: "One day a tall, lean, energetic man, with a pale face, black side-whiskers and drooping moustache, a big nose, a steep, high forehead and a black bush of hair, rushed out of the office to my work bench. That was my first acquaintance with Alexander Graham Bell." The two men now worked together, first on the telegraph and subsequently on the electric telephone. Bell drove himself and Watson continuously, neglecting his profession to work at night on his deeply-rooted ideas. A characteristic saying of his was: "Watson, we're on the way to making a great discovery."

They discovered the secret of electric speech transmission by a coincidence. In May and June 1875 they were working in their attic in Boston; Bell held the receiver to his ear, while Watson operated the transmitter, sixty feet away in the workshop. The apparatus was suddenly disturbed by a short circuit. The steel spring vibrating above the pole of the magnet produced an electric current which varied in intensity with the density of the air surrounding the spring; this was the idea Bell had been seeking to crystallise. The current was transmitted over the wire to the receiver in Bell's room, and fortunately this part of the apparatus was capable of transforming the current into a rough but recognisable reproduction of the sounds produced by Watson. Bell heard the sound, and at once realised that they had made a great discovery. The telephone had been born. Moses G. Farmer, an American engineer, related years later with tears in his eyes that, after the publication of Bell's description of the telephone, he could not sleep for a whole week, so angry was he not to have made this discovery long before. "Watson," he said, "in the last ten years I have had that idea a dozen times, but each time I was too blind to see it."

If Bell had known anything of electricity he would not have become the inventor of the telephone.

But this fortunate advance did not eliminate all the difficulties. Bell lived to compare himself at that period with Morse, who "although he was only a painter had conquered electricity". Bell, too, would not give in to difficulties, but the harsh facts of an inventor's life began to blunt even his bold imagination. He ran into debt, was unable to pay his rent and finally had to recognise that his contemporaries did not regard him as a genius, but rather as a troublesome youngster who neglected his profession to follow a will-o'-the-wisp.

However, Bell did not abandon the telephone; he drafted a patent, which was finally lodged in the Patent Office at Washington — after some delays — on 14th February 1876. A few hours later another document was lodged, when the American inventor Elisha Gray handed in a description of his still unrealised proposals for electrical transmission of the spoken word. Although this was not a complete invention and patent claim, the fact that Bell's patent application and Gray's advance proposal were lodged on the same day gave rise to the mistaken idea that Gray had discovered the telephone at the same time as Bell. A few weeks later, on 7th March 1876, Bell was granted his patent. The text described the principle and its potential applications so fully and clearly that it withstood all subsequent claims and litigation.

Three days later Bell spoke the first sentence over his telephone, after five years of arduous experiment: "Watson, come at once. I want you." It was a genuine call for help, for Watson saw as he hurried into Bell's laboratory that his chief had spilt the acid from a battery down his trousers. But the acid stains were forgotten as Bell and Watson repeatedly changed places to convince themselves how clearly the telephone transmitted speech.

At the great Jubilee Exhibition in Philadelphia, held in 1876 to celebrate the Centenary of the United States of America, Bell and Watson successfully demonstrated the telephone in the presence of the Emperor of Brazil, Sir William Thomson (later Lord Kelvin) and other specialists in communication technique. Thomson, whose research had made possible the first Atlantic cable, and who was knighted for this work in 1866, described the transmission of the human voice as the greatest miracle of electric telegraphy. He prophesied that it would be possible to make oneself understood over electric cables several hundred miles long.

Bell not only met with approval. In spite of his successful demonstrations he also encountered indifference and scorn. Many leading business men doubted the potentialities of his apparatus. The ordinary visitors to the Exhibition paid far less attention to his telephone — which was probably to affect the economic pattern of the world far more than many other technical achievements of the 19th century — than to the attractive commercial exhibits on other stands. And although Thomson described Bell's telephone as the "most astonishing thing I have seen in America", it was treated in London first of all as the 'latest American humbug'.

OPPOSITION TO THE TELEPHONE

The first Bell Telephone in Germany was tested by the Post-master-General, Herr Stephan, in the Berlin Telegraph Office in the autumn of 1877, and by 30th October Berlin was linked to Schöneberg. Although users of this 'long-distance talking'

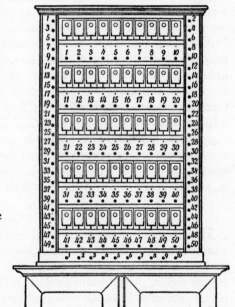

19th-century telephone switchboard.

needed a powerful voice and had to repeat themselves frequently, and although the hearer readily misunderstood the conversation and often had to guess at it, all this was readily accepted for the sake of this exciting new means of communication.

Like everything new the telephone also met with opposition. Many Berliners gave cheap telephones as Christmas presents in 1877; these simple gadgets were sold for a thaler apiece. Two wires running from window to window across the street enabled neighbours to talk to each other. The postal services erected small masts on the roofs for the official telephone wires and were constantly opposed by the occupiers. One outraged lady protested to the Postmaster-General that she would in no circumstances allow the virtue of her three daughters, who slept in the attic, to be threatened by the immoral conversations carried by those wires over her roof! Even in the 1880s doctors were issuing warnings against the dangerous pleasure of telephoning. It was even 'proved' statistically that the mortality of telephone subscribers was three times that of other people, since telephoning caused diseases of the brain, chest and nerves. Moreover, if the innumerable curses hurled at the innocent operators were treated — and punished — as 'insults to an official', all the prisons would have been filled for years.

Automatic telephones were not immediately accepted when they were introduced somewhat later, as dialling was said to do away with the ease and rapidity of telephoning. When an automatic exchange was planned in Munich, a report issued immediately afterwards said that directors and senior officials refused to waste their precious time dialling and listening to "ingenious noises". The good old non-automatic telephones should therefore be preserved since they would have to be restored one day. In any event it was wrong to waste Bavarian money on crazy experiments like that.

PATENT DISPUTES

The struggle for the telephone, when it did become violent, was not concerned with morality, convenience, health or other reasons advanced by objectors, but with economic power, patent rights, priority and profits. Bell's successes were not so much attributable to his technical knowledge as to his endurance and that little bit of luck needed for new ideas and projects to succeed.

The *Boston Globe* carried the following statement on 13th February 1877: "Received by telephone — the first verbal message by wire. We have pleasure in presenting our readers this morning with the first news received by a newspaper over the newly-discovered telephone, the system of sound transmission by wire invented by Professor Alexander Graham Bell . . ."

Bell himself worked on unperturbed and gave several public lectures on his telephone. May 1877 saw the beginning of the

first great patents dispute. The Western Union Telegraph
Company purchased the telegraph patents of Elisha Gray and
Thomas A. Edison with the intention of developing an alterna-
tive form of telephony. In December of that year, when the
Bell Associates Company already had more than 3,000 telephones in service, Western Union and Elisha Gray founded a
competitor organisation, the American Speaking Telephone
Company. Bell and his collaborators were directly faced with
considerable dangers. This struggle for a new invention was
suddenly something more than an effort to overcome public
inertia — it was a fight for patents, for rights and for priorities.
Even though the very existence of the apparatus was still
doubted in England, across the Atlantic the dispute about the
telephone was beginning, and some people were not even
ashamed to call the inventor a plagiarist and a thief.

The subsidiary company of the wealthy Western Union easily
stirred up more difficulty for the Bell group, which was fighting
for its existence. Whenever the Bell Telephone Company
reached out, the 'charged cable' of Western Union lay across its
path. A patent dispute in England was settled by the courts in
Bell's favour in 1877. And yet when Bell wrote to the Board of
the Electric Telephone Company of London, who used his
patents, he knew perfectly well that his ideas seemed Utopian
and misguided, although he suggested that the telephone should
be recommended immediately to the public as a means of communications for banks, merchants, factories, shipping companies, gas and water services, police and fire services, newspaper editors, hospitals, government offices, railway systems,
mines and divers, and that contracts should rapidly be nego-
tiated for its use by the Army and Navy and by the Telegraph
Service. When Bell tried, years later, to find a copy of his letter,
one of the addressees told him, in some embarrassment, that he
had not taken the letter over-seriously and had thrown it into
the waste-paper basket.

The first American court case began in the summer of 1877;
the Bell Company accused the Western Union of manufacturing
and selling telephones of the kind covered by Bell patents. Bell
was a tough fighter, but fair and honest, sick of a struggle which
he had not sought. The Western Union would not yield at first;
it took a whole year for the evidence to be collected on both

sides. When it was finally established that Bell was the un-challenged inventor of the telephone, an agreement was reached, and the two parties combined their patent rights.

Bell's telephone patent has often been considered the most valuable single patent ever issued. Once its great importance was realised, Bell's opponents were no longer satisfied with the minor slanders they had begun with, but instead branded him as a greedy swindler and thief. Notwithstanding this, Bell won all of the six hundred patent cases brought against him over the years.

Sometimes very strange situations arose. The opposition pro-duced steel basins and pepper pots as evidence that they had discovered the telephone before Bell. One of them actually claimed to have constructed a telephone earlier, without know-ing what it was! In another case an apparatus based on Reis's proposal was produced in court, and when it failed to work the counsel for the plaintiff declared that it could speak but did not want to at that moment.

After numerous attacks had been defeated, the opposition started in September 1887; bringing the greatest patent case in history, they sought to deprive Bell of all rights in his invention. The United States Attorney-General brought a case against the American Bell Company and Bell himself on behalf of the Pan Electric Telephone Company, which had already had judgment given against it for misusing Bell's patents; the intention was to cancel the patents Bell held. He was accused of having prac-tised the biggest deception of the century. Although Pan Elec-tric was unmasked as a fraudulent company run by share-pushers, the struggle developed into a gigantic scandal, far less judicial or economic in character than political.

This struggle of the giants lasted for three years and de-veloped into a drama of the pioneer era in America. The mat-ter had to be taken up by Congress and finally the investigation was quashed. With Bell completely victorious, the case came to a natural end. The long night hours which he had spent preparing his patent claim had been rewarded.

*   *   *

We shall not go any further into Bell's activities as an in-ventor. The one-time Professor of Speech Studies invented a

Studio No. 1 at the B.B.C., Savoy Hill, in 1928.

The beginning of a tradition; King George V making his Christmas
broadcast from Sandringham in 1934.

The original Baird television apparatus as used in 1925. Note the ventriloquist's dummy, the first object ever seen on television.

The first Telefunken experimental television unit, 1926. The Nipkov discs gave a thirty-line picture.

speedboat as well as the electric telephone, and was one of the great pioneers of flying. Edinburgh, his birthplace, which he visited once more as an old man, conferred on him the freedom of the city. Surrounded by the seventy-two town councillors in their scarlet robes, the Lord Mayor presented the world-famous inventor with the traditional casket, bearing the inscription: 'Alexander Graham Bell, Doctor of Philosophy, Doctor of Laws, Doctor of Science, Doctor of Medicine.'

When the transcontinental telephone link was opened in 1915, Bell spoke from New York to Watson in San Francisco. He hailed it as a triumph for the many engineers who had developed his discovery and who had created the modern telephone.

A replica of his first telephone was connected, the old appara- tus made of 'boiler plate', which Bell always considered the most efficient telephone ever made. He was asked to repeat his historic message: "Watson, come at once. I want you!" Wat- son recalled how forty years previously he had hurried up the narrow attic steps to Bell's laboratory, and replied, from a distance of 3,000 miles, that this time it would be a week before he arrived!

*　　　*　　　*

Let us look back once again to the path of development from the runners and horsemen to the world-wide telephone net- work. Sömmering's bubble telegraph with its thirty-five leads was never used. The needle and dial telegraphs, together with the Morse telegraph, covered the world. When a transatlantic cable ultimately linked Europe and America, the first 'cabled' news was sent on 27th July 1866, and the next day Londoners read for the first time the previous day's Wall Street prices. Nothing was better suited to impress them with the value of this new means of communication, for previously such news had taken twelve days to cross the Atlantic.

Bell and his collaborators developed the second great means of communication. A huge network of wires and cables of ever- increasing density began to cover the earth's surface. Where the wires could not be hidden underground or laid, in the form of cables, on the ocean bed, they could be clearly seen in the sky above the big cities. It is difficult to imagine the size of these

L

masses of wire which spread over town and country; the world had literally spun itself a web.

Before this web could be removed, the third step — that of wireless transmission of speech and music — had to be taken.

THE ELECTRIC WAVES

The idea of dispensing with wires and transmitting speech and music by 'wireless' through the 'ether' probably struck even the authors of Utopian novels as too far-fetched in the latter part of the 19th century; they preferred to look for less highly imaginative solutions.

When Edward Bellamy, the American journalist and social reformer, wrote his *Looking Backward* in 1887, he described a 'time-traveller' who involuntarily fell asleep and first awoke in the year 2000; even so he did not venture upon fantastic technical speculations, although his story was not lacking in revolutionary ideas. Bellamy's listeners of the future hear concerts at home, transmitted not by wireless but by the telephone, already in use in the author's time. The orchestras perform in central halls connected to the homes by telephone lines. The time-traveller from 1887 is very impressed by this progress, considering that such an invention, bringing music into every home, would have been the acme of enjoyment if introduced in his day.

Exactly ten years after the publication of this book Guglielmo Marconi, then a student only twenty-three years old from Griffone near Bologna, demonstrated a transmission of wireless signals over a distance of three miles between Flatholm Island in the Bristol Channel and Penarth. He signalled the Morse letter 'V' — three dots and a dash; this was the letter that fifty years later, in England, took on a double meaning: the Germans used it for V-weapons in which V stood for 'revenge' (*Vergeltung*), while the Allies adopted the letter as a symbol of Victory.

*   *   *

Radio telegraphy, wireless waves and the broadcasting system were three concepts which originated early in the 20th century, as the third means of communications began to develop. The germ of this development can, however, be traced far back into the 19th century.

As early as the 1840s and 1850s Michael Faraday, a smith's son who had obtained extensive scientific knowledge by private study, began to investigate electric current; his experiments demonstrated a connection between magnetism and electricity. His friend and colleague, Professor James Clark Maxwell, of King's College, London, took up his idea and was able to confirm and explain the experimental results by a mathematical theory. His calculations showed that magnetic and electric fields affect each other, and that light is a form of electromagnetic waves; the latter statement was bitterly opposed by the adherents of traditional physics to whom light was a mechanical phenomenon.

The ideas which Maxwell had to defend so strongly in 1865, after publishing his epoch-making theory, have long since been self-evident. We know today that a particular type of electromagnetic wave occasions chemical changes in the retina of the eye, and that the stimuli so produced are passed to the brain and there experienced as 'light'. These waves are given the name of 'light rays', and belong to the great group of electromagnetic waves, all of which ultimately originate from the atom. Nature has not provided us with sensory organs for any other electromagnetic waves; consequently they were only gradually discovered by scientists. These waves are grouped according to wavelength, spread over a long scale which includes not only light, but also radio waves, X-rays and cosmic radiation. This scale is very wide indeed, for at one end we find alternating electric current with wavelengths of more than 10 million kilometres, and, at the other, short gamma rays one thousand-millionth of a millimetre and cosmic rays one thousand-billionth of a millimetre in wavelength.

The conflict aroused by Maxwell's hypothesis that electric waves are propagated at the speed of light, i.e., 186,000 miles per second, lasted for many years; in fact Maxwell did not live to see experimental proof of it. It was only in 1888 that Heinrich Hertz, Professor at the Technical College at Karlsruhe, finally closed the debate on the wave character of light. He demonstrated that the electric sparks produced by him caused electrical vibrations which were propagated into space at the speed of light. Hertz liked to call himself a practical engineer and yet considered his discovery to be of only theoretical importance.

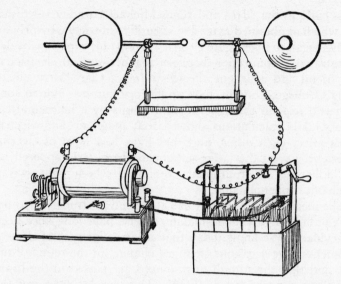

Heinrich Hertz's oscillator for producing electric waves.

When a Viennese colleague asked, shortly after the publication of his experimental results, if his apparatus could be developed for wireless telegraphy, the young professor answered that he did not think it had any practical application. He did not live long enough to see the contrary proved for he died in 1894 at the age of thirty-seven. In his honour the unit used to indicate the frequency of electric waves is called 'Hertz'.*

Hertz's discovery was one of the most important for the development of wireless telegraphy and radio communications. The first need was to develop detectors for the invisible electric waves. In his search for a suitable apparatus, the French Professor Edouard Branly made in 1890 the second basic discovery in wireless telegraphy — a small glass tube filled with iron filings; Hertz's classical demonstration of electromagnetic waves was just two years old. Branly called his apparatus a 'coherer', because the filings cohere under the influence of the electric current and complete the circuit in a Morse receiver. This apparatus made it possible to receive Morse signals by wireless.

The third basic discovery was made four years later in Lenin-

* Abbreviated to Hz; in English it is usual to use the term 'cycles per second' instead of 'Hertz' (Translator's note).

grad, by Professor Alexander Popov. He had been experimenting with wires attached to balloons to measure electricity in the air during storms, and still called them 'air wires'; without knowing it he had discovered the wireless aerial.

RADIO TELEPHONY

In 1895, a year after the death of Hertz, Marconi, who had heard lectures in Bologna University on Professor Hertz's work in Bonn, began to experiment on his father's estate near Bologna in an attempt to transmit Morse signals over long distances by wireless. All he had to do was to assemble the discoveries made independently by others: the electromagnetic wave theory of Maxwell, an Englishman; the transmitter of Professor Hertz of Germany; the coherer, invented by Branly, a Frenchman; and the aerial, discovered by the Russian, Popov.

Initially Marconi's transmitter and receiver were only fifteen feet apart. But this young man without academic qualifications succeeded in ringing a bell by wireless at this distance. Marconi's father, who still had a low opinion of his son's scientific capabilities, was unimpressed by this achievement; he considered there were easier ways of ringing bells. But Guglielmo had enough imagination to recognise the importance of this first successful experiment.

Early in 1896 he travelled with his mother to England. Suspicious English Customs officers entirely dismantled the peculiar apparatus which the young Italian carried in his luggage; Marconi had to rebuild the apparatus completely before he could continue experimenting. On 2nd June 1896 he filed his first patent application for wireless telegraphy at the London Patent Office. The Postmaster-General became interested in Marconi's experiments; the Press took note of them and soon he received enquiries and offers for the commercial exploitation of his invention from several countries. A bank in Milan offered 300,000 lire. Marconi was not a romantic inventor, but a sober man who knew exactly what value his discovery would have as soon as he could achieve a major success.

When he transmitted wireless signals over a distance of eight miles across the Bristol Channel in 1897, there was among the spectators a professor from Berlin, Adolf Slaby, who had studied electromagnetic waves for some time and had heard of Marconi's tests. The relatively great range of the apparatus aroused his curiosity and he immediately decided to get in touch with Marconi. The wind was so strong that Marconi, Slaby and three other observers took cover in a large wooden crate, where, greatly excited, they heard the first clear Morse signals which reached them 'silently and invisibly' from the rocky coast opposite.

Slaby returned to Berlin with a considerable number of ideas for his own research which he continued together with his young lecturer Count George Arco. By June 1897 they had wirelessed from a lecture room in the Technical High School in Charlottenburg to a water tower some 500 yards away to which the aerial was attached. The race to signal over long distances had begun. But no one yet thought of the bitter commercial conflicts which were to grow from these first seeds of a great technological development.

A few weeks after Slaby's experiment in Charlottenburg, the Wireless Telegraph and Signal Company was founded in London. Marconi, still only twenty-three, was granted half the share capital; in return he gave his patent to the Company. Perhaps the other shareholders thought they had to do with an inexperienced inventor, but Marconi had a sound business sense. Not only was he an engineer, he was also a salesman and manager. Money was to him a measure of personal success.

Marconi's company began to erect the first radio stations in England. And about the same time Slaby and Arco succeeded in sending telegrams by wireless between Rangsdorf and Schöneberg, a distance of some thirteen miles. On 1st November 1897 Slaby declared in a speech in Berlin: "Nature has opened a new door to us; the sea of electric waves is now ours."

*   *   *

The large-scale application of Hertzian waves for wireless telegraphy ushered in tremendous developments. Even in 1897 Slaby considered the new means of communication fit for ordinary use. He considered the most important possibilities to lie in military communications, e.g., with besieged fortresses, advancing armies or airships. He also prophesied the use of jamming in war-time.

Even before international competition had reached its height, a notable rivalry arose inside Germany; opposed to the Slaby–Arco system developed by A.E.G. was the system of Professor Braun of the Siemens and Halske Company. Ferdinand Braun had discovered in Strasburg during 1897 one of the most important electronic devices, namely the cathode-ray tube, known in Germany as the Braun tube. A year later he founded his own company: the Professor Braun Telegraphic G.m.b.H.

At this time the firms as such were not of great importance, and the systems were referred to rather than the individual inventors. The day of the solitary inventor was ending and the lone worker had only the slenderest chance of success. If he wished to put his own ideas into practice he needed the support of undertakings with the capacity to deal with such developments. Thus Slaby and Arco sought the help of A.E.G., while Professor Braun turned to Siemens and Halske.

While 'cabling' across the oceans was now accepted, the pioneers of wireless telegraphy increased their efforts to extend the range of transmission. In 1899, the year when the Telegraph Research Bureau was founded in Berlin, Marconi wirelessed across the Channel. Two years later, on 12th December 1901, he transmitted from England to Newfoundland · · · the Morse letter 'S'. For the first time wireless had spanned a distance of 2,000 miles. At the same time Marconi had proved that wireless waves do not travel through space in a straight line like light, but along the curved surface of the earth. The 20th century, which was to be not only the century of flight, but also that of radio and television, had opened appropriately.

*　　　*　　　*

While Marconi set out to challenge the cable companies in signalling across the Atlantic, competition in Germany between the A.E.G. and Siemens and Halske was growing steadily. It had now become more than a sporting race to achieve better range and quality. All permissible means were used, even some which were undoubtedly unfair, such as the use on both sides of jamming to disturb tests and demonstrations. An 'armistice' was only reached in 1902, when the Leipzig High Court was appealed to as the last resort. After months of difficult negotiations the two firms founded, in the spring of 1903, the Wireless

Telegraphy Company, later known as Telefunken. It was high time, for Marconi had meanwhile made considerable progress. His company had already fitted twenty-five coastal stations, thirty merchant ships and thirty-two British naval vessels with wireless. Since 1902 Marconi radio stations had been exchanging complete telegrams across the Atlantic. At a banquet in Canada, Marconi spoke of the bridging of the distance between Europe and America to the benefit of the nations on both sides. The wealthy cable companies promptly increased their efforts to bring Marconi into financial trouble through their English banks.

The cabled word, once a novelty, which had overcome much opposition, had now itself become traditional and its commercial exploiters were both strong enough and willing to fight the rapidly increasing competition from radio. Nonetheless, soon hardly anyone on either side doubted that radio would be accepted. Coastal radio stations were built. During the Herero revolt in German South-West Africa, military wireless stations received their baptism of fire, and in 1906 the first World Radio Congress was held in Berlin; twenty-seven countries signed an International Radio Agreement.

During this time the Marconi and Telefunken systems were engaged in a hard struggle around the world. Marconi attempted to set up a world-wide monopoly in radio. In the meantime, Count Arco pushed developments at Telefunken more and more vigorously, trying to reduce Marconi's technical lead. By 1906 Telefunken had completed the preliminary work for the erection of a large experimental station near Berlin. Dr. Hans Bredov, a promising young man recently appointed departmental head and secretary, immediately began searching for a suitable place; the choice fell on Nauen. The transmitting mast, over 300 feet high, was not shaped like the Eiffel Tower but rather like a pencil, standing on a tiny base and guyed at different heights. In 1906 the daring structure was completed and the experimental transmissions began.

Meanwhile the conflict for patents, rights, priorities and financial agreements continued. Marconi opposed the cable companies, Telefunken opposed the cable companies, Marconi opposed Telefunken. Successes were followed by failures. Marconi ran into financial difficulties and Telefunken also had considerable trouble. Ship-borne radio was still considered a luxury; shipowners refused to install expensive radio equipment so that the captains could, as was ironically suggested, wish each other a safe journey on the high seas. Even the German Post Office was not able to settle down with wireless at the beginning. Accustomed to reliable operation with wires and cables, they demanded more from the pioneers of wireless telegraphy than they could then provide. Wireless communications were more easily disturbed and were therefore initially not considered as serious rivals.

Marconi and Braun were awarded the Nobel Physics Prize in 1909 in recognition of their services to radio. Radio telephony was already being suggested about this time. But the general public still doubted that they would soon be able to call through the ether with an electric 'voice' and be heard and understood by their friends at the other ends of the earth.

Nauen was to be the centre of the world radio traffic from Germany. The installations were enlarged and twelve 100-foot masts added, while a larger and more powerful transmitter was also to be constructed. In addition a second experimental station was to be built in the German colony of Togoland, to provide a link with Nauen. Two heavy setbacks occurred during this stage of the struggle with Marconi. The Togo transmitter was destroyed by a whirlwind. A year later a tremendous squall brought down the main mast at Nauen. This was a great blow, considered in Germany as almost a national calamity and compared with the Zeppelin catastrophe at Echterdingen. Nevertheless the fight went on, and within four weeks an auxiliary mast was erected. Like the Echterdingen catastrophe, the destruction at Nauen gave considerable impetus to the spread of wireless.

After long and laborious negotiations between Marconi and Telefunken, the two giants finally reached agreement in Brussels on 5th March 1913. From this moment there was no longer a monopoly and the way to a genuine world radio system was free.

The outbreak of the First World War dispelled all doubts as to the importance of radio at sea. On 4th August 1914 all German ships on the high seas received wirelessed instructions to proceed to neutral ports. This order circled the earth in a few minutes, and the major part of the German Merchant Navy was actually saved in this way.

The invisible net round the earth was now complete. In 1914 a foreign journalist visiting Nauen asked Count Arco how far messages could be sent from Nauen; receiving the answer "as far as Oberschöneweide", he remarked disappointedly that this did not seem very far. The Count smilingly pointed westwards and added "the other way round".

*   *   *

Up to the First World War there were three means of world-wide communication: cable, telephone and radio. The time was now ripe for the fourth step: public radio and television services with the transmission of speech and music and of moving pictures.

As early as 1904 Professor Fleming had discovered the thermionic valve. Soon after, one of the most important of many improvements was discovered by the American inventor Lee de Forest of Council Bluffs, Iowa. He inserted a metal grid between the filament and the plate of a Fleming valve; when the grid was negatively charged it restricted the flow of electrons, but reinforced it when charged positively. Thus it worked either as an attenuator or as an amplifier. Lee de Forest became the American prophet of radio. In 1907 he founded the de Forest radio company, and only three years later Caruso sang into the mysterious electrical apparatus which carried his voice through the air to the fifty amateur constructors in New York. Five years later a transmitter in Arlington in the U.S.A. sent out a few words which were received and understood in Paris.

Inevitably the pioneers of wireless signalling also began to study the latest form of communications. In 1908 Slaby and Count Arco demonstrated a radio transmission of music at the Technical College of Charlottenburg to the German Emperor and Empress. Arco played a record of Caruso into the microphone at the Tempelhofer Ufer and the music was received by radio in Slaby's laboratory in Charlottenburg. After the Professor's explanation of the technique involved, the Empress, deeply impressed, remarked, "I had no idea that Count Arco could sing so well!" That is the story told by the radio pioneer Kurt Krüger-Lorenzen.

Radio technique continued to develop rapidly. The *Baltimore Sun* reported on 23rd February 1913 that a "certain Bredov from Pomerania" had strikingly demonstrated the wireless transmission of music in America, and that the spectators thought it the devil's work.

The birth of the German broadcasting system really dates from 1917, for in May of this year Bredov transmitted music and talks to the troops on the Western Front. Two years later he put before the National Assembly in Weimar plans for extending the Press and business radio system to a general broadcasting system, but his idea was not taken up.

On 16th November 1919 Bredov became the director of the new broadcasting department of the German Postal Ministry. The authorities opposed his plans without understanding them, and he therefore decided to address the Urania Lecture Society in Berlin on 'Broadcasting for the Public'. He also wished to bring large numbers of people to an understanding of what broadcasting was by means of experiments. His success exceeded his expectations and he encountered excitement, scepticism, astonishment, ready agreement and scorn. The stir created was considerable. Director Bredov had actually transmitted music and speech by wireless during his lecture!

Bredov's new chief, the German Postal Minister, had heard the lecture. Bredov was particularly interested to know what impression his talk had made and was horrified to hear the Minister declare: "You could easily have dispensed with your experiments. No one will believe you." And when Bredov replied: "Herr Minister, in ten years you will, from your desk, be able to speak to all the postal officials in Germany simultaneously," the Minister sympathetically patted him on the shoulder.

The representatives of the technical press also showed considerable reserve, and even Hans Dominik — later famous for his futuristic novels — commented in the *Berliner Lokalanzeiger*: "Even though the speaker kept firmly to a foundation of fact, his ideas were often of a boldness worthy of Jules Verne, for instance, when he referred to the speaker of the future whose words will be heard by millions by means of wireless."

*   *   *

The main radio station set up in Königswusterhausen now began daily experimental speech transmissions, with a 5,000-watt transmitter, to Moscow, Sweden, Yugoslavia, Britain and Holland. But the modern confusion of wireless transmissions was still a long way off. On 22nd December 1920 Königswusterhausen broadcast a big concert on the 2,700 and 3,500 metre wavelengths; it was received over almost the whole of Europe by the many enthusiastic radio amateurs who were already at work. In the same year a Pittsburgh station reported the results of the Presidential Election. Shortly afterwards the famous singer Nellie Melba sang on the English radio and was heard by an amateur in Milan.

By 1922 there were 400 transmitters in the United States and 60,000 receivers. While inflation was crippling the economic life of Germany, America was producing 5,000 valves a month; a year later the figure was 20,000.

From 1921 Bredov was responsible, as Secretary of State, for the entire German Postal broadcasting system. In this capacity he was able in 1922 to propose to the Postal Minister the introduction of public broadcast programmes. A German Society for Instruction by Wireless was founded and the Post Office decided to build and operate a transmission network, and also to permit private transmitters.

THE SPREAD OF BROADCASTING

Even in this period of the development of broadcasting warnings were not lacking. Now and again the doctors gave their familiar warning that radio waves would be a threat to health. In America, where broadcasting was already operating on a large scale, there were stories of its very bad effects on the weather.

On 17th July 1923 the Bavarian Government in Munich made the first serious objections to the introduction of broadcasting in Germany. Despite this and similar protests, despite the strikes and threats of civil war which marked this period, and despite political disturbances and inflation, the German broadcasting system was officially inaugurated by Bredov on 15th October. A fortnight later the first broadcasting station built by Telefunken began transmitting from Berlin.

After this broadcasting was discussed a good deal. But it was almost a breach of good manners to mention culture and radio in the same breath. The Prussian Minister of Culture forbade the members of the Berlin State Opera to broadcast; the journalist Adolf Zimmermann said one day to Bredov: "I have always supported your plans and will continue to do so, but if you use the word culture once more in connection with your new-fangled broadcasting, we shall part company." Many people were offended at the idea of considering that the technical achievement of broadcasting had any cultural value. They could not approve of 'pumping out' serious music to the masses by means of imperfect apparatus, for the broadcasts were frequently interrupted. The mechanical transmission or reproduction of music horrified them.

Broadcasting spread like an epidemic. The year 1924 saw a 'wireless craze' in the United States. What actually happened was that a great technical innovation which was to affect everybody had begun to spread. It brought in transformations and completely changed cultural life. Creative man had made a new plaything for pleasure-seeking man (*homo ludens*), who now faced a period of confusion before entering on a new stage of his existence. Radio brought public life into private homes and critics held that this destroyed man's last defences. The listeners were caught up with the rhythm of broadcast music. "For instance, take dance music. Under the loudspeakers the couples dance in a thousand halls in Berlin, Stettin, Königsberg and Breslau, all observing the same rhythm, as though guided by ghostly hands."

Wireless was often branded in those days a fleeting craze. But the craze caught on. On 1st December 1923, shortly after the introduction of broadcasting, there were 467 registered receivers in Germany. By 1st April 1924 the number had reached 8,600 and by 1st January 1926 had passed a million. By 1927 there were 700 radio transmitters around the world and over six and a half million receiving sets. In 1928 it was reported that in the first five years of its existence radio had spread in Germany as far as the telephone had spread in fifty years.

In 1930 the great Radio Exhibition in Berlin was opened by Albert Einstein with the following speech: "Dear hearers, present or absent. As you listen to your radio, think how this remarkable apparatus has come to us. Remember Oersted, who first used the magnetic effect of electric currents, or Bell, the first to apply this effect to reproduce sound electromagnetically; or Reis, who first turned sound waves into fluctuating electric currents by a microphone and sensitive electric contacts. Think, too, of Maxwell, who proved mathematically the existence of electric waves, or Hertz, who first demonstrated their production by sparks. Think especially of Lieben, who devised an incomparable means of revealing electrical vibrations — the cathode-ray tube; and remember gratefully the host of unnamed engineers who simplified radio instruments and adapted them for mass production, so making them available to everyone. People should be ashamed of themselves when they use the miracles of science and technology with no more appreciation of them than a cow of the botanical structure of the plants it blissfully crops."

In the same year registered wireless sets in Germany numbered 3 million and in America 11 million.

*   *   *

By 1957 the world total of radio sets exceeded for the first time the total world sales of newspapers. There were 290 million radio sets and 60 million television receivers — in all 350 million — windows on the world which could be opened or closed at will with a flick of the finger. The total daily sales of daily newspapers throughout the world at the same period was 255 million.

The struggle to introduce and extend broadcasting has long since ended. If a famous poet, a statesman or a scholar speaks into the microphone, either in the studio or from his desk, his voice is heard by millions. And if today anyone tried to call this an idea worthy of Jules Verne he would not be understood.

THE FACE OF THE WORLD

Man had hardly accustomed himself to broadcasting's intrusion upon the privacy of his home, and *homo ludens* had hardly learned to use the new toy properly, when there came the irruption of a new 'enemy' into his home — television. This was accompanied by a serious misunderstanding. When television was introduced in Germany in the 1930s, the public feared that it was really a 'far-seeing' apparatus and that its 'evil eye' could penetrate walls and buildings.

In his reminiscences of the infancy of television Kurt Krüger-Lorenzen recorded: "The worried mother who, with tears in her eyes, besought a high official responsible for broadcasting to close the television system down, because everybody could now watch her two young daughters going to bed or getting up, was far from mad!" The little group in front of and behind the primitive television camera in the Berlin studio of the 'Paul-Nipkov transmitter', the first television station in the world, had to meet a great deal of opposition. Much emphasis was laid on the threat to personal liberty and on the despicable attempt to penetrate into the most intimate aspects of private life.

The television specialists had to come down among the public in much the same way as the early fliers had done with their aircraft to pave the way for the coming era of flight. For instance, at the great Radio Exhibition in Berlin, the Paul-Nipkov station had its own stand, so showing the public that television was not a Peeping Tom. Reports show that the visitors constantly moved back and forth from the stand to the receiver, painstakingly convincing themselves that they were not seeing a film. They were so amazed that they could not see enough. Nevertheless, many suspected a trick; they were repeatedly heard to say: "It's impossible, and even if they can show it here, a thing like that could never catch on."

*   *   *

Once man had succeeded in transmitting the human voice electrically, he set about solving the problem of transmitting pictures similarly. But sight is a more complicated process than hearing, and the technical problem of transmitting moving pictures over long distances by electro-magnetic waves proved one of the most difficult to solve.

In 1944 Robert E. Lee wrote in his book *Television*: "If we wanted an exact explanation of the mathematical and physical processes in the iconoscope during a television programme, then even Professor Einstein would end up in a sanatorium after giving the lecture." While this may be very exaggerated, it does show how difficult the subject is.

If we examine a half-tone illustration under a magnifying

glass, we see that it consists of a large number of dots of varying size; in some places they almost disappear, while in others they run together in dark patches. This gives the observer the impression of a continuous picture with gradations of light and shade. The picture transmitted by television has to be broken down into dots and built up again in a similar manner.

As early as 1842 Alexander Bain had proposed a transmitter and receiver for the transmission of pictures; it was a kind of forerunner of the 'wire-picture' apparatus of today. In 1875 C. R. Carey developed a primitive selenium cell which transformed light into electricity. By the time Hertz began, in 1887, to experiment with photo-electric effects, the theoretical problems of what was later known as television were already to some extent solved. However, in practice, it required more than twenty years to work out the details. The pictures first scanned had to be broken down into 40,000 dots, transformed into electrical impulses, and then transmitted to the receiver, where the picture was to be reconstituted from these dots in a fraction of a second. If the individual pictures were to produce the effect of a continuous movement — as in a film — a large number of pictures was necessary, up to as many as twenty-five per second.

The first step towards television was literally a Christmas present for mankind. It was during Christmas, 1883, that the student Paul Nipkov, sitting in his poverty-stricken study in Berlin, conceived the idea of the Nipkov disc which transmitted a picture dot by dot, instead of all at once. Very simply the basic idea of television became clear to him. He made a circular disc with a spiral of small holes around its periphery. Rotated in front of a camera, it dissected the picture, so to speak, into separate dots. The differing brightness of the dots affected the selenium cell behind the disc; bright dots increased the resistivity of the selenium and dark dots reduced it. On reaching the receiver the current impulses varied the intensity of a light source set behind a similar disc rotating at the same speed; the flickering dots of light, projected on a screen, built up to form a picture.

Paul Nipkov patented this discovery. But if ever an invention was ahead of its time it was the Nipkov disc. Nobody, not even the inventor, knew what to do with it; he published an article

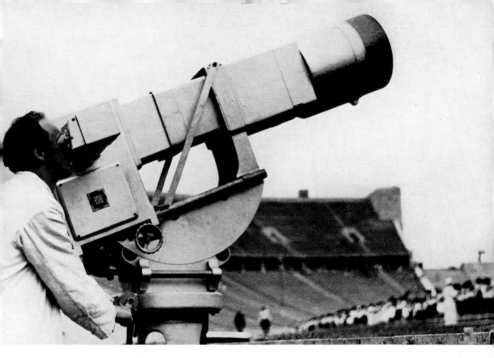

An outside broadcast television camera at the 1936 Olympic Games in Berlin.

A modern studio camera, in the B.B.C.'s Studio G at Lime Grove.

Smaller and smaller valves; *left:*
old thermionic valve; *right:* a m.
cased transistor; *centre:* a mo
miniature valve.

Progressive reduction in the size of
rocket instrument packages; *left:*
for a V-2; *right:* for an Aerobee
rocket; *centre:* for a Vanguard
satellite 1957–8.

A printed-circuit television receiv

or two, and lectured to societies. Polite people told him it was an interesting invention, and less polite people made fun of it. The Nipkov disc and its potentialities for the transmission of pictures were forgotten. The discoverer entered the railway service. His patent lapsed. Then suddenly there came wireless telegraphy, broadcasting and, finally, a renewed interest in the transmission of pictures. It was found that the Nipkov disc could still be used. Nothing better had yet been invented. And so it came about that the first television station in the world was called after Paul Nipkov.

When in 1944 Dunlap published in New York his book *The Hundred Radio Scientists*, he put Paul Nipkov in the first row of the world-famous. The despised engineer from Pomerania thus took his place with Thales, Otto von Guericke, Benjamin Franklin, Ampère, Morse, Faraday, Helmholtz, Slaby, Ferdinand Braun, Heinrich Hertz and Marconi.

Nipkov lived long enough to see his idea employed. Krüger-Lorenzen relates how the old inventor stood in front of the receiver "while we pupils conjured up the first moving pictures on the screen as he had shown us. But his enquiring spirit was still too active and his vision still too penetrating for him to be bound by the practical application of his own discoveries. And thus he was the first to propose that the Nipkov disc be superseded when better technical means paved the way for the perfection of television."

*   *   *

Better, brighter television pictures were required. It had to be possible to write with a beam of light and make electric impulses visible in the form of light. Professor Ferdinand Braun was the man who showed the way to this objective with his cathode-ray tube. His first purpose in constructing it was to make rapid electric impulses visible.

His cathode-ray tube was introduced in 1897. It consists of an evacuated tube filled with a fluorescent gas. A heated cathode emits a straight, invisible beam consisting of numerous fast-moving electrons which strikes the screen at the other end of the tube. It is on this screen that the picture appears and can be seen from the outside. The cathode ray is deflected by an electromagnet and thus 'draws' a picture, line by line. Accord-

M

ing to the intensity of the incoming impulse, more or fewer electrons are emitted, that is, the beam becomes brighter or dimmer. Moving rapidly over the screen it thus gives rise to line elements of the picture, made up in turn of dots of varying brightness; the slow human eye sees this pattern as a complete picture. In 1909 Braun shared the Nobel Prize with Marconi. He died, aged sixty-eight, in 1918 as a war internee in New York.

The Nipkov disc and the Braun tube were early steps towards television. When television was first achieved, the apparatus consisted of an old tea-chest, a Nipkov disc of cardboard, an empty cake tin, a projection lamp from a bicycle shop, an electric motor from a scrap heap, components from a discarded telegraph, a few knitting needles, scrap timber, pocket lamp batteries and, quite incomprehensibly, glue, sealing-wax and string.

This was the apparatus with which John Logie Baird experimented in his attic. Baird was born in 1888 in Helensburgh, Scotland, and when his experiments began he was a sick and disappointed salesman of shoe polish, jam and razor blades. In the spring of 1924 he succeeded in transmitting a silhouette of a Maltese cross over more than ten feet. He knew that he was on the right track, and the principle of picture transmission seemed very simple to him. However, being without funds, he had to sell his invention for a song to a cinema proprietor in London.

A year later Baird took a poorly-paid job in the largest London store and actually demonstrated 'television' to the customers. But his apparatus was still incapable of transmitting a human face clearly; only dark patches of outline appeared on the screen. Baird had a difficult time, but he worked on despite often being near to starving or freezing. He could not pay his rent, his shoes were in holes, his landlord threatened to throw him out, and all this while he was looking for a backer. But even newspaper editors turned the 'mad inventor' away very quickly.

Finally, on 2nd October 1925, his hopes were fulfilled; he succeeded in transmitting an image of the head of 'Bill', an old ventriloquist's doll. The inventor ran from the attic in his slippers, without socks or collar, his hair all awry, into the office on the ground floor and there caught hold of the nearest human being, an office boy who was more frightened of the wild-looking

inventor than of his mysterious experiments. But he was persuaded to place himself under the bright lamps and, after some
adjustments, his image appeared on the screen, the first televised picture of a living man.

The ice was at last broken and Baird received sufficient
money for his tests. He became famous overnight. His miserable apparatus was transferred to the Science Museum in Ken-
sington, a curious muddle of wires, motors and discs, focused
on a dilapidated ventriloquist's dummy.

'Bill' looks confused and a little frightened as he gazes at this
new technological marvel.

*   *   *

But Baird's pictures were still unsharp and badly lit. It was
the cathode-ray tube which made possible a completely
electronic television system of maximum clarity.

In 1923 Vladimir Zworikyn, a Russian living in America,
discovered the iconoscope, an electronic tube which is the heart
of the modern television camera. Thus one invention after
another contributed to the realisation of television, the magic
mirror.

The German Postal Service began to study television closely
in 1927. In the same year pictures were transmitted from New
York to Washington over a cable link. Television engineers still
had radio in their minds, and from the beginning of their work
it was obvious that their successes with wire-transmitted pictures could be repeated with wireless. In Germany Hans
Bredov had the historic honour of being the first man to
approve practical experiments with television.

The first experimental wireless transmissions were sent out
from the Berlin–Witzleben station. Now it became clear that
existing transmitters for long, medium and short waves were
not suitable for television. These waves are not of sufficiently
high frequency to carry the many tens of thousands of points
composing a picture. The broad frequency bands produced for
picture transmission could only be carried by ultra-short waves.

*   *   *

The development of ultra-short-wave techniques was long
and laborious. Wireless telephony had used very long waves;

for instance, a giant transmitter at Bordeaux operated on a wavelength of 27,000 metres, and the Nauen station, which provided the link with New Zealand in 1916, on 13,000 metres. Today we can listen to long-wave stations in the 1,500-metre band. Medium-wave broadcasting spread soon after the First World War. Gradually it was supplemented by the far-ranging short-wave transmissions, although for a time radio engineers thought that wavelengths below 100 metres were useless for broadcasting. New circuits made it possible to go below ten metres in 1925. Professor Abraham Esau of Jena was experimenting with ultra-short waves and succeeded in telegraphing over twenty-five miles on a wavelength of three metres.

Thus ultra-short-wave radio gradually came in, bringing some surprises. The long, medium and short waves used until that time had a virtually unlimited range. It is a strange coincidence that the man who had given a theoretical explanation of the multiple reflection of radio waves from an ionised layer in the upper atmosphere died in the year which saw the first successful experiments with ultra-short waves. This layer is situated between sixty and seventy miles above the earth and enables the waves to cover very long distances after reflection. His name was Oliver Heaviside and the Heaviside layer is named after him.

The new ultra-short waves could only travel as far as a beam of light emitted from the same point. They are therefore similar to light waves and of very high frequency. For instance, with a wavelength of one metre, they vibrate 300 million times a second. Consequently a large number of stations can transmit on closely adjacent wavelengths without interference. Some 3,000 stations could operate comfortably between nine and ten metres.

A subsequent surprise brought the first into prominence again, as it were. It was noticed that occasionally signals were received from ultra-short-wave transmitters thousands of miles away, and the theory had to be extended. It was then discovered that these waves can be broken by sharp features, such as mountain ridges, thus enabling them to cover surprising distances. Since these waves behave like light, it must be possible to concentrate them into beams, as with a searchlight reflector. This was found to be the case and the engineers installed great screens behind the transmitter aerial, to concentrate the radio waves in a directional beam. The longer waves in a normal short-wave band required huge reflectors suspended from 150-foot masts. The ultra-short waves made it possible to use more manœuvrable reflectors a few feet in diameter. The shorter the waves the sharper they could be focused.

Then began the contest to achieve the shortest wavelengths. At the first International Short-Wave Congress in Vienna in 1938 the Americans demonstrated transmissions on an eight-millimetre wavelength, and Professor Abraham Esau announced the successful production of a wave of 4·4 millimetres. Shortly before the Second World War, he reduced this to two millimetres. Finally, the gap between electric waves and heat radiation was closed. The band from 30 microns (one micron is one-thousandth of a millimetre) to 750 microns — more than four octaves in the frequency scale of electromagnetic waves — was now overlapped on both sides. Levitski of Russia produced wavelengths of 30 microns with a surface transmitter, while from the other side, i.e., that of heat radiations, wavelengths of 750 microns were reached.

The general public hardly took any notice of this fascinating struggle for progress in the unknown; otherwise they might have posed the bewildering question as to when a radio wave ceases to be one, or when a heat radiation becomes a radio wave.

As always the road from pure research to practical application was a long one. It was possible to produce ultra-short waves; now it was time to discover by laborious precision work how they behaved and were propagated, and what could be done with them.

*   *   *

The first television transmitter began operating in 1934 in Berlin–Witzleben, transmitting sound and pictures on ultra-short waves. By 22nd March 1935 the trials were far enough advanced for a regular television programme to be announced. The first public television installation was opened in the Postal Museum in Berlin. This Nipkov television transmitter remained in service for ten years, from the trials of 1934 to the cessation of programmes in 1944. By 1936 Berlin had a regular two-hour television programme each evening. The Berlin Olympic Games were televised and 150,000 people visited the twenty-eight television saloons in the capital. A public television-phone service was opened between Berlin and Leipzig.

In Britain the Coronation of King George VI was televised in 1937. The television-phone linked Berlin and Munich in 1938. In 1939 the German Post Office demonstrated television in all the major towns of South America. German troops were provided with six-hour programmes daily in 1940. Hamburg began a television service in 1941, relaying the Berlin programmes. In the same year television in America began with the licensing of the first commercial transmitter, while Baird, still actively experimenting, demonstrated stereoscopic television in Britain. The Berlin television transmitter was destroyed by bombs in 1943.

The British Broadcasting Corporation was the first in Europe to begin television programmes after the war, in 1946. In 1950 Nordwestdeutsche Rundfunk in Hamburg was the first to resume experimental television transmissions; Berlin followed in 1951 and Frankfurt in 1953.

*   *   *

Television's struggle is now over. Man the pleasure-seeker has won another round, and man the inventor is free to turn to new problems.

There is no lack of problems, but new, wide horizons have been opened. Transistors are replacing valves, which have grown smaller and more reliable with the years. Transmitters and receivers are becoming ever smaller and lighter, and have shrunk to the size of a small watch or a bean; they can thus be inserted in the ear or worn like a wrist watch. Transmitter units as big as a four-ounce tin of preserves are installed in artificial satellites and shot into space. Tiny devices, complete with power supply, measuring equipment and transmitter — the whole no bigger than one-half of a bean — can be swallowed by a patient, so that the doctor can easily find out what is happening in the body without operating. Minute television 'eyes' are inserted in boreholes, revealing to the scientists on the surface buried treasure, archæological remains or minerals which may be there.

The story of Prince Ahmed and the fairy Paribanu has come true, even though in somewhat modified form. Man can transmit his voice and his image anywhere at will, on the earth, into the ionosphere or even into space.

SEEING BY RADIO

On 30th April 1904 the German engineer Christian Hülsmeyer of Düsseldorf received from the Imperial Patent Office in Berlin a patent for a process "for detecting distant metallic objects by electrical waves". The drawing in his patent specification shows an apparatus on board ship detecting the presence of another ship by electrical waves. The illustration and the description clearly indicate that even in 1904, when neither

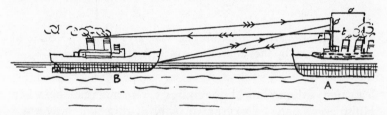

Sketch from Hülsmeyer's specification, 1904, explaining his method of ranging.

broadcasting nor television were known and wireless telegraphy was only in its infancy, this patent had established the basic idea of what was later known as radio ranging.

That this important discovery was unknown for some time is shown, for example, by a futuristic novel by Hugo Gernsback published in 1911. The author 'invented' colour television and a "device for detecting solid bodies in the sky and in space", among other things. He wrote in his preface: "This novel is intended to give readers the truest possible picture of future developments. The author would emphasise that even the most fantastic ideas proposed have a scientific foundation. Their realisation is possible." The bare existence of Hülsmeyer's patent shows that it is not quite correct to consider this novel as the 'source' of the invention of radio-ranging.

But why was it necessary to wait thirty years before the first trials in this field were held? There are several reasons. At

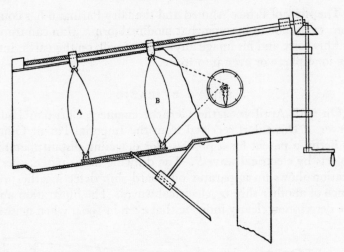

Hülsmeyer's projection apparatus for a beam of waves, concentrated
by the adjustable lenses (A and B).

least two of the technical prerequisites were not available when
Hülsmeyer's patent was granted: neither ultra-short waves nor
pulse techniques were yet known. Even so, their development
need not have taken thirty years. It was only in the early 1930s
that the German Navy decided to develop devices for the detection of objects by radio waves, known as 'reflection apparatus', until the code name 'radio measurement' ('*Funkmess-
technik*') was introduced. The original English term was 'radio-
location', and only later was the American term 'radar'
adopted, an abbreviation from 'radio detection and ranging'.

Tests on behalf of the German Navy were begun with a wavelength of fourteen centimetres. Unfortunately this promising
beginning was abandoned, and wavelengths between eighteen
centimetres and two metres used instead. Nevertheless satisfactory apparatus was developed. The centimetre wavelengths
which give better results were only used after a considerable
detour in development. The "Freya" set, working on a 240-
centimetre wavelength, gave good results as an aircraft detector. The first model was installed on Wangerooge Island
and was also used for fighter control. It scored its first large-
scale success in air defence, according to State Secretary Leo

Brandt, by detecting a bomber formation about to attack Wilhelmshaven in December 1939.

*   *   *

The question may now be asked as to whether radar is exclusively of military application. It is basically an extension of sight, the most important human sense, much as broadcasting extends hearing. True, radar does not go so far in this as radio, and its tasks are more difficult. Nonetheless, it does a great deal. Radar helps us to see at night or in fog, to measure exactly distances or speeds of moving bodies. Moreover, its range corresponds approximately to visual range — some thirty miles in the case of shipping, and about two hundred for a high-flying aircraft. It is quite obvious that artificial eyes of this kind are of the utmost importance in peaceful uses, for instance, in sea or air travel.

Despite this, for ten years — at least from 1935 to 1945 — no one mentioned this possibility, not even in technical journals. Even the fact that the French had fitted a 'reflection apparatus' on the *Normandie* to detect icebergs was ignored. And all this because, the world over, a curtain of military secrecy had fallen on developments in this field, although the 'method for detecting metallic objects by electrical waves' had either been neglected or scorned for years.

Once metre and decimetre waves could be focused by special aerials or reflectors and beamed to a target, the objective was almost reached. It was then only necessary to send out very short pulses (e.g., a ten-millionth of a second) of energy in a spherical wave front thirty metres deep. Reflected back by the target, part of this energy reaches the receiver, standing next to the transmitter. This shows that the target lies in the direction in which the aerial is pointing. The target distance is given by the time taken for the pulses to travel outward and return, since their speed is known to be 186,000 miles per second.

*   *   *

In 1939 Telefunken began fundamental research on radar.

The first properly-developed Telefunken radar set was the 'Würzburg' aircraft detector of which some 4,000 were constructed. The set had a completely rotating aerial and could therefore also be used for height measurement. This made it possible to locate not only ships but also aircraft up to twenty-five miles away. The construction of the aerials proved difficult; this task was entrusted to the Zeppelin engineers, who were highly successful. Subsequently the Würzburg aerial was enlarged to a diameter of twenty-five feet and its range increased to forty-five miles. Fifteen hundred of these new sets were built under the name 'Würzburg Giant'.

The new devices were also soon used in aircraft. The 'Liechtenstein SN 2' was installed in 1,500 night fighters. Siemens built a rotary aerial and 'star-detector' for the Freya. Under the code name 'Hunting Lodge' it became indispensable for determining the situation in the air.

When Britain was suddenly threatened from the air in 1939, she had to provide new defences at all costs. Sir Robert Watson-Watt designed a radar chain which operated on the twelve-metre wavelength. It soon became clear that this was too long, and so, in two steps, the British experts advanced to shorter wavelengths, thus reaching the centimetre range, which is ideal for radar work. They first used nine-centimetre waves, and finally three-centimetre waves, which give much better reflected pulses. Thus England took a sudden lead in the new technique of radar. Her scientists even received an unexpected windfall as a kind of reward for their bold step forward. An airborne nine-centimetre set with a rotary scanning aerial, intended for submarine detection, was left on as the aircraft flew over the land, and suddenly an image of the earth's surface below was seen on the radar screen.

Immediately recognising the great importance of this discovery, the experts gave a warning that the apparatus should not be used over Germany. It was used, nevertheless, and experimental model No. 6 was shot down near Rotterdam and recovered by the Germans, who called it as a result the 'Rotterdam' apparatus. Professor Leo Brandt, chairman of the 'Rotterdam' working party, suggested that all German radar sets should be converted to operate in the centimetre band, between nine and three centimetres.

As early as 1940 radar was used in the defence of German towns against air raids, and in 1941 airborne radar was used to combat enemy bombers. In 1943 the British and American air-

craft released tons of tinfoil strip to confuse the radar installations. The slowly-dropping strips created on the radar screens
images exactly like those of real aircraft. An accurate representation of an aircraft's shape only became possible with
improved radar sets after the war.

Radar sets consisting solely of receiver units were ultimately
developed. To counter the 'Rotterdam' apparatus, German
night fighters were fitted with a ranging apparatus known as
'Naxos Z' which had a range of forty miles. Ground-based
range-finding receivers could operate at a distance of 250 miles,
so that the aircraft gave themselves away by means of their
'Rotterdam' sets as they took off from England. This led to the
'Rotterdam' sets being abandoned for Pathfinder work.

*   *   *

Perhaps all this gives the impression that radar is only for
aerial use, as it were a privilege of the third dimension. This
is not true. The functions which radar can perform led to its
being used in aircraft first of all. But for a long time now a
whole series of very interesting applications of radar has been
known. We have already referred to shipping, which can use

'Blips' on the radar screen
show that the emitted
signal is being reflected
from an object.

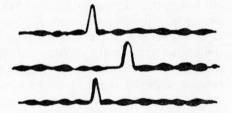

radar most successfully. At the 1953 Hanover Technical Fair
a well-known German company exhibited the first shipborne
radar built in Germany since the war. The aerial, which both
scans and receives, rotates twenty-four times a minute. The
screen picture is synchronised with this, and the set can be
adjusted to four ranges — one, three, ten and twenty-four
nautical miles — for locating shipping at sea.

Even apart from problems of transport there are peaceable
uses of radar, and specialised branches of the technique have
arisen. One such is radar meteorology. It is well known that

light waves are scattered by molecules of air or minute particles in suspension in the atmosphere. Otherwise we should have on earth only blazing light and very deep shadow, and the sky would appear black. We now know that radar waves behave similarly to light waves, and radar emissions on wavelengths of one to ten centimetres, known as micro-waves, are scattered by raindrops, snowflakes and hailstones in the atmosphere.

Such waves can be used to make meteorological observations. Showers, squalls, thunderstorms, cold and warm fronts and even cyclones can be seen on the screen. The important thing is to know how to identify them. When precipitation occurs along a warm front, horizontal cloud layers occur, between thirty and several hundred yards in thickness; these layers reflect radar waves very strongly. Thus radar provides the meteorologists with an up-to-date picture of the weather. One such apparatus was installed in Berlin in the summer of 1957. It shows the meteorological phenomena over a radius of several hundred miles. The screen images indicate the dimensions, intensity, speed and direction of any feature of the weather.

During the last war a fifteen-centimetre experimental set installed at Rügen was used to watch the aerial combats over Berlin. From time to time, when the transmitter was switched off, a long trace remained on the screen for two seconds. For a long while the observers sought for an explanation of this curious phenomenon until they noticed one day that, low on the horizon and in the direction of the fading trace, there lay the moon. This convinced them that they had made radar contact with the moon; the radar waves would need a little more than two seconds for the outward and return journey, the moon being some 239,000 miles away. In this way a coincidence produced the first link between radar and astronomy.

Radar can actually reach out into space. Since solid bodies reflect radar waves, the moon must also do so and it offers a clearly visible target. American scientists directed a sharply-focused beam of separate pulses to the moon. The near-by receiver recorded the returning pulses after 2·5 seconds. That was the first electronic ranging operation in space.

Messages were sent to the moon for the first time on 8th November 1951. As usual the waves were reflected back to earth. A suitable receiver on the moon could naturally have

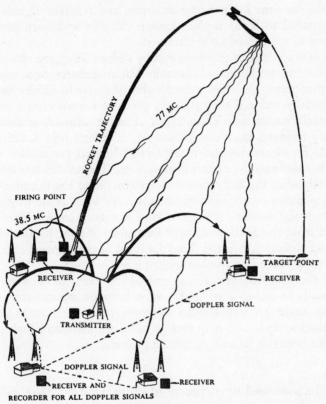

Radar tracking of research rockets.

picked up these signals and transmitted them a further 240,000 miles from the earth. The Collins Radio Corporation twenty-kilowatt transmitter was at Cedar Rapids, Iowa, and the receiver 680 miles away at Sterling, Virginia. The transmission aerial was seventy-five feet long and the parabolic receiver aerial thirty-three feet in diameter. The directional aerial was not movable, but observers saw the moon move into the directional field, leaving it again thirty minutes later. The nearer the moon was to the centre of the field, the stronger the reflected signals became, maximum intensity being reached after ten minutes and continuing for roughly the same period. Naturally reception was weak. The field strength was only about one-millionth of that normally received by a television set. Once again the time lag between outgoing and reflected signals was compared with the moon's known distance and once again a figure of 2·5 seconds was obtained.

Even meteors can be followed by radar. They are often tiny bodies, whose diameter is measured in millimetres, or at most in centimetres. They are so small that they could hardly be detected by radar if they did not produce known effects in the upper atmosphere. Three types of radar echo are simultaneously received in such experiments. The first type is reflected from an electron cloud formed close behind the meteor as it rushes through the earth's atmosphere. The second sort follows shortly after the first, once the electron cloud has become very diffuse; these echoes can still be observed seconds after the passage of the meteor. The third kind of echo is caused by reflection from the ionisation layer formed in the air by the ultra-violet radiation emitted from the front of the meteor, which is strongly heated by friction with the air.

Exact measurements on several meteors were made in Canada in 1949. Their paths were between 25 and 120 miles long, their average heights between 12 and 35 miles, their initial speeds between 13 and 37 miles a second and their final speed between 10 and 35 miles a second.

*   *   *

The successful development of radio occurred more quickly than that of telegraphy, and radar in turn developed more quickly still. Soon after the principle had been discovered, the location of distant objects with electric waves was possible, as Hülsmeyer had prophesied early this century.

As I drove one day to the Rhein-Main base of the American Military Air Transport Service to meet Dr. Wernher von Braun, I examined the huge multi-engined machines — Globemasters, DC-6s, Hercules, Skymasters and many other types — which were all characterised by striking black noses. This attachment, apparently small but actually quite large, contains the radar installation with which the modern aircraft finds its way across continents and oceans, through darkness and fog, cloud and storm.

Radar eyes are even gazing out into space, for this, too, is no longer considered impossible. And so one day new worlds re-

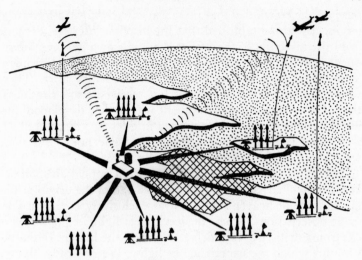

Radar in defence, as a means of guiding aircraft or
missiles against enemy planes.

vealed themselves. Our eyes can see the sun and stars, and it
would be bold to assume that they radiate only in the narrow
band of visible radiations. In fact, they 'transmit' over a wide
frequency range, and there are regions of the firmament which
send out radiations which our senses cannot detect.

When the last war ended, releasing radar sets in large numbers, a new and independent science developed very rapidly
from the fortuitous link between radar and astronomy, obtaining undreamed of results; this science is known as radio-
astronomy.

WAVES FROM SPACE

Initially, the waves from space were misunderstood. People
spoke of radio waves and radio transmitters, and the unscientific
layman believed that this meant that they were possibly
artificial signals from intelligent beings. This is not so. It is
much more true to say that we have turned to our own uses
these naturally-occurring waves which reach us from space, and
which we have suddenly been able to detect.

Radio waves of cosmic origin were observed in 1931 by the
American engineer Karl Janski. He was investigating atmospheric radio interference by means of a sensitive short-wave

receiver; he concluded that these waves were of extra-terrestrial origin. He also established that the heaviest interference came from the direction of the Milky Way, our own galaxy. Subsequent, more exact measurements have shown that the strongest 'cosmic noise' comes from the centre of our Milky Way. These were very important discoveries but received scant consideration. Only when radar equipment was further developed during the war were further sources of interference discovered. It was found that there was not only 'galactic noise' but there were also radio emissions from the sun.

As long as man relied on his eyes or on optical aids, all our knowledge of space, of stellar structure and of the origin or disappearance of heavenly bodies was exclusively based on telescope observations. These devices collect light, i.e., that part of electromagnetic waves which produces in the human retina the stimulus which we experience as light. We can only observe from a distance objects which emit radiations. Large telescopes receive many million times more light than our eyes. The Mount Palomar reflecting telescope has a 200-inch mirror. This giant telescope possesses a range of 1,000 million light-years; that is, it can receive light that has been travelling through space for a thousand million years and has covered ten trillion kilometres. This tremendous research instrument cost six and a half million dollars and its manufacture, which was exceptionally difficult, took more than twelve years. If a 500-inch reflecting telescope were built, the mirror would have to be cast next door to the observatory, being too heavy to transport far. Such an apparatus would cost about 100 million dollars and its range would be approximately double that of the Mount Palomar telescope.

Our 'window into space' for optical observation is very narrow, since the earth's atmosphere only lets through a band of light waves from part of the ultra-violet to the infra-red. Gamma-rays, X-rays and the major part of the ultra-violet radiations are absorbed. We said earlier that it would be overbold to suppose that stars emit only radiations visible to our eyes. Stars and clouds of cosmic gas produce radiations of every imaginable wavelength. However, only the waves from the centimetre band up to some ten metres in wavelength are allowed to pass; the remainder are reflected back into space by the ionosphere. Nevertheless, this 'second window' gives a much wider view into space than the first. What is more, radio-telescopes have the advantage that they are independent of clear skies or pure air, and can be used day or night and even through thick cloud. Radio-astronomy thus consists of 'seeing' with artificial electric eyes; or, rather, of listening to the strange emissions from space, which sound like a thousand confusedly murmuring voices. Hearing it for the first time, one might easily imagine that these are messages from inhabitants of other worlds.

* * *

A radio-telescope resembles the reflecting telescope. They both have a large collecting surface, that of the radio-telescope serving to concentrate as much as possible of the energy emitted from cosmic sources. These sources are exceedingly intense; a broadcasting station is considered large if it has a power of 1,000 kilowatts. The energy sent out by one source of radiation in the constellation of Cassiopeia is approximately 1,000,000,000,000,000,000,000,000 kilowatts! Yet this source is small in comparison with the whole universe. The energy radiated from a source in the nebula in Cygnus amounts to some 1,000,000,000,000,000,000,000,000,000,000 kilowatts.

Despite this the cosmic signals are very weak to us. The total radiation falling on the entire surface of the earth from the Milky Way is only one watt, and would not be enough to light a small lamp. Consequently the apparatus required to detect cosmic radio waves is generally very large. Nowadays the scientists principally use parabolic mirrors with a dipole receiving aerial at the focus. The power of resolution of a radio-telescope is small in comparison with that of the reflecting telescope, because the cosmic waves lie in the centimetre and metre bands; they thus have a wavelength a million times that of the light waves. That is why large radio reflectors are generally needed. To enable a radio-telescope to operate with the same power of resolution as the 200-inch Mount Palomar mirror, it would be necessary to build a reflector as large as the Pacific Ocean. On the other hand radio-telescopes have the advantage of being able to penetrate cosmic dust, and therefore reach far farther into space than optical telescopes.

The radio-telescope at Cambridge, Massachusetts, which

N

operates on a wavelength of 3·7 metres, is so large that its aerials alone cover one acre, while those of the Ohio State University radio-telescope are 23 feet high and 160 feet long. The gigantic Jodrell Bank radio-telescope near Manchester has a parabolic mirror 250 feet in diameter, and although it consists of a lattice of light-alloy wires it weighs 300 tons. It can, however, be turned and tilted to point to any part of the firmament. The total weight of equipment for this huge installation exceeds 1000 tons. On 17th September 1956 a large radio-telescope for the Bonn University Observatory was inaugurated on the Stockert near Münstereifel. This radio observatory has a parabolic mirror of aluminium alloy 80 feet in diameter, standing open to the sky on a several-storeyed concrete pillar; its total collecting area is 5,580 square feet. It is made up of a large number of separate components, forming a slender lattice, and yet weighs nearly 20 tons.

To meet the stringent requirements of radio astronomers with regard to resolution, amplification and reliability, the Telefunken development engineers had to improve and surpass every known receiver characteristic. The result was a masterpiece of electronics — known as the 'Space Super' — a fifteenstage receiver with nearly 200 valves and several thousand coils, condensers and other components.

A fairly recent dictionary defines the 'music of the spheres' as the harmony of the heavenly bodies in their appointed paths, adding — almost resignedly, as though saddened by the unattainable — 'inaudible to men'. Telefunken's spectrometer has thrown doubt on this definition. The receiver for the radioobservatory on the Stockert detects these weak cosmic signals, 'the music of the spheres', already referred to by Pythagoras 2,400 years ago. It detects them, not by making them audible, since these radiations from space lie in a very different frequency band, but by electrical means. The word spectrometer shows that the heart of this radio-telescope is an apparatus intended to measure clearly-defined radiations which occur in the spectrum of interstellar hydrogen, although they are well outside the visible light band. The radio engineers call this radiation 'noise', even though it is an electronic phenomenon and not an acoustic one.

*   *   *

It is remarkable that not even the boldest scientific prophets of the last ten years have foretold this reaching out into space. Radio-astronomy, developed from radar, enabled man to cross new frontiers and form a new picture of his world. This makes the earth appear even smaller. Our sun has three hundred thousand times the mass of the earth. There are many other suns; but even the nearest of them is many million times further away than our own, so that we see them as points of light — the fixed stars. This great collection of suns forms our galaxy, which we call the Milky Way. It is as tremendous in size as in the number of its constituent suns. In addition to the hundreds of millions of stars it also contains gas and dust. The gas is very irregularly distributed in space, between the stars, concentrated in enormous clouds containing the cosmic dust, which renders them opaque.

There are many more star systems of this kind. In fact, we do not know how many, for our telescopes have not yet reached the boundaries of this universe of galaxies. There may be as many as 1,000 million such systems within the range of our largest telescopes. It is generally assumed that the galaxies are the main components of the universe, as it were the largest independent 'bricks' in its structure. Neither do we really know whether this universe really has any boundaries, nor whether the number of these systems is infinite or finite; most astronomers prefer the latter hypothesis. Their total number may even be no more than one thousand times greater than the number we can already see and identify.

It is widely held that the universe has, moreover, a most remarkable characteristic: it is expanding. All the galaxies are moving away from us and each other, and the further they move, the quicker they travel. This is shown by observation of the wavelengths of certain light rays which they emit. Like radio transmitters, the hydrogen atoms in these systems send out radiations of quite clearly defined wavelengths; most of the radiations are still in the visible band, but there is one with a wavelength of twenty-one centimetres in the ultra-short radio band. If a source of light or of radio waves is moving away from us at high speed, the received radiation has a somewhat lower frequency or longer wavelength than the radiation sent out. This phenomenon is known as the Doppler effect. Measurement of this displacement gives an exact indication of the velocity of the source of radiation.

If the universe is expanding, it must initially have been smaller. A simple calculation allows us to determine how long ago it was that the galaxies were very close together, assuming that they are moving away from each other at a constant speed. This gives us a period of 6,000 million years. Consequently the universe must have had a beginning, perhaps originating with an enormous explosion, like that of a hydrogen bomb, but immeasurably larger in scale — a cosmic hydrogen bomb whose mass must have been made up of all the matter in the universe. According to this theory the galaxies which are flying apart must be the debris of this cosmic explosion.

This cosmogony suggests that the galaxies began to separate out of the chaotic mass of exploding gases in the early stages. The dimensions, aspect, density and rotation of the star systems must be studied to check this theory; examination shows that most galaxies have a curious spiral structure. Their bright components are concentrated in spiral arms, of which there are in most cases two, extending in opposite directions from a central structureless nucleus and continuing in two coils to the extreme edge of the system. It is hoped that the investigation of the spiral structure and a deeper knowledge of this striking phenomenon will help us to understand the physical conditions in the early stages of the universe.

Before the advent of radio-astronomy the spiral structure could only be observed in distant systems. The situation suddenly changed when, in 1944, a Dutch astronomy student (later Professor) Van der Hulst, suggested that it must be possible to observe the twenty-one-centimetre waves emanating from interstellar hydrogen atoms by means of radio receivers. Seven years later such observations were successfully made.

Thousands of radio sources in space have been discovered and thousands still cannot be identified with visible objects. Those which can be so identified fall into two very distinct groups. The radio sources of the first type can be traced back to explosions and are therefore the results of what are called supernovæ. The second type of intensive radio emission is attributed to the collision of two galaxies. Collisions between stars are exceedingly rare, the distances between them being so colossal compared with their diameter that the probability of one of the hundred trillion stars in observable space colliding with another is unimaginably slight.

Matters are very different in the case of the galaxies. In their denser concentrations, the distance between two individual galaxies will on the average be not more than ten times their diameter. Consequently colliding galaxies, one passing through another, must occur fairly frequently in space. The individual stars are not involved, being far too far apart to collide, but the widely diffused clouds of interstellar gas strike each other with considerable force, owing to their high speed, producing strong electric potentials. In these circumstances electrons can be accelerated to such an extent that they emit the synchronous type of radiation.

The best known of these radio sources are the cosmic 'transmitting stations' known as Perseus A and Cygnus A. Perseus A is some 100 million light years away, and Cygnus A some 300 million.

*   *   *

Radio-astronomy was still in its infancy in the middle of the 20th century, one of the youngest sciences developed by man in his efforts to comprehend the universe. This great new development took place unnoticed and unreported, far from the criticisms of the sceptics. No one doubted that perfected radio-telescopes would soon give even better results.

Where this will lead we cannot say. A distance of twenty times that of the striking source of radiation in Cygnus brings us into a most mysterious region. At eighteen times the distance of the Cygnus source the velocity of the galaxies equals the speed of light. Since no movement can even exceed the velocity of light, some radical change must occur at distances of the order of twenty times that of the Cygnus source.

Either we reach in this way the uttermost bounds of the universe, or the linear relationship between speed and distance, or that between intensity and distance, no longer holds good. It might also be said that this is the outer limit of the mass of matter scattered by the explosion in which the universe originated. Or, to speak in terms of the curved universe, we would say that the distances reached must be of the order of magnitude of the radius of curvature of the universe.

It is as though science is daring to leave a safe harbour, to cross a wide ocean whose shores are completely unknown.

*   *   *

Let us recall the laboratory of Heinrich Hertz towards the end of the 19th century. The young physicist was twenty-nine years old when he discovered that electromagnetic waves behave like light waves. When he showed that a wave rebounds from a metal surface, he was in a sense making the first radar experiment. Had anyone wished at that time to list the developments based on that discovery — wireless telegraphy, television, radio ranging, radar, radio-astronomy to the edge of the universe — he would have been a visionary, giving vent to ideas of a boldness worthy of Jules Verne. And yet scarcely more than half a century has passed, one second in man's history.

FIFTY YEARS OF RADIO PROGRESS

The invisible net thrown around the earth by wireless telegraphy, radio telephony, broadcasting and television is made up of waves. Electrons, the smallest particles of matter in our universe, have played a part in its formation.

When Ferdinand Braun improved Marconi's original apparatus and introduced the coupled transmitter, the way to the creation of this world-wide net was clear. Yet the Professor took a prudent view of the potentialities of the newly-developed system of wireless telegraphy. In a lecture in the winter of 1900 he said: "If you ask what are the prospects and the practical value of wireless telegraphy, I would answer, from present knowledge, somewhat as follows: its value for improved signalling, unaffected by weather, time of day, fog, rain or snow is already recognised . . . But it must be considered illusory to think that it would ever supersede wire telegraphy . . . We may lay our best wishes in the child's cradle and rejoice if it fulfils them in growing up, but who can say with certainty, even after five years, what sort of man it will make? It will grow and be of service, even if it is not a Hercules . . ."

Doubt is one of the greatest teachers of research workers. We can understand that that which is new can only progress slowly, because the conservative spirits can and do only see the facts which follow the rule while the critics concentrate on the exceptions. For them repeated deviations from a formulated law are a continual spur to further investigation.

When Marconi declared that he would wireless across the ocean, many thought it a pipe dream, since it was well known that electric waves "are only propagated in straight lines, while the earth is round". When his experiment nevertheless succeeded, the capacity of very long waves to adjust themselves to the earth's curvature was recognised. This fact encouraged Marconi to make further trials with shorter waves. Once again failure was prophesied, it being accepted that these waves "travel into space in straight lines". Contrary to this expectation, however, the fact that these waves were reflected from the Heaviside layer gave improved communications of greater range.

For many years radar development in Germany was hindered because the application of decimetre waves to this field was considered useless on theoretical grounds. True, Hülsmeyer had demonstrated his 'Telemobiloscope' in 1904; he aimed it at a steamboat 600 yards away on the Rhine near Cologne, and as the ship came into the beam sent out by the apparatus the bell rang in his receiving set. But no reliable detector was available at the time. Hülsmeyer was years too early with his idea; he shared the fate of Paul Nipkov, who had invented his scanning disc forty years too soon. To the end of his days Hülsmeyer deplored the 'blindness' of his contemporaries. Undoubtedly his ideas would have contributed to accelerating considerably the introduction of radar.

By the middle of the 20th century the tasks performed by electronic devices were innumerable: broadcasting and television, radio pictures, all kinds of sound recording, motor and generator controls, induction heating, temperature measurement and control, testing and control of quality in all sorts of manufacturing processes, fever therapy, electric surgery, X-ray photography, long-distance telephony, electron microscopy, electronic calculations, radar, remote control, rocket guidance, electron micrography, electronic welding.

A Hercules has indeed grown from those small beginnings. No one can foresee all the social impact of this knowledge, or its effects on further scientific and industrial development. But it cannot be denied that, even today, new applications can be discovered.

CHAPTER V

NEW FIRE FOR PROMETHEUS

The revolution in physics — The bricks of the universe — A new type of radiation — The Curies and radium — Splitting the atom — A world-shaking discovery — The Bomb — The sorcerer's apprentice

THE REVOLUTION IN PHYSICS

PROMETHEUS, the Titan of Greek legend who stole the fire of the Gods and gave it to man, was chained to a rock by Zeus in punishment. But mankind used the gift to make life easier, and for a long time the fire-giver was worshipped in Athens at a torch race. Thousands of years later, as the atomic era opened, research workers named a new element — Promethium — after him.

This was when man laid hands on new fire, the fire of the atom. No one can tell who brought this new Prometheus gift to mankind, for many contributed to it. An entire branch of science — physics — served by thousands of professors, lecturers, research workers and their assistants, had to undergo a revolutionary change before the fire which heats the sun could be lit on earth. Physics was a branch of science which seemed to have reached its full, triumphal development early in the 1890s, and the tremendous change which followed was completely unexpected.

About this time many young physicists, who later received high honours, were asked by well-meaning friends why they were studying a subject which had no future. In fact, shortly before the end of the century not a few people feared that the great scientific and technological developments of the previous decades had left little to be discovered. They thought that it now only remained to formulate the known laws rather more precisely and to establish more firmly the foundations of knowledge already obtained; in a word, they must carry their calculations to five, six or even seven places of decimals. When Max Planck, on entering Munich University in 1875, ques-

The lodestone rock; from an old print.

tioned the famous physicist Philipp von Jolly — his professor of physics — about this branch of study, the professor answered wearily: "Physics is a branch of knowledge which is stable and very largely exhausted, and is really hardly worth studying any longer."

*   *   *

The idea that physics had reached 'a stable state' was one of the greatest misunderstandings of modern times, for at the precise moment when the research workers thought they had reached the end of their task, there opened before them the door which had until that time barred them from staggering new discoveries and undreamed-of knowledge. There now began a revolutionary period of physical research, the first half of which closed the 19th century while the second half provided a spectacular beginning to the 20th. This era opened in 1887 with the discovery of Hertzian waves, followed in 1895 by wireless telegraphy and, in the same year, X-rays. Radioactivity was first observed in 1896, the free electron discovered in 1897 and radium in 1898. The year 1900 saw the introduction of the Quantum Theory, and the Theory of Relativity was published in 1905.

One surprise followed another. Young physicists were creating an entirely new picture of physics, making the most radical changes of all in connection with a concept which was later to symbolize a new era in the history of mankind — the atom. The chemists had employed this concept of the atom for a very long time. The existence of a minute, indivisible particle of matter had gradually come to be taken for granted; and yet the existence of these atoms was questioned. The Atomic

Mediaeval physics; Jacob Grandamico demonstrating the effect of a magnet on a magnetic needle, 1645.

Theory of the chemist was a good working hypothesis; but was it really anything more? Leading physicists and chemists, for example, men like Ernst Mach and Wilhelm Ostwald, recalled with great emphasis that there was no convincing proof that atoms existed. Was it not therefore incumbent upon a precise and objective scientist to reject this hypothesis, however useful it might be?

But soon the necessary proof was provided — once more in those stirring years at the turn of the century — that atoms were a reality. Radioactivity and X-rays provided the answer. Once this knowledge spread, and the atom had been revealed to the research workers as a divisible body of complicated and remarkable structure, the way was open for man to enter a new era in his history, the atomic age.

*　　　*　　　*

Far from a broad high-road, this 'road into atom-land' was rather a maze of tracks and by-paths, many of them leading to the objective, until on 'day X' the second gift of Prometheus was presented to mankind.

On 16th July 1945, in the desert not far from Alamogordo in New Mexico, an electronic robot was switched on when the clocks in the observation station showed 5.29 and 15 seconds a.m., Western American Time. This simple operation ushered man into the atomic age, in the presence of a group of prominent scientists and soldiers who had come to witness the first atomic explosion initiated by man. Zero point of the atomic age was a steel tower 100 feet high on which the bomb was mounted. Zero hour was 5.30 a.m. A darkened sky, covered by low cloud, pouring rain and lightning flashes served to give the scene a dramatic setting. "The strain before the actual explosion reached a frightful pitch," recorded the official report on the development of the atom bomb, issued in 1946. "Failure was an ever-present possibility. But excessively good results, such as were feared by some observers, would mean that the weapon was uncontrollable, and consequently unusable."

The revolution in physics, initiated as the century opened, began to near its climax when final assembly of the atomic bomb was commenced in an abandoned farmhouse, during the night of 12th July 1945. Various components were brought in from widely-scattered points and while Dr. R. F. Bacher, of Cornell University, installed the core of the bomb, the 150 men concerned with the project, normally so calm, could ill hide their excitement. This first trial bomb and its components represented the sole product of the cost of the undertaking, which totalled 2,000 million dollars. The money had gone into the building of entire towns and completely new installations spread over many acres of land, or into experiments of a nature unique in man's history. The scientists clearly understood the importance of this final assembly before the ultimate test, and they realised that they were daring the greatest experiment ever. They also knew that no other country in the world could have provided the mental or technical resources available. Moreover, they were fully aware of their responsibilities as the pioneers of the new age and knew that the slightest mistake would destroy them and their work.

After two days of strenuous work the finished bomb was hoisted to the top of its lattice tower. Operations continued for the next two days, since apart from the bomb it was necessary to install a battery of instruments to measure every detail on which the success or failure of the experiments depended. The lightning flashes and rolling thunder not only sobered the experts but also prevented proper observation of the test from the air; consequently the explosion, which was originally timed for 4 a.m., was delayed.

The nearest observation point was about five and a half miles south of the tower in a timber and earth shelter, while the principal spectators were assembled at a point ten miles away which provided a better view. The bomb was to be set off by Dr. Kenneth T. Bainbridge, who was one of the last to inspect the tower with its terrible load. He reached the control station at about three o'clock and shortly afterwards the decision was taken to continue the experiment, despite the uncertain weather; zero hour was set at 5.30 a.m. Green flares and loudspeakers marked off the last seconds; at the signal '45 seconds to go' the automatic mechanism was tripped. From this moment onwards the entire complicated experiment continued without human intervention. Nevertheless, an emergency switch had been provided, controlled by an Army scientist who was to try to stop the test, if the order came to do so. But it did not come.

The whole desert, grey in the early light, had become quite silent. Suddenly, exactly on time, there shone out on the horizon a searing light, a light not of this earth, in the form of a gigantic greenish ball of flame, many hundred times brighter than the sun.

In the millionth part of a second the matter split up by the explosion had been heated to more than $1,000,000°$ C., and a pressure of several hundred thousand atmospheres was produced. The rapidly-climbing fireball spread, changing in colour from dark purple to bright orange-yellow. Directly above it seethed an enormous multi-coloured cloud, rapidly rising to a height of 41,000 feet, dispersing the clouds in its path. The explosion created a storm of tremendous intensity, sweeping millions of tons of pulverised earth along with it. A huge pillar rose at great speed from the ground in the train of the expanding fireball towering ever higher until, within eight minutes, its peak reached the stratosphere.

Just before, when the artificial sun — hundreds of times brighter than the real one — appeared, the observers ten miles away felt a blast of hot wind. Two men standing outside the command post were thrown to the ground by the powerful pressure wave. Then the air was filled with the thunder of a thousand block-busters, the earth trembled and the mountains around re-echoed the tremendous roar.

The test was successful.

The steel tower had been completed vaporised and an immense crater now spread where it had stood. The sun rose on a pillar of smoke and dust eight miles high, towering above ground zero — the first atomic mushroom of man's history, the symbol of an epoch just begun.

Dazed, but relieved by the success of the operation, the scientists gathered to make their first estimates of the new weapon they had created for their country; special tanks were driven into the crater to examine the ground around the blast point. In that inconceivably small fraction of time which had sufficed for the transformation of a small quantity of matter into radiation and energy, man's world was changed.

*   *   *

THE BRICKS OF THE UNIVERSE

With unimportant exceptions (the heat of the earth, for instance), all forms of energy utilised by man derive from the sun. This was an unquestioned fact, an iron law, until man entered the atomic age. Once he began to tap the energy locked in the atomic nucleus, the source of solar energy itself was at his disposal.

Even in 1890 the atom was still considered the smallest possible particle of a chemical element and thus the smallest constituent of the matter which makes up the world. An element — that is, a substance which cannot be separated into other substances, e.g., hydrogen, oxygen, gold or iron — consists of minute, completely identical particles called atoms. The atom was clearly indivisible; hence its name, derived from the Greek ἄτομος, the indivisible.

But then came the revolution in the concept of the universe which we now have to consider, and the stable structure of physics was heavily shaken. Professor Arnold Sommerfeld of Munich gave a humorous warning to students eager to begin to study physics with the words: "Danger! The building is likely to collapse and is temporarily closed for reconstruction."

Many of us still learnt at school that matter and energy can neither be created nor destroyed, but only transformed. The atomic explosion on Zero Day had, however, proved conclusively what physicists had known and taught since the beginning of the 20th century, namely that matter and energy are equivalent and therefore nothing else than two forms of the same unknown thing. Our world is full of energy sources although the forms used by man for thousands of years, all drawn originally from the sun — wood, coal, petroleum and natural gas — were only like crumbs from a richly-spread table. Inconceivable reserves of energy had been stored up since the creation in Nature's strongest safe deposit, the atomic nucleus, which Sir Arthur Eddington described in 1930 as the cosmic storehouse of energy.

The first inroads upon this store were made by man in the explosion of the device in the tower in the New Mexico desert. After this there was a little less matter in the earth than before, for some of the energy embodied therein had been released and the mass associated with it had been destroyed.

*   *   *

This relationship between matter and energy had been discovered by Einstein when still young; forty years before, he had succeeded in expressing it in a formula of remarkable simplicity: $E = m \times c^2$. That is, the energy embodied in matter is equal to the mass of that matter multiplied by the square of the speed of light. Einstein had established a firm relationship between matter, energy and the speed of light, and this cosmic trinity led to the code name Trinity being applied to the historic event of 16th July 1945.

Einstein's formula says nothing about the type of matter involved. To find the amount of energy which corresponds to a gram of matter, it is necessary to multiply a mass twice, each time by the speed of light (i.e., 186,000 miles per second), and express the result in familiar energy units. This calculation gives the astounding result that one gram of matter corresponds to twenty-five million kilowatt-hours. It is essential to use practical examples to obtain a clear idea of the incredible fact that such tiny amounts of matter contain such enormous quantities of energy. For instance, were it possible to utilise completely all the energy in two grams of coal, this would be enough to supply Western Germany with electricity for a whole year.

In the 4th century B.C. the Greek natural philosopher Democritus of Abdera held that matter consisted of very small, indivisible particles of the same material which were identical in shape, size and weight. This conception of the structure of matter is very close to our own, although his atoms are not the ultimate bricks of which matter is made, but those which make up the chemical elements. A salt crystal can be mechanically ground so small that we ultimately obtain molecules of salt, which the chemist can split up into atoms of sodium and chlorine. However, if graphite or diamond be similarly ground, the final product is always an atom of carbon which the chemist cannot break down any further.

The writings of Democritus were lost over the centuries and his atomic theory forgotten. Only towards the end of the 18th century, when scientists renewed their investigations into the constitution of matter, was the theory revived. Over 2,000 years had passed since the Greek philosopher produced his picture of the world, and, in less than 100 years, it was experimentally proved that matter really does consist of exceedingly small particles.

A series of striking discoveries revealed its structure. The entire universe accessible to us consists of ninety-two basic chemical elements. Thus the atom of the ancient Greek finds a new form; yet in 1890 no one was quite certain whether atoms really existed.

A NEW TYPE OF RADIATION

The new discoveries and physical theories which initiated and accomplished the revolution of physics did not simply form a wave of successive events like beads on a string, but were to some extent interrelated, while others were based on older findings. Moreover, they were the fruit of the life's work of many unknown research workers, who are overshadowed by the great men of science. In a brief survey depicting the struggle to introduce new inventions these numerous links and connections can be but imperfectly recorded. We shall therefore mention only the major milestones along the course of this revolution in physics.

One of the first to follow this path, without knowing it, was Wilhelm Conrad Röntgen.

*   *   *

During the night of 8th November 1895 Röntgen, Professor of Theoretical Physics at Würzburg University, was experimenting with a cathode tube — an evacuated glass tube, bear-

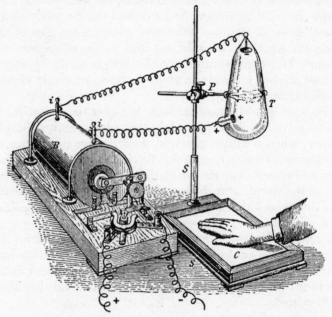

Röntgen's experimental apparatus for photographing a hand, 1895.

ing at each end a metal plate connected to a battery. He knew that as soon as the electricity was switched on it would pass through the vacuum inside the tube. The cathode or negatively charged plate would then begin to glow, emitting a new type of radiation.

As he worked on, a sheet of paper coated with a phosphor-

An early spark transmitter used by Marconi in 1897.

The huge Jodrell Bank radio-telescope. The bowl measures 250 feet in diameter and can be rotated and tilted in any direction.

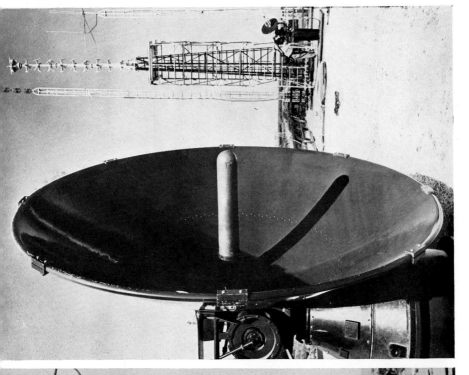

Left: Rocket observation and remote control aerials.　*Right:* Rocket tracking aerials.

escent layer suddenly began to glow in the dim laboratory. This could only be caused by the cathode tube, which was housed in a box; it was, however, so light-tight that not even a glimmer could escape. And yet the paper continued to shine until Röntgen switched off the current. To study this striking phenomenon more closely, Röntgen decided to see whether this new type of radiation could cast a shadow. He passed various objects between the tube and the paper, obtaining various degrees oi shadow. As this rather childish-seeming procedure continued, he suddenly saw a skeleton hand outlined on the paper. These new rays had the remarkable property of penetrating opaque substances and revealing their internal structure. The modest discoverer simply called these new rays 'X-Rays'.

As time went on Röntgen received more than 150 honours and commendations for his great scientific achievement. But it is only today that we realise that he was introducing a new era in the natural sciences. When he demonstrated his discovery in public for the first time in Germany, the rays were called Röntgen-rays, a name still used. He did not patent his great discovery and made no claims whatsoever when other research workers, professors and other students were spurred by his work to carry out their own investigations. All over the world people built X-ray apparatus to see for themselves what had been demonstrated for the first time at Würzburg in January 1896; namely, that one could see bones through the flesh, painlessly and apparently without injury.

Nevertheless, a strange thing happened. On several occasions features exposed to X-rays began to turn red, as they would from a burn. No one recognised immediately the hidden danger in these still mysterious radiations until Professor Henri Becquerel began to study them in his own way.

*　　　*　　　*

Becquerel's father was a notable specialist in the subject of phosphorescence, and his son Henri was consequently familiar with the self-luminous character of many chemicals. He assumed that this must be a similar effect to that which occurred in the cathode tube and therefore began to experiment with uranium compounds.

This decision was to have very far-reaching consequences.

o

Becquerel had unconsciously begun to follow a trail to a major discovery, and chance favoured him. He had been storing crystals of uranium in a drawer and one day unthinkingly put in a packet of films. Wanting to use them some days later he must have had misgivings, and unwrapped the packing; to his surprise he found that, although the uranium salts did not phosphoresce, the outline of the crystals was clearly marked on the emulsion. Thereupon Becquerel began to take an interest in the unusual capacity of uranium compounds to blacken films. For months on end he continued his experiments systematically and the uranium continued the whole time to produce its invisible rays, which affected photographic films. His astonishment grew daily. Soon he discovered that the almost inexhaustible radiation could penetrate not only black paper, but also metal, and that it had nothing to do with phosphorescence. He had discovered something entirely new, then known as 'Becquerel rays' but soon to be known as 'radioactivity'.

THE CURIES AND RADIUM

Becquerel was the friend and teacher of a young Polish immigrant to France named Marie Sklodowska. She had originally come to Paris to study and had married Pierre Curie, who later became a professor. The Curies immediately began to investigate more closely the phenomenon discovered by Becquerel, and Marie Curie chose the subject of Becquerel rays for her doctorate thesis. This was a choice of considerable importance.

"Professor Curie and I then worked in the laboratory of the School of Physics and Chemistry," said Marie Curie later. "I was busy with some work on uranium radiation, which had been discovered two years previously by Professor Becquerel . . . I wanted to know whether other elements emitted similar radiations . . . I therefore began to examine various minerals and found that several, containing either uranium or thorium, or both, were active . . . It then struck me that there might be an unknown element in the minerals with much stronger radioactivity than uranium or thorium; it was this element I wished to find and isolate. Professor Curie and I therefore set to work. We thought we would finish in a few weeks or months, but this was not so. It needed many years of hard work."

The Curies ultimately found the strongest radiation in a uranium-containing ore, called pitchblende, from the St. Joachimsthal in Bohemia. The ore had been lying for years on the waste heaps of the old silver mine and work was just beginning on clearing the rubbish when the Curies ordered ten tons of pitchblende. In an uncomfortable and badly-equipped shed the Curies began to look for the unknown radioactive substance in the pitchblende. The further their work progressed, the more restricted was their field of investigation. It seemed that two constituents of the pitchblende were the principal carriers of the radioactivity they sought, and this told the Curies that pitchblende contained two unknown elements. In the summer of 1898 they were able to announce the discovery of the first, which was named 'polonium' after Marie Curie's homeland.

In a little grey exercise book Marie recorded every day during these months the weight of her little daughter Irène, her diet and the cutting of her first tooth. Some three months after the discovery of polonium she proudly wrote on 17th October 1898: "Irene can already walk very well and no longer crawls on all fours." On 5th January 1899 the notebook shows the entry: "Irene has fifteen teeth!" Between these two entries you will find another important note, made by Pierre and Marie Curie with one of their helpers. It said: "The various reasons listed here lead us to believe that the new radioactive substance we have found contains a new element, to which we give the name radium. The radioactivity of the substance is considerable, so that of radium must be enormous."

*　　　*　　　*

The Curies had, it is true, discovered radium, but it still only existed in their minds and remained locked up in the substance they had isolated from the pitchblende.

Their discovery disturbed a large number of traditional ideas and contradicted the most deeply-rooted views on the constitution of matter. The physicists were still reserved, although intensely interested in the Curies' work, and began to realise its far-reaching consequences. Nevertheless they preferred to wait for the final proofs before accepting the new doctrine. The chemists were even more decided in their reactions. A chemist really only begins to believe in the existence of a substance when he has seen, touched and weighed it, investigated it, tested it with acids and determined its atomic weight. When the Curies announced the discovery of radium no one had seen it. No one knew its atomic weight. So the chemists declared, firm in their opinions: "No atomic weight, no radium. Show us some radium and we will believe you."

To show the sceptics polonium and radium, to prove the existence of these 'brain children' to the world, and lastly to convince themselves, Pierre and Marie Curie had to work extremely hard for four long years. Even so, they only had a tiny quantity of radium, having isolated less than one-tenth of a gram out of an enormous weight of pitchblende.

Radium was — and remained — very rare. It was exceedingly difficult to obtain it in a pure state and was therefore more expensive than gold. Three years and nine months after the day on which the Curies announced the probable existence of radium, Marie finally succeeded, in 1902, in isolating one-tenth of a gram of pure radium and in determining its atomic weight. The sceptics yielded to the facts and to the tremendous endurance of one woman. Radium was officially recognised.

*   *   *

The Curies had no money, no laboratory and no help to carry out their important and difficult task. They had to start from nothing and Marie Curie subsequently described this period as the 'Heroic Era' of their married life.

Her life would have been happier if she had been able to turn all her forces to unlocking the secrets of Nature. Instead she had to carry on other struggles in which she was not so successful. She wanted a laboratory, but this was asking too much; it was a dream. Pierre Curie was only made a professor in 1904 when the whole world had recognised his work, but he was never given his laboratory. "Death makes sure of important personages before he touches the general public," wrote Eve Curie in her biography of her mother. And when one day Professor Pierre Curie was proposed for a decoration, he replied: "Please inform the Minister that I have no wish for a decoration, but need so much the more to be given a laboratory."

After Henri Becquerel had discovered the radiations emitted by uranium compounds the scientific world used the term 'Becquerel rays' for some time; but the name did not last. Only two years after the discovery of these radiations, Madame Curie finally named them radioactivity. This was the title of the book which she finished in 1934, shortly before her death. The simple cover bore the inscription Madame Pierre Curie, Professor at the Sorbonne, Nobel Prizewinner for Physics, Nobel Prizewinner for Chemistry . . .

Rays as such were nothing new to physicists at that time. Röntgen had discovered his penetrating X-rays only a little earlier and experiments with cathode rays had been carried on for several decades. Gradually, like a multi-coloured mosaic, the new picture of physics was created. One very important problem was the nature of these radiations. Many scientists considered X-rays to be a wave radiation closely allied to visible light, but then William Henry Bragg — a Nobel Prizewinner working as a physicist in Australia — stated that they were corpuscular radiations, that is to say they consisted of minute particles of matter. This was an error, and an argument continued for some time until Max von Laue — then thirty-three years old — finally demonstrated, to the Bavarian Academy in Munich on 8th June 1912, that X-rays are, in fact, wave radiations. Only then could X-rays be classified as radiations of extremely short wavelength in the scale of electromagnetic waves.

Max von Laue always insisted on experimental proof as an indispensable tool for the research workers, since — as he wrote in the introduction to his book on X-ray diffraction — "Nothing is more disturbing to science than that physicists should give way to surmise when proofs are both necessary and possible." On the other hand, it had been known for some time that cathode rays are corpuscular in nature. But this did not settle the question as to the nature of the particles which, moving at high speeds, constituted the cathode rays. They might be charged molecules or atoms, and many people speculated about the mysterious atoms of electricity which, although nothing more than an hypothesis at that time, already had a name — electrons.

At the end of the 19th century many research workers were studying these particular radiations. If they really were electric particles, it must be possible to demonstrate and measure their deflection by an electric or magnetic field. The first great success in this field was achieved in 1897 by the famous English physicist J. T. Thomson, the head of the Cavendish Laboratory at Cambridge. Shortly before his death in 1940 he wrote in his autobiography:

"After long consideration of the experiments it seemed to me that there was no escape from the following conclusions:

"(1) That atoms are not indivisible, for negatively electrified particles can be torn from them by the action of electrical forces . . .

"(2) That these particles are all of the same mass, and carry the same charge of negative electricity from whatever kind of atom they may be derived, and are a constituent of all atoms.

"(3) That the mass of these particles is less than one-thousandth part of the mass of an atom of hydrogen.

"I at first called these bodies corpuscles, but they are now called by the more appropriate name 'electrons' . . . At first there were very few who believed in the existence of these bodies smaller than atoms. I was even told long afterwards by a distinguished physicist who had been present at my lecture at the Royal Institution that he thought I had been 'pulling their legs'. I was not surprised at this, as I had myself come to this explanation of my experiments with great reluctance, and it was only after I was convinced that the experiment left no escape from it that I published my belief in the existence of bodies smaller than atoms."

The results were indeed surprising and the negative particles moving in the cathode rays weighed less than one-thousandth of the weight of the atoms. They were the long-awaited free electrons. Although minute, they had a definite weight. Subsequent precise measurement revealed that the mass of an electron (at rest, since its mass increases at high velocities) is $1/1,837$ of that of the lightest atom, the hydrogen atom. The very next year the radium emissions also gave up their secret, and three entirely different types of rays were found; these were called alpha, beta and gamma, after the first three letters of the Greek alphabet. These rays could be separated by a powerful magnet; the gamma rays were not affected at all, the alpha particles only slightly, while the beta rays were strongly deflected in the opposite direction.

It was later discovered that alpha rays could only penetrate metal foil a few hundredths of an inch thick, while beta rays could penetrate a few tenths of an inch of metal. In the air alpha rays die out after a maximum travel of three inches, beta rays last for several yards; gamma rays, however, could still be detected some 100 yards away. Clearly, as their behaviour in the magnetic field had already shown, they must be three entirely different kinds of radiation. Alpha rays are helium nuclei, beta rays are made up of electrons, and are therefore corpuscular, consisting of minute particles of matter moving at high speeds. Alpha particles reach a speed of 12,000 miles per second and beta particles about 180,000 miles per second. Gamma rays are clearly related to X-rays and visible light, and are propagated at exactly the same speed as light.

It might almost be thought a fortunate circumstance that there are a few elements in Nature whose nuclei undergo a natural change and emit radiations in so doing. In this way the materials which were, so to speak, left over from the creation betray their presence. The greater the rate of change, the smaller the amount of material still remaining; that is why radioactivity was discovered only at the end of the last century. Until then scientists thought that the elements were immutable. Now they suddenly learnt that radium gradually turned into lead, meanwhile giving out strong radiations. That must mean that a tremendous quantity of energy was locked up in the atoms of radioactive elements.

The Curies and other scientists were puzzled to know the origin of the inexhaustible radiation from radium and the other known radioactive elements, uranium and thorium. It seemed to be a contradiction of the law of energy formulated by Dr. Robert Mayer sixty years before. Mayer's ideas had been forgotten for a long time and he himself taken for mad. He advanced the suggestion that energy could manifest itself in various forms, for example, as movement, heat, light or electricity, but that it could never originate from nothing nor be destroyed. The law of energy overcame heavy opposition and was finally accepted. Yet now certain remarkable substances had arisen in the laboratories — uranium, thorium and radium, which was very rare — which seemed to disobey the law of energy, emitting energy in the form of radiation.

Pierre Curie discovered that one gram of radium gives out approximately 100 calories of heat per hour; this was not much, since 100 gram-calories will heat a small glass of water by just one degree. One gram of radium would therefore take one hour to do this. And yet this low heating effect was a sensation for the scientific world. Anybody who took the trouble to make a trial calculation came to the fantastic result that this meant 2,400 calories every twenty-four hours, 1,000 kilo-calories a year, or one million kilo-calories per thousand years. But did it continue for thousands of years? No one knew if radium would continue to radiate with the same intensity after a thousand years or whether it would still exist. The pure radium salts isolated by the Curies were hardly a year old.

A few years later it was known that this radiation does not continue indefinitely, only lasting some 2,000 years in the case of radium. In 1903 the first calculation of 'Atomic Energy' showed that, before its complete disappearance, one gram of radium produces three million kilo-calories, that is three thousand kilowatt hours, or as much heat as seven cwt. of coal.

Thus nuclear energy was discovered before science ever knew of the existence of the atomic nucleus.

SPLITTING THE ATOM

In the 20th century, when distance no longer means anything, it is a commonplace for students to finish their studies in well-known universities, however far away they may be. But when Ernest Rutherford, then twenty-four years old, came from Nelson in 1895 to finish his studies under Professor Joseph John Thomson of the Cavendish Institute, Cambridge, it was rather unusual; the young student came from Nelson, New Zealand, and had travelled almost halfway round the world to study in England.

Rutherford soon earned the name of 'the young rabbit from New Zealand', but respect for his penetrating questions made them add, 'who burrows very deep!' His first work was allied to radioactivity. He took part in investigations in the properties of electrons, ions and X-rays, thus laying the foundation for his later achievements. Actually he never completely abandoned this field. He was fascinated by the scientific adventure in the zone between matter and energy. Radium, a 'dead metal', was almost a living thing to him. He eventually became so familiar with radiation that he declared: "Ions are such jolly little beggars; you can almost see them," although there was as yet no question of making individual atoms visible. This was first achieved fifteen years later by C. R. T. Wilson, in his 'cloud chamber'; free ions, e.g., alpha particles, produced visible trails as they passed through it and revealed their presence exactly like an aeroplane flying at a great height.

At the early age of twenty-seven, Rutherford became a professor at McGill University, Montreal, where he worked for three years with Frederick Soddy. This collaboration proved very fruitful. Rutherford and Soddy developed the idea that radioactivity must depend on transformation of the elements. When an atom emits a radiation, e.g., an alpha particle, it is transformed into another element. This single fact was sufficient to show that the 'indivisible' atom was, in fact, divisible! On this basis Rutherford and Soddy formulated their famous theory of radioactive decay; radioactive elements are transformed into other chemical elements by emitting radiation, after which they decay. The new elements are generally also radioactive and decay further, so that ultimately whole series of elements are formed.

Their work on the theory of decay was published in London in September 1902 and Rutherford became world-famous. But although his work met with ready acceptance on one side, it received fierce opposition on the other. For his ideas shook the scientific world, destroying the accepted picture of a chemical element, which — unlike chemical compounds — can neither be transformed nor broken down. For years the decay theory was a subject of bitter discussion; Soddy himself described the period as 'pretty hectic'. Several colleagues even suggested that Rutherford should postpone publication of his theory, because of their serious misgivings, and their fear that "these radical ideas would damage the university's reputation".

After nine years of almost superhuman work in Montreal, described in some fifty publications, Rutherford was called back to England. Famous, and now holder of three honorary doctorates, he became a professor at Manchester in 1907. "So striking is the contrast between youthfulness and fame," wrote

Professor Werner Braunbeck, "that when Rutherford was introduced shortly after his arrival to Baron Kikuchi, the Japanese Minister of Education said: 'Rutherford? Would that be a son of the famous Professor Rutherford?'" His predecessor in Manchester not only left him a well-equipped laboratory, but also his lecturer Hans Geiger, the young German physicist who later invented the Geiger counter.

For ten years Rutherford worked with his favourite, the alpha particle, which was finally shown to be the helium atom. It is 7,000 times heavier than an electron and penetrates metal foil relatively easily. Finally, Rutherford instructed Geiger to investigate this process thoroughly. The results were quite astonishing. Almost all the alpha particles underwent only slight deflection, but one or two clearly struck an impenetrable part of the atom and were deflected at a considerable angle.

Now something remarkable happened; Rutherford had an idea which seemed fantastic at that time. He suggested that the atom must have an exceedingly massive nucleus. The deflection of the alpha particles must be due to a positive electrical charge on this nucleus, since they themselves were also positive. The discovery of the atomic nucleus must not be taken too literally. Rutherford simply concluded from the deflection of the alpha particles that the entire mass of each atom must be concentrated in an exceedingly small space. This highly concentrated structure, which neither he nor other scientists were ever able to see, he called the nucleus.

Professor Geiger told me much later how Rutherford expressed this vague idea in formulæ, and then impatiently demanded the exact test results. Geiger hardly had time to write his observations down before Rutherford tore the sheet out of his hands. Moreover, experimental results were in accordance with the theoretical prediction! That was the revelation of the atomic nucleus, the beginning of a tremendous new development. For fifteen years the scientists had had the nucleus in their hands without knowing it.

Two years later the Danish physicist Niels Bohr produced his famous 'atomic model', a miniature solar system in which the nucleus represented the sun, surrounded by electrons moving in planetary orbits. Although subsequently Bohr no longer insisted that his model corresponded to physical reality, being only a practical and graphic working hypothesis, it has penetrated deeply into men's minds as a symbol of the atomic age. Ultimately, in fact, it became the symbol of the 20th century.

In 1912, however, the idea of the atomic nucleus, which no one had seen or could see, was not yet accepted. The traditionalist physicists maintained their opposition, although the idea enlightened many of them. But the majority repudiated it vigorously. Bohr's atomic model and its theory brought undreamed-of successes but scepticism and rejection continued. His proposals were simply too bold and far too contradictory to the fundamentals of mechanics and electrodynamics. Even Rutherford was uneasy and wrote to Bohr: "The mixture of Planck's ideas with classical mechanics makes it very difficult for me to form a physical picture of what it all means." The aged Lord Rayleigh, Nobel Prizewinner in 1904 and a recognised authority, declared: "I do not believe that Nature behaves in this way and cannot consider this theory a true picture of what actually occurs."

Nevertheless, Bohr's atomic model was eventually accepted. The fundamental objections were for a time lost sight of in the triumph of the theory. It was only much later, in the 'thirties, that it became clear that this very practical picture of the atom as a planetary system would have to be abandoned.

* * *

The First World War broke up the world-wide collaboration of the physicists. Once the war was over, scientific research gradually revived. Rutherford is said to have missed a sitting of the British U-Boat Defence Committee in the last year of the war and to have declared on being reproached for his absence: "I was just determining whether we can split the atom. If this idea turns out right, then it is much more important than your whole war." Now almost fifty, he had found his work thrown back several years by the war, but was about to take the third great step in his career of scientific discovery.

He had already toyed with the idea that the relatively large atomic nucleus might perhaps be destroyed by the tremendous forces achieved by bombarding it with alpha particles travelling at 12,000 miles per second. He discovered the splitting of the nucleus almost by chance. One day, completely astonished, he observed that long-range hydrogen nuclei suddenly occurred during the bombardment of nitrogen with alpha particles, although there was no hydrogen anywhere near. Rutherford's genius enabled him to bridge the gap between observation and explanation in one step. These very long-range particles must, he concluded, be hydrogen nuclei, which he later called 'protons'. The hydrogen nuclei must have been knocked out of the nitrogen nuclei by the alpha particles. This meant that the nitrogen nucleus had been destroyed.

Rutherford, now the head of the Cavendish Institute in Cambridge, which he had left twenty-one years before to begin his overthrow of the classical conception of physics, expressed himself with extreme caution when he published his results: ". . . we can hardly escape the idea that the long-range particles are not nitrogen nuclei, but probably hydrogen nuclei . . . If this is so, we must conclude that the nitrogen nucleus has been split by tremendous forces exerted by the impact of fast-moving alpha particles . . ."

The atom, once thought to be indivisible and now known to be theoretically divisible, had finally been experimentally proved so. But while Rutherford's pupils and friends excitedly discussed atom-splitting, and plunged into a tremendous new programme of research to try to repeat this sensational process with other elements, Rutherford's work was still sceptically received and hotly contested by the conservative physicists, guardians of the traditional picture of science.

*   *   *

In spite of their scepticism the scientists gradually began to repeat and copy Rutherford's experiments, as far as they had the facilities, all over the world.

The Americans soon applied considerable effort to the study of an idea which still seemed somewhat fantastic, splitting the atom. The University of California discovered that Rutherford's apparatus was ridiculously primitive, and built for Professor E. O. Lawrence a cyclotron, a gigantic atom-splitting machine.

Lawrence had conceived the idea that atoms of heavy hydrogen, with two protons, would be ideal projectiles with which to smash other atoms. The cyclotron was intended to impart a high speed and a considerable penetration force to these atoms, known as deuterons. Although this tremendous apparatus weighed eighty-three tons, it worked well. The atoms were broken open and released their neutrons, which in turn became very effective projectiles. Lawrence subsequently built a cyclotron weighing 4,900 tons, which provided him with streams of particles having an energy of more than 100 million volts. The cyclotron was based on a simple principle. Lawrence accelerated the sub-atomic particles to the required high velocities by leading them around a powerful electromagnet, thus raising their speed at each circuit.

Röntgen, Becquerel, Pierre and Marie Curie, Thomson, Rutherford and many other famous or obscure collaborators of the great physicists had, during the hectic years of the new physics, captured the outer defences of Nature's fortress, the atom. Science was now to storm its keep, the atomic nucleus. Rutherford himself would have liked a pause for reflection. "When I look back on my activities as a scientist for more than thirty years," he wrote later, "I know that I am always longing for a breathing space, in which no important advances were made for several years. But this moment never came and is not likely to come very soon. It strikes me that the rapid development of physics, which began thirty years ago with the discovery of X-rays, shows no sign of slacking off; on the contrary development seems to be more and more rapid as time goes on."

As the revolutionaries of physics, who had turned the picture of the world completely upside-down, grew older and began to blend the new and the old in fresh physical theories, they inevitably became themselves the conservators of the new physical concept of the world. Thus Einstein, for example — the 'revolutionary of 1906', who had shaken the entire scientific world with his Theory of Relativity — later became a conservative who refused to recognise the radical conclusions of the Danish physicist Niels Bohr.

On the other hand when Einstein was prompted by experimental results to revive the old theory that light is corpuscular, consisting of light quanta, Bohr, the intellectual leader of the new generation of physicists, criticised this bold new step jokingly: "When Einstein sends me a telegram, saying that he has now found the final confirmation of his light quanta, the bare fact that the radio-telegram reaches me proves that the theory of electromagnetic waves is correct, and that Einstein is wrong."

Inevitably, the general public, stirred by the scientific discoveries and radical new theories, now began to speculate about the tremendous energy locked up in the atom and to form bold visions of the future.

On the other hand, those who did not wish to make fools of themselves or appear to be visionaries exercised sober restraint. For instance, W. de Haas, writing in 1931 under the pseudonym

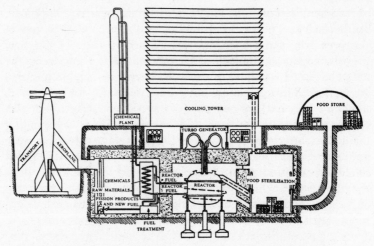

Undreamed-of in 1930. An atomic power station.

Hanns Günther, described in simple terms how world energy demands would be supplied in the future, in an eighty-page pamphlet which depicted the potentialities of the next hundred years. He advanced the view that the physical problem of releasing the energy of the atom by artificial fission would defeat the engineers for a long time. No one could tell whether it would take years or generations before this, the capital problem of technical physics, was solved. Although he described a world without coal, in which the Mediterranean was shut off from the Atlantic to provide enormous quantities of energy, with tidal power stations and wind-power plants for energy supplies, and the utilisation of the heat of tropical oceans or the cold of arctic regions, he did not dare to prophesy that world power needs would in the future be supplied from Nature's real energy store-house, the atom.

In 1921 the German physicist Walter Nernst, attempting to make the results of Rutherford's experiments intelligible to the general public, wrote: "We are living, so to speak, on an island made of gun-cotton, for which, thank God, we have not yet found a match."

Rutherford was also assailed by doubts. He believed that mankind might never learn to utilise the energy of the atom, or, at best, not for a hundred years. The man who had turned physics upside-down did not really believe in the possibility of using nuclear energy in practice, and frequently declared: "Anyone who pursues such ideas is living on the moon." He maintained this opinion until his death in 1937; was it an attempt to close his eyes to possible risks? Robert Oppenheimer, one of the young physicists of those exciting years, once said subsequently that the new discoveries filled all those who participated in them with excitement and fear.

But the barrier had been broken; man had uncovered a large number of Nature's secrets and the new concepts of physics called for imagination and courage. When Rutherford died, one of his pupils, Dr. Otto Hahn, was already engaged in Berlin on freeing the giant, atomic energy, from its chains.

A WORLD-SHAKING DISCOVERY

It was 1932. The history of mankind was passing through a deep trough. For years the economic crisis had been crippling the industrial nations, and there were millions of unemployed. It was a year of the great depression. And yet this was a wonderful year for the physicists. Nuclear physics was beginning to reap what had been sown in the years since the physical revolution which occurred about the beginning of the century. The harvest was so rich that 1932 really constituted the starting-point of what was to become practical nuclear physics.

Heavy hydrogen was discovered at the beginning of this year. The nucleus of a normal hydrogen atom has a charge of one and a mass of one. It is a proton. The nucleus of an atom of the newly-discovered heavy hydrogen was revealed as a particle with a charge of one and a mass of two. This nucleus is twice as heavy as that of ordinary hydrogen and is called a deuteron. But nobody yet knew what else the deuteron contained besides the proton. A little later another long-awaited nuclear particle, which already had a name, revealed itself to the scientists; this was the neutron, a neutral particle, that is one without electric charge.

Frédéric Joliot, once a colleague of Marie Curie, and his wife Irène, Madame Curie's eldest daughter, were experimenting at this time with a new type of radiation, produced by irradiating beryllium with alpha rays. These rays from beryllium released protons from paraffin wax. Irène and Frédéric Joliot-Curie almost had the secret in their hands, when Chadwick announced from the Cavendish Laboratory at Cambridge his discovery of the neutron.

A beam of neutrons! This discovery was like a bombshell in the scientific circles concerned. And even before its effects had worn off there came another shock. The announcement was made, again from Cambridge, that the transformation of numerous different atomic nuclei by means of artificially-accelerated beams of protons had been successfully carried out.

A new science had been created. The transformation of large numbers of atomic nuclei was now possible. The atomic nucleus, once the impregnable fortress of Nature, had yielded. Once more there were believers and unbelievers, timid doubters and bold pioneers. When Frédéric Joliot-Curie prophesied that one could now envisage the possibility of producing or breaking down elements at will, and that nuclear reactions of an explosive character were conceivable, the interest he aroused was only transitory.

As Rutherford in 1933 declared the liberation of atomic energy on a large technical scale to be a Utopian dream, Leo Szilard, a physicist who had emigrated from Hungary, began to think about the problem, concluding that a chain reaction would be achieved if one could only discover an element which would release two fresh neutrons for every single neutron absorbed.

*   *   *

Let us once again look at the new picture of the atom as the scientists now saw it.

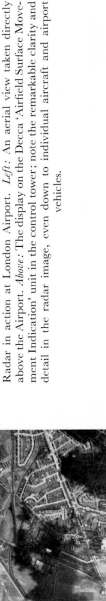

Radar in action at London Airport. *Left:* An aerial view taken directly above the Airport. *Above:* The display on the Decca 'Airfield Surface Movement Indication' unit in the control tower; note the remarkable clarity and detail in the radar image, even down to individual aircraft and airport vehicles.

Calder Hall, the world's first full-scale atomic power station. The twin 300-feet cooling towers are in the background, with Number 1 reactor and the turbine hall. In the foreground is the Central Electricity Authority sub-station which feeds the current produced into the national grid.

Since the individual components of an atom are inconceivably small, we cannot lay them out on the table and examine them in detail; it is therefore most difficult to compile a specification of the basic unit — the 'brick' — from which the world is built up. Consequently, ideal models were used. In Professor Niels Bohr's model, the nucleus — surrounded by an envelope of electrons — lay in the middle of the atom. The electrons were considered to be arranged in 'shells', but this must be understood figuratively and not structurally. Comparison of the atom to the planetary system, with the nucleus representing the sun and the electrons moving like planets around it, was a graphic aid to a better understanding of the phenomena within the atom.

Speculative laymen for some time took this model representation too literally. They thought that there might be inhabited worlds among the 'planets' in the atom, with a flora and fauna like that of the earth, while in a far larger universe our planets — Earth, Mars, Jupiter, etc. — were perhaps no more than electrons. We must, however, clear our minds of the idea that matter really consists of an enormous number of minute planetary systems.

Hydrogen has the simplest atom, its nucleus being an indivisible positively-charged particle, some 1,800 times as big as an electron. Hydrogen is the first element in the Periodic Table, and its nucleus is therefore called a proton. In addition, the hydrogen atom contains a negatively-charged particle or electron.

Now it is easy for us to find our way round Nature's great 'box of bricks'. The combination of two protons and two electrons gives a helium atom, three protons and three electrons make up a lithium atom, four protons and four electrons an atom of beryllium, the fourth element in the series. Continuing, still with equal numbers of protons and electrons, we find carbon with six of each, nitrogen with seven and oxygen with eight. We reach the provisional end of the series with uranium, which has ninety-two protons and ninety-two electrons. The atomic numbers of the elements indicate both the number of protons and electrons in their atoms.

The number of protons and electrons governs the chemical properties of an element. For instance, an atom with seventy-

P

nine protons is indubitably gold. If it has one proton less it is platinum; if it has one more it is mercury. The mediæval alchemists, seeking to turn lead into gold, would have had to remove three protons from the eighty-two which make up the nucleus of the lead atom; this exceedingly difficult problem was only to be solved by the physicists of the 20th century.

Another important number also serves to distinguish the atoms; this is the atomic weight. For instance, the atomic weight of gold is 197. If we remove the seventy-nine protons from its nucleus, we are left with a large number of uncharged particles almost as large as the protons. These are the neutrons — particles without electrical charge — which Chadwick discovered in 1932. Thus the nucleus of the gold atom contains 197 − 79 = 118 neutrons.

But what happens if we add two further neutrons to the 118 in an atom of gold, i.e., if we increase the atomic weight to 119? The atomic number remains unchanged and therefore the substance is still gold; what we have is a 'brother' of gold. In fact, there are whole families of 'brother and sister' atoms, all of them bearing the same family name but distinct from each other in atomic weight and in physical (not chemical) properties. These related forms are known as isotopes. The oxygen in the air we breathe is a mixture of three of the naturally occurring isotopes of oxygen; their nuclei contain either eight, nine, or ten neutrons, but they all have eight protons, and their atomic weights are sixteen, seventeen and eighteen respectively. Iron has four isotopes which occur in Nature, tin ten, lead eight and uranium three.

Of recent years physicists have considerably increased the number of isotopes; it is now very large, and increasing steadily. Initially there were 100, but in a few years the number became 1,000 and then 2,000. Every atomic nucleus was subjected to scientific experiments.

But this was not enough. It was even possible to create new elements, hitherto unknown and not found in Nature. For many years uranium, with the atomic number 92, was the last element. It was now followed by element 93, called neptunium, while number 94 was the artificial element plutonium, which is made in relatively large quantities and has achieved economic importance. Number 95 is americium, number 96 curium. By the autumn of 1955, the number of artificially-produced trans-uranian elements had risen to ten. Element 97 was named berkelium, number 98 californium, number 99 einsteinium and number 100 fermium. Element 101 was eventually artificially prepared in the laboratory, and although at first only seventeen atoms of this new substance were obtained — and they soon decayed — this element was christened mendelevium. In the summer of 1957, Swedish, British and American research workers at the Nobel Institute in Stockholm prepared arti-ficially an isotope of element 102, for which they proposed the name nobelium. This element — the last to be discovered up to 1957 — is short-lived and strongly radioactive.

An illustration will show how minute a quantity seventeen atoms of a substance represents. If all the atoms in a thimbleful of water were counted separately at the rate of ten a second, then the 50,000,000 inhabitants of Western Germany would have to count for 40,000 years, atom by atom, until the thimble was empty.

*   *   *

All this followed from the rich harvest of 1932, the wonderful year of physics. The importance of the discoveries made in that year could only be assessed fifteen years later, when the world learned of the secret advances in atomic energy.

The atom bomb, the development of which had been ordered by President Roosevelt, ended the war which Hitler started. It is a very striking coincidence that three events, which were to affect the fate of mankind, took place within twelve months:

> In February 1932 the neutron was discovered.
> In November 1932 Roosevelt became President of the United States.
> In January 1933 Hitler seized power in Germany.

In Paris the Joliot-Curies discovered artificial radioactivity in 1934. By means of irradiation with alpha particles they produced radioactive isotopes which could actually be separ-ated chemically from the non-radioactive isotopes.

During this period Enrico Fermi, already famous despite his youth, was working in the Physics Institute at Rome Univer-sity. Instead of alpha particles he used neutrons as projectiles with which he bombarded sixty-eight different elements from hydrogen to uranium; forty-seven of them became radioactive. Shortly afterwards Fermi observed that the effects were more marked when the neutron source was surrounded with water or hydrogen. The hydrogen clearly slowed the neutrons down; Fermi had discovered 'slow' neutrons. But then Fermi, hitherto so successful, reached a wrong conclusion, with the consequence that the really world-shaking discovery was made by someone else.

Fermi bombarded uranium with slow neutrons, obtaining new and unknown elements. In June 1934 he published his hypothesis that the new artificial radioactive substances produced from uranium by neutron bombardment were new 'transuranian' elements, following uranium in the atomic series. Once more enthusiasm and scepticism were stirred up. Had man really created artificial elements? Then a new era in human history had begun. But when Fermi's terrible mistake became known the sceptics smiled with satisfaction — the impossible would be for ever impossible.

The news of these astounding results reached Berlin-Dahlem, where Professor Otto Hahn, Director of the Kaiser-Wilhelm Institute of Chemistry, and Lise Meitner, Head of the Physics Department, had been working on this problem for several years.

Dr. Meitner went to Berlin in 1907 and rapidly became Hahn's indispensable partner. But things were not easy for her; the entrance of a woman student into the laboratories used by the male students was considered a feminine challenge. She was therefore only able to work with Hahn in a special laboratory in the basement of the Institute.

Otto Hahn and Lise Meitner had grown older, but age had not dulled their scientific zeal. When Fermi's transuranian elements were announced, it seemed as though the two physicists had been beaten in the scientific race; but they did not give up. Together with Professor Fritz Strassmann they also began to use neutron beams, concentrating on the most promising elements, thorium and uranium. Years of hard work passed. Finally, on 22nd December 1938, Professors Hahn and Strassmann published their famous report in *Die Naturwissenschaften*, which included the words: "Our radium isotopes possess the characteristics of barium; as chemists we ought really to say that the new substances are not radium but barium, as we have no other elements here . . . as nuclear chemists we cannot yet bring ourselves to this step which is in contradiction to all experience hitherto in nuclear physics."

Hahn and Strassmann — Lise Meitner having meanwhile had to leave Germany — had discovered the fission of the uranium nucleus by neutrons. But this result was so frightening that they dared not yet draw the conclusions which follow. But one thing is now certain. Fermi was mistaken. The world-shaking discovery had fallen to Hahn and Strassmann. The two German scientists had unknowingly opened a door, and vast new fields of research lay before them. Who would be the first to enter upon them?

The news reached Lise Meitner in the little village of Kungelv near Gothenburg. She talked the frightening discovery over with her nephew, Dr. O. R. Frisch, who had been working with Niels Bohr in his Copenhagen institute since 1934. Hahn and Strassmann had spoken of a 'splitting' of the atomic nucleus. Lise Meitner and O. R. Frisch thought of the similarity of this process with the fission of baccilli, and therefore used in their first publication the expression 'nuclear fission'.

Even before the world learned what had been achieved in the laboratory and what the consequences might be, many scientists began to have doubts as they faced the vision of a gigantic new source of energy. Frisch felt "like a man who has suddenly caught an elephant and now has no idea what to do with it".

As 1939 opened, Niels Bohr listed fifteen important reasons for his opinion that the fission process discovered would not have any practical application. The American author William Laurence wrote that Einstein once told him that he did not believe in the release of atomic energy. Even Otto Hahn is reputed to have said, when the possible effects of the discovery were discussed: "But surely that is not God's will!"

THE BOMB

Science had wrested one of Nature's greatest secrets from her, but the world public took no notice of the event. Only the few initiates concerned themselves with artificial radioactivity, free neutrons, high-energy particles and atomic fission. They recognised the gigantic source of energy in the nuclei of the heavy elements of high atomic number.

Only once in his lifetime did Professor Albert Einstein intervene in world politics. As fears grew that Hitler's power would spread, Einstein drew President Roosevelt's attention to the military potentialities of the fission of the uranium nucleus, discovered by Otto Hahn. He signed a letter, written by others, to the President of the United States, beginning with the following words: "Some recent work by E. Fermi and L. Szilard, which has been communicated to me in manuscript, leads me to expect that the element uranium may be turned into a new and important source of energy in the immediate future . . . This new phenomenon would also lead to the construction of bombs . . . A single bomb of this type . . . exploded in a port, might very well destroy the whole port, together with some of the surrounding territory . . ."

These phrases were the introduction to several fateful years, even though the beginnings were slow and hesitant.

Fear of Hitler's atomic bomb, which was believed to be in an advanced state of development, spurred the physicists and research workers assembled in the United States to ever greater efforts. After the war Einstein once said with regret that had he known that the Germans would not be able to build an atomic bomb, he would not have lifted a finger to further its development in the United States.

The United States did not follow the proposals of the atomic physicists enthusiastically. On the contrary, the military authorities at first showed considerable opposition, especially as they were by nature suspicious of all new weapons. Least of all could they reconcile themselves to the atomic bomb project. Shortsightedness, false assessment of the possibilities, underestimation and mistrust determined their attitude to the scientists' plans. This may sound like an old gramophone record, but it is completely true. Repeatedly representatives of the military gave the scientists to understand, as they reported on their plans, that they had hardly more confidence in them than in the innumerable other 'mad inventors', who — in other countries as well, incidentally — plagued the services and the authorities with thousands of senseless and impracticable proposals for new weapons.

On the other hand, the scientists — accustomed to unfettered research — were unable at first to adjust themselves to the military's requirements which inevitably imposed strict discipline and, above all, absolute secrecy as to the research results. They were used to discussing the results of their experiments with colleagues, publishing theories and experimental data and drawing encouragement from the work of colleagues abroad. Then again the practical engineers were outraged at being suddenly called upon to accept vague theories and build giant factories without any data, or at best with information which often seemed uncertain.

Up to the beginning of the summer of 1940 not even financial support could be expected for atomic research. Instead the criticisms of many individuals and organisations grew against a 'senseless project' for which the prospects painted by the physicists were, to say the least, dubious.

Once again Einstein intervened, and once again a committee established that an atomic bomb could be manufactured before the end of the war. Only then came the long-delayed decision to proceed in all earnest with the construction of the new weapon. It happened by chance that this came exactly one day before the Japanese onslaught on Pearl Harbour and America's entry into the war.

*   *   *

The 'Manhattan Project' began to gain impetus. General Leslie R. Groves was put in charge of it. When he met his staff at Los Alamos for the first time, he told them always to remember that they would have to deal with the biggest collection of 'crackpots' ever assembled. Despite many difficulties the enterprise was started. The scientists sought — and found — U 235, the uranium isotope responsible for nuclear fission. In 1941 they produced the first two artificial transuranium elements — neptunium and plutonium. It was discovered that the isotope of plutonium with an atomic weight of 239 was also fissionable. Initially only infinitesimal quantities of this new material, too small to be weighed, were obtained, and yet human genius succeeded in studying these minute traces of material and in building a gigantic industry on this foundation.

On 2nd December 1942, Enrico Fermi, who had meanwhile

emigrated to the United States, having in 1939 become a Professor at Columbia University, succeeded in making the last, decisive step. He and his co-workers achieved the first, long-awaited chain reaction, which had until then been no more than an idea. An atomic pile, composed of blocks of graphite and uranium, yielded an increasing number of free neutrons, as soon as a bar of cadmium, which absorbs neutrons, was withdrawn. This was the first nuclear reactor in the world.

Nuclear fission releases energy continuously in the form of heat which tends to hinder the continuation of the chain reaction. The reactor must consequently be cooled. That is why the first large reactor was built at Hanford, Washington, where the Savannah River provided ample cooling water. However, heat is more than an unwelcome concomitant of chain reactions; it is the only usable form of the energy obtained from the nucleus. It can be used to heat the boilers at a power station, the cylinders of an engine or the combustion chambers of a rocket. The production of heat, which is a considerable nuisance in the research reactor, became the principal task of the power-producing reactor. The nuclear reactor's other function is to produce artificial radioactive isotopes and fissile elements, such as plutonium 239; this was its main task in the early days of nuclear reactors.

The intense bombardment of free neutrons smashes the uranium 235 nuclei, and nuclei of numerous lighter elements are produced. The more stable uranium 238 nuclei do not break up, but absorb one neutron each. The product is the radioactive isotope uranium 239, which has a half-life of twenty-three minutes. In this short time one half becomes transformed into the new element neptunium, which is also short-lived, since half of it decays within two or three days, forming another new element — plutonium. This is more stable, its half-life being 24,000 years. But its fission by means of slow free neutrons takes place more easily than that of any natural element.

*   *   *

At the beginning of 1943, the atomic scientists were faced with complicated problems. Research installations of a new kind were needed to prepare the atomic bomb. A gigantic industry had to be built up from scratch to manufacture uranium 235. In addition, nuclear reactors had to be built to produce plutonium. Simultaneously there began the struggle with the dangers of this many-sided operation — dangers still not fully known, but already glimpsed — for it was known that a speck of plutonium, one-millionth of a gram, slowly destroys bones and tissue, with fatal results.

There also existed the risk of a spontaneous, unintentional explosion. Nobody knew how much plutonium could be brought together without running this risk. The only information available was theoretical, based on calculation. As long as the quantity of easily-fissionable plutonium remained small it could not explode, because the majority of the free neutrons released as it decayed were dissipated, without causing the fission of further nuclei. The bigger the quantity of plutonium, the fewer neutrons escaped. Once the mass had reached a certain figure, enough neutrons remained to cause the fission of further nuclei; the chain reaction then grew at a tremendous rate, and an atomic explosion occurred. This mass was given a special name — the critical mass.

The main charge of the atomic bomb had therefore to be slightly smaller than this critical mass. Only when it was set of could enough plutonium be added for the critical mass to be exceeded. The exact data for the solution of this frighteningly difficult problem could only be obtained experimentally. With infinite care the physicists groped for the key to the puzzle. At any moment the entire experimental assembly might explode, but by good fortune the experiment was successful.

Louis Slotin, Canadian-born son of Russian refugee parents, was the young physicist charged with carrying out these deadly dangerous investigations. It was a task after the heart of this young scientist, who had only become acquainted with the problems of nuclear physics during the war, and was not assailed by as many doubts as were the older research workers. Slotin was also the man who assembled the first atomic bomb for the Trinity test at Alamogordo.

Almost a year later, while he was preparing the second atomic bomb which was to be exploded in the waters of Bikini Atoll in the Pacific, his screwdriver slipped; the two subcritical hemispheres came together and a chain reaction instantly began.

Instead of retreating, Slotin seized the hemispheres with his bare hands and interrupted the reaction. Although by so doing he saved the lives of the men working with him in the room, he himself had received so intense a dose of radiation that he was from that moment doomed to death. Nine days later the man who had determined the critical mass of the atom bomb died.

*   *   *

On 12th July 1945 the first atomic bomb was assembled in an old ranch house in New Mexico. Two days later it was raised to the top of its steel tower, and after another two days it was set off.

Meanwhile President Roosevelt had died and was succeeded by President Truman. His was the heavy responsibility of deciding on the use of this frightening new weapon, the effects of which were now known. For instance, General Farrell, an eye-witness of the explosion, had stated: "Thirty seconds after the explosion came, first, the air blast, pressing hard against the people and things, to be followed almost immediately by the strong, sustained, awesome roar which warned of doomsday and made us feel that we puny things were blasphemous to dare tamper with the forces heretofore reserved for the Almighty."

President Truman later wrote in his memoirs that he decided that the bomb should be dropped to end the war more quickly. General Groves considered, however, that in actual fact he had only refrained from saying 'No', because at that time it would have required great courage to say 'No'.

Thus on 6th August 1945, three weeks after Trinity Day, the American Super-Fortress 'Enola Gay' took off from Tinian, an island 2,000 miles from Japan, heading for Hiroshima. This was the aircraft which dropped the first atomic bomb. In a blast of heat, fire and radiation, a capital city died. The appalling phenomenon was repeated three days later over Nagasaki. Two bombs, in which the actual charge was not much bigger than a clenched fist, brought the Second World War to a flaming end.

*   *   *

Ten months after the destruction of the two Japanese cities by atom bombs, Operation Crossroads began in the lagoon of the tiny Pacific Island of Bikini. Was it the intention to demonstrate that mankind had reached a decisive turning-point in its progress towards the future?

The first bomb was dropped from an aircraft, the second exploded three weeks later some ten yards below the surface of the sea. Deep down in the lagoon the fireball appeared, almost as though the sun itself had fallen into the sea. Then the explosion ripped the waters apart and a pillar of water, some 2,200 feet in diameter, rose to a height of over 8,000 feet. This gigantic fountain, composed of a million tons of water, formed a hollow chimney through which the fireball leapt skywards. Three million cubic yards of sludge and sand, the pulverised bottom of the Pacific Ocean, followed at the base of the pillar.

In 1947 the U.S. Atomic Energy Commission began its work. New research centres were built, the atom towns grew, and there were already in America alone thirty installations producing fissile material. In other countries work on the same problems and objectives was going on with no less determination behind security barriers.

From this time onward more and more test explosions shook the earth. Operation Sandstone took place at Eniwetok in the Pacific. In 1949 the Russians tested their first atomic bomb, which was already more powerful than those dropped on Japan. During January and February 1951 five American test explosion were set off in the Nevada Desert. In May the preliminary test for Operation Greenhouse was held at Eniwetok. This was the first thermonuclear reaction, the new hydrogen bomb. The fire which burns in the stars was lit for the first time on earth, for the reactions in this bomb are the same as those which occur in the sun. Science had advanced from nuclear fission to nuclear fusion. Henceforth man had even greater quantities of energy at his disposal. A further seven atomic explosions shook the Nevada testing grounds in the autumn of 1951.

During 1952 mushroom atom clouds rose eight times above the Nevada Desert; one of these bombs was fifty times as powerful as the Hiroshima bomb. In October 1952 Great Britain held her first atom bomb test, on Montebello Island, near the Australian coast. In November 1952 the island of Elugelab, in the Eniwetok Atoll, was vaporised. A piece of the planet Earth disappeared from the map without trace. Within four seconds

the bomb was transformed into a fireball nearly nine miles
across, with a mushroom cloud reaching a height of ten miles;
the energy released corresponded to the yield from three million
one-ton T.N.T. bombs.

And so it went on, year after year. In 1953 came the fourth
series of Nevada tests, with nine bombs; the first Russian hydrogen bomb exploded in August. In 1954 there were at least four
tests with American 'deliverable' hydrogen bombs. More and
more atom bombs, more and more hydrogen bombs; then one
day, in 1957, Britain too exploded her first hydrogen bomb on
Christmas Island in the Pacific. Man had turned the whole
earth into a proving ground for his ideas. After a long and
weary journey, the promised atom-land was reached. He had
begun by turning Nature's most liberal gift, abundant energy,
into a destructive weapon, not least because the decisive years
of development happened to coincide with a world-wide war.

In the spring of 1955, Dr. Otto Hahn, one of those who had
involuntarily contributed to the beginning of this development,
warned mankind in the following terms: "If the hydrogen bomb
is surrounded by a thick layer of cobalt, the very numerous
neutrons released by the reaction produce large quantities of
the long-lived and highly radioactive cobalt 60, which would
be thrown into the atmosphere as a fine dust by the tremendous
power of the explosion and would thence be carried by the
winds. Wherever this dust gradually drops to earth, it produces its frightful effects. It has been calculated or estimated in
the United States that ten large hydrogen bombs, with thick
cobalt shells, would produce such a large quantity of cobalt 60,
whose radioactivity would continue for several years, that the
continued existence of mankind would be seriously threatened
thereby."

THE SORCERER'S APPRENTICE

On Friday, 12th July 1957, an 'enemy' air force crossed Alaska
into United States territory and dropped a total of 175 atomic
and thermonuclear bombs on 162 vital targets. From the air-
raid alarm to the dropping of the bombs there were only two
hours in which to evacuate the civil population from the cities.
The President and his Government were accommodated in
emergency quarters a hundred miles from Washington. The

destruction in the areas attacked was inconceivable, but some
defence installations throughout the country remained intact.
Atoms bombs with a total destructive capacity of 451·7 million
tons of explosive were dropped on the target towns, which had
a total population of more than ninety-five million. New York
was wiped out, huge areas of the New England States, the east
coast down to the boundary of Virginia and North Carolina,
the middle-west as far as Illinois and Iowa, the north-west to the
Pacific Coast and the big towns of California became nothing
but heaps of debris, which were moreover poisoned by radioactivity.

That is the outline of a gigantic atom air-raid exercise held in
the United States of America in the summer of 1957. The results were highly disquieting. A few decades previously an exercise like this would have been considered an idle game. But
now the game had become deadly earnest.

*   *   *

Long before, man had repeatedly used new inventions for
military purposes in the first case. When early man learned to
use fire, he threw blazing brands at attacking wild beasts to
ward them off, and used fire arrows against other men and their
dwellings. The wheel was used in the chariot, the lever became
part of the huge primitive catapult; hammer and axe were not
solely tools but weapons for close combat; the horse was not
only man's helper in tilling his fields or carrying burdens, but
also served him as a cavalry charger. The aeroplane carried
not only peaceable passengers but also bombs. This list of
detours and by-paths in the development of technical devices
could be continued almost indefinitely.

It is bitterly ironical that one of man's greatest achievements,
the release of the energy locked up in matter, should first of all
be used almost exclusively to supplement the modern arsenal.

The number of atomic and hydrogen bombs already manufactured is a secret. However, sober estimates show that
roughly one-fifth of the reserves of atomic bombs accumulated
by the Eastern and Western blocs up to the summer of 1957
would suffice to annihilate all life on earth and burn up all the
continents to permanent deserts. The explosive force of all the
atomic bombs made hitherto by one nation alone, the United

States of America, is so huge that the equivalent of ten tons of explosive is held in stock for every one of the 2,500 million inhabitants of the earth. In other words, this stock of atomic bombs has the explosive power of approximately 25,000 million tons of chemical explosive!

The enormous scale of the energy suddenly made available to mankind in the form of the most frightful weapons is shown by an American senator's fantastic illustration; he stated that the existing stock of hydrogen bombs in the summer of 1957 would be sufficient to displace the earth's axis by 16 degrees.

*   *   *

It would be unjust and wrong, however, to quote only the destructive effects of atomic bombs. Since that memorable day in 1942, when the first controlled chain reaction was initiated at the University of Chicago, advances with important effects on human life have been made. Valuable methods of treating disease and new scientific tools were discovered and gigantic energy sources opened up.

"Why do not the world's responsible atomic scientists refuse to handle such material?" asked Professor Hahn in his warning on the dangers of cobalt 60. "They do not object, but on the contrary are very actively studying it, because they wish to apply the beneficial potentialities of cobalt and many other substances artificially rendered radioactive by neutron bombardment, not to cause damage but to help mankind." If peace is maintained, the unravelled secrets of the atom offer almost overwhelming possibilities. Inexhaustible sources of electric power can be created, making it possible to open up regions today considered too remote or too poor in natural resources. Cheap electricity can be produced and used to irrigate dry soils and turn deserts into fertile agricultural land. Greater exploitation of the seas and their resources can be expected, unknown mineral deposits extracted and many entirely new products manufactured. The atom must be used as a research instrument to discover new elements. It will yield new medical products and will also help us to deepen our knowledge of the world around us.

It would be unwise to peer into the future. Who can say what will happen in the next twenty-five, fifty or seventy-five years? And yet we can, if we cast a backward look for the sake of comparison, form an approximate idea of what can happen in the world in years to come.

Once atomic research can be concentrated on peaceful objectives, plutonium will be used less for bombs and more as an

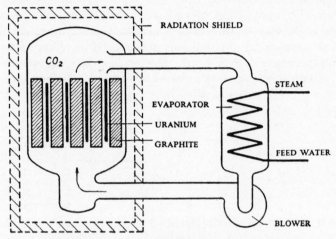

Diagram of a Calder-Hall type reactor.

energy supplier, providing enormous quantities from compact sources; these will be used to drive machines, ships, trains and aircraft. Further research could yield not only improved atomic fuels, but also new substances of higher atomic weight than either uranium or plutonium; they would be of great practical importance in connection with stationary nuclear power stations. It is fairly certain that uranium will not be the only raw material of the atomic era. Yet uranium is already twenty million times stronger than T.N.T. as an explosive, while as a fuel its calorific value is many million times in excess of any other known fuel.

The erection of nuclear power stations is in full swing. One day they will be able to provide electricity more cheaply than the conventional sources of supply. There will be further gains from the increased yield of by-products, since the reactors can be used to create radioactive elements and isotopes — substances which are being applied to an ever-increasing extent in science, in industry and in medical research.

A whimsical comparison once likened radioactive isotopes to 'modest flowers', which the scientist, on entering this world of ultra-small things, discovered at the edge of the path. One could say that the radioactive isotope is a flower of science, which man's questing and classifying mind has learned to raise in innumerable varieties.

A major application of radioactive isotopes is the use of tracers. Minute quantities of a radioactive substance can be added to any kind of circulatory system and be traced exactly along the whole of their route. Devices like the Geiger counter are so sensitive that they can still detect one 40,000-millionth part of a gram of radioactive substance. Thus if one gram of

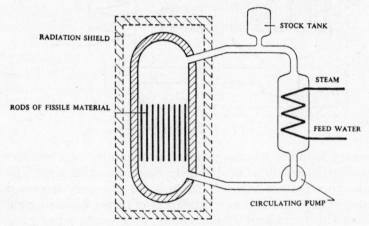

Diagram of a pressurised-water reactor.

radioactive sugar were uniformly distributed over 80 million normal one-cwt. sacks of untreated sugar, it could still be detected.

Many factories are already using radioactive isotopes for the measurement, during the manufacturing process, of the thickness of tinplate, foil, paper, plastic, glass, film base and many other products. The 'twin brothers' of the elements can also be used for the study of chemical reactions and processes. They can serve to follow fluids passing through pipes, to check the recovery of chemical catalysts or the state of the catalysts themselves during the reaction.

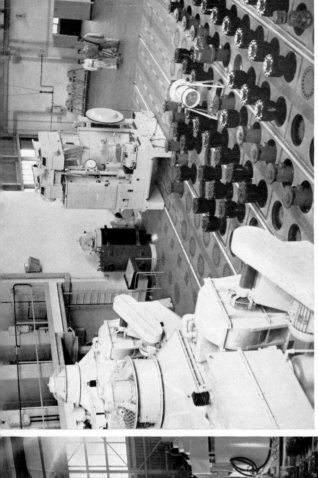

General view of the charging deck of Number 1 reactor at Calder Hall, showing one machine for charging and discharging fuel elements and the control-rod actuating gear.

Loading fuel elements into the machine which lowers them into the core of the reactor.

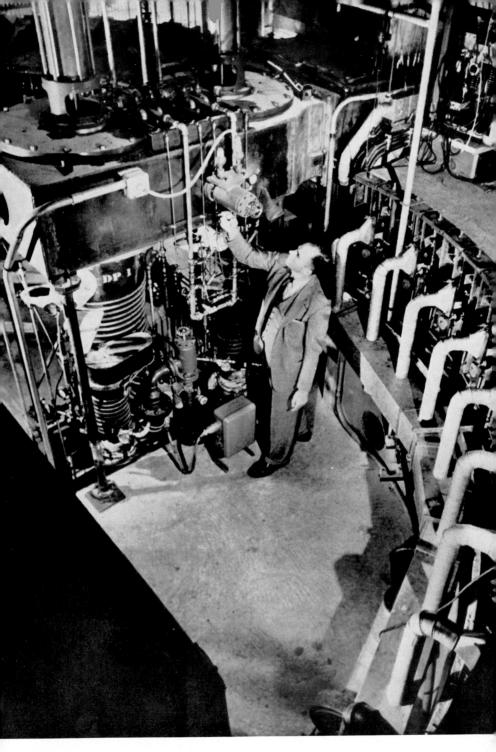

A physicist adjusting a vacuum pump inside the magnet of a one-fourth size working model of the 10,000-ton bevatron at the University of California radiation laboratory. The model is used to study problems of operation and design.

The doctors treat many diseases with radioactive isotopes, whose radiations to some extent replace X-rays. X-ray therapy is not however dispensed with but rather supplemented by valuable new methods, since irradiation apparatus using radioactive gold or cobalt are lighter and therefore more easily car-

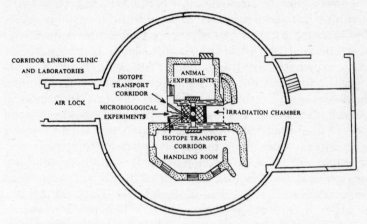

Medical research reactor at Brookhaven National Laboratory.

ried. Radioactive phosphorus is applied in the treatment of leucæmia, and radioactive iodine for hyperthyroidy. Those are only a few examples of the many wonderful possibilities.

In the early stages radioactive isotopes were undesirable by-products from nuclear reactors which had to be disposed of as 'radioactive waste'. Even by the summer of 1954 there were in the United States alone almost a thousand industrial users of radioactive isotopes. They brought about an annual saving of some 100 million dollars. By 1965, it is estimated, the savings will exceed 1,000 million dollars solely in the many fields of application opened up by the development of simplified methods.

*   *   *

Although fire will burn a man's finger, and repeatedly takes its toll of goods and of human life, it has not yet occurred to anybody to forbid the use of fire. During the years of controversy on the great dangers of the atomic era, caricatures were published showing prehistoric men experimenting with their

Q

newly-discovered fire, while in the background the wise old folk declared warningly: "They'll soon have the whole forest alight."

True, a local forest fire cannot readily be compared with a widespread atomic fire; nevertheless, scientific and technical progress cannot be arrested simply because the dangers to living creatures have been increased to begin with. It would be sense-less to try to turn the wheel of progress backwards. Anyone who was attracted by this idea learned to know better in August 1955, when the first International 'Atoms for Peace' Confer-ence was held in Geneva. The large-scale industrial exhibition held at the same time was virtually the first International Atomic Exhibition. It showed how the world would very soon benefit from the results of atomic research, and what prospects were already opened up in this first phase of completely new scientific and technical development. It was a huge congress, serving as a prelude to a new era. "In all, 1,260 sorcerers' apprentices sat in the cream-coloured leather seats, cradled in a newly-recovered peace of conscience." This was a reporter's impression of the opening session. Atomic power stations were discussed instead of atomic bombs. A total of 1,139 papers, occupying 17,000 pages, contained a vast amount of scientific material, including, in the first place, exhaustive reports on the nuclear power stations in Britain, the Soviet Union and the U.S.A.

Transportable nuclear engines were already powering American submarines, such as the *Nautilus* and the *Seawolf*, on undersea voyages of several months' duration without refuel-ling. Atomic engines for merchant ships were being developed and fourteen atom-powered ships were under construction. American aircraft firms had begun designing the first proto-types of nuclear-propelled aircraft.

In the autumn of 1956, the Düsseldorf periodical, *Atomwirt-schaft*, published the first detailed survey on the world's reactors. In those countries carrying out atomic research there were, according to this survey, 76 reactors in operation; projects existed for 109 research reactors, while 138 power reactors were planned or under construction. Power reactors deliver energy from atomic nuclei. In 1955, world power requirements were almost twenty billion kilowatt-hours. Approximately half of

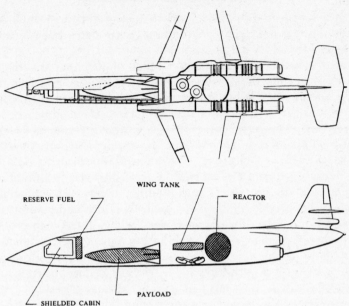

Diagram of a nuclear-powered aircraft; the pile heats the jet
turbines.

this was provided by coal, a quarter by petroleum and a tenth
by water power. Although the world energy economy changes
with time and it is hardly possible to predict likely developments, it is already clear that some of the traditional energy
sources are gradually giving out, and that the others will not be
able to meet fully the increasing demand.

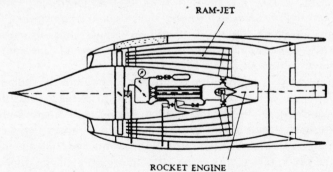

Diagram of a coleopter-type aircraft, with reactor heating of
the ram-jet. (After H. von Zborowski.)

It lies with man himself whether nuclear energy with all its possibilities is to become a threat or a promise to mankind, and whether the successful unlocking of the mighty forces of Nature means existence or annihilation. One of the leading atomic physicists of our day, Professor Robert Oppenheimer, who, as first Director of the Los Alamos Research Station in 1945, was known as the 'father of the atomic bomb' and subsequently — after leaving Government service — became Professor of Theoretical Physics at Princeton, New Jersey, drew a pleasant picture when he wrote in 1953: "We know that our work is rightly both an instrument and an end. A great discovery is a thing of beauty; and our faith — our binding, quiet faith — is that knowledge is good and good in itself. It is also an instrument; it is an instrument for our successors, who will use it to probe elsewhere and more deeply; it is an instrument for technology, for the practical arts, and for man's affairs. So it is with us as scientists; so it is with us as men. We are at once instruments and end, discoverers and teachers, actors and observers. We understand, as we hope others understand, that in this there is a harmony between knowledge in the sense of science, that specialized and general knowledge which it is our purpose to uncover, and the community of man. We, like all men, are among those who bring a little light to the vast unending darkness of man's life and world. For us as for all men, change and eternity, specialization and unity, instrument and final purpose, community and individual man alone, complementary each to the other, both require and define our bonds and our freedom."

From 1946 to 1956 the U.S.A. alone spent more than 12,000 million dollars on atomic energy developments. Since then the figure has been about 2,000 million dollars annually and is steadily increasing. And still the major part of this sum is devoted to weapons.

Generally speaking the technique is only in its infancy. There is no doubt that many additional peaceful applications of atomic energy will be discovered. From the force which once wrought destruction will come a huge new industry beneficial to mankind. This is the promise of the atomic era. But the man in the street, seized with fear of the unforeseeable consequences of using atom bombs, is still groping in the dark in this epoch of great scientific illumination; he is disturbed almost daily by

wild prophecies about the fearful consequences of the radioactive pollution of large tracts of the earth, as well as being
bombarded with superficial — sometimes positive, but more
frequently negative — judgments about the 'atom'.

This alone would explain the stir in 1956 and 1957 — among
the people in areas where it was proposed to construct nuclear
reactors — in Germany where no practical application of
atomic energy had been possible since the end of the war. For
instance, early in 1957 eleven communities in the Karlsruhe
Landeskreis lodged an objection with the Government of Hesse
against the construction of the German Atomic Centre near
Karlsruhe. Perhaps reports of farmers opposing the approaching physicists with scythes and flails were exaggerated; but the
fears that the future operation of the nuclear reactor would
pollute the whole neighbourhood — farmland, meadows and
woodland — with radioactivity were real. Even while the research station was being built, two communities did take up
this very aspect of the problem, not like their forefathers with
scythe and flail, but by recourse to the appropriate courts of
justice.

Ignorance, exaggeration, unscientific speculation and perhaps some lingering superstition may very well be at the bottom
of this attitude. But concern about the future, fear of the uncontrollable effects of a development which even the experts
concerned cannot clearly foresee, and the sense of responsibility
to children and grandchildren are undoubtedly real and
sincere.

The history of the revolution in physics, which overturned an
established picture of the universe and unlocked for man the
energy in the atomic nucleus, is a typical example of the great
struggle for innovation, particularly as this struggle is still continuing. After the revolution it is an easy matter to shake one's
head over what was considered in the 19th century to be a
stable science at the end of its development. Since then physics
has been transformed. Yet people stand up and declare that
progress is now at an end, and any thought of it nonsense, and
that the signs of an imminent falling-off are clear. In fact the
new scientific revolutionaries are in our midst. Perhaps the new
idea which will overthrow everything has already been conceived and expressed, and perhaps the unfamiliar elements of

future development are stored up as yet unrevealed in the mind of a young genius.

At the beginning of 1955 Albert Einstein wrote to Max von Laue: "If I have learnt one thing in the tribulations of a long life it is that we are much further away from a deep insight into Nature's fundamental phenomena than most of our contemporaries think . . ."

In the following words Robert Oppenheimer wrote about the necessary, inevitable, constantly-renewed tension between the New and the Old: "The principle of correspondence — the requirement that the new laws of atomic mechanics should merge with those of Newtonian mechanics for large bodies and events — thus had great value as an instrument of discovery. Beyond that, it illustrates the essential elements of the relation of new discovery and old knowledge in science: the old knowledge, as the very means for coming upon the new, must in its old realm be left intact; only when we have left that realm can it be transcended . . .

"This is one reason why, however great the novelty or scope of new discovery, we neither can, nor need, rebuild the house of the mind very rapidly. This is one reason why science, for all its revolutions, is conservative. This is why we will have to accept the fact that no one of us really will ever know very much. This is why we shall have to find comfort in the fact that, taken together, we know more and more."

> "The initial period of application of these new methods
> will lead directly to an era of complete confusion."
>
> Norbert Wiener (1949)

CHAPTER VI

ROBOTS EVERYWHERE

*The crowning achievement of technology? — "Artificial men with a
little intelligence . . ." — Robots everywhere — Calculating machines
— Machines with consciousness? — The automatic factory — Automation, with or without tears? — Visions.*

THE CROWNING ACHIEVEMENT OF TECHNOLOGY?

SIX years after the flight of a fully automatic Skymaster from
America to Europe, I sat with the then Chief of the Experimental Group for Automatic Flight in the All-weather Branch
of the American Air Force, in Wiesbaden. Major James L.
Anast told me: "There were fourteen of us on board, a crew of
nine and five observers. The Captain of our machine was
Colonel James L. Gillespie, Head of the All-weather Flying
Branch. We took off from Stephenville in Newfoundland and
landed, after a safe flight, at Brize Norton in Oxfordshire.

"It is a well-known fact that a modern large aircraft makes
very heavy demands on the pilot, especially during blind flying.
In the Skymaster there were no fewer than thirty-six instruments for checking temperatures, pressures, r.p.m., fuel
reserves and so on, as well as more than twenty devices for
flight control and navigation.

"There were great potentialities in radar; it could be used to
relieve the pilot and to increase flying safety. However, what
we wanted was to develop automatic devices which would
relieve the fliers very much more. That was our reason for
flying this completely automatic Skymaster over the Atlantic
on 21st September 1947. The pilot's seat was empty — a
strange sight for anyone who is accustomed to glance occasionally over the pilot's shoulder.

"Nevertheless, we had a very skilled flier on board; although
he had never taken flying courses he had all the necessary data.
This automatic pilot, named 'Joe', awoke when the Chief

pressed the start button in Stephenville. The pilot revved up the motors to take-off speed and then set the aircraft rolling. As soon as the prescribed speed was reached, he pulled the control column back. Our flight had begun. Completely calm, Joe waited for information from the altimeter, which would govern his next operation. The undercarriage had to be retracted, the engines throttled down to cruising speed and the flaps pulled up. In the meantime he was setting the plane on her compass course.

"A few hours later Joe detected weak, distant radio signals from our first transmitter, on board a ship in the Atlantic. The signals brought Joe into action again and aiming, so to speak, at the ship, he corrected his course. Having flown over the ship, he followed the compass course again.

"When the Skymaster flew over Ireland several hours later, Joe took no notice, as Ireland was not included in his programme. Only when the second experimental transmitter started signalling from England did he resume his activities. This was his destination; he turned towards it and began to bring the plane down as soon as he reached the predetermined distance. At this moment the approach signal from the Brize Norton airfield reached him, together with the signals from the blind-landing transmitter, giving his approach path.

"He set the machine down on the runway unerringly, allowed it to slow down and then applied the brakes. The experiment had been successful. The crew and the observers breathed a sigh of relief. Joe was naturally unconcerned; he had done his job and neither blame nor praise could touch him. After all, he was only a robot.

"Joe, the robot who had flown the experimental four-engine aircraft, had no resemblance to a human being. To anyone who thought that the pilot's place was behind the control column this automaton was quite invisible; his complicated 'body' consisted of a maze of meters, switches, relays, aerials, receivers, transmitters, batteries and control circuits, distributed over the entire aircraft and linked by cables and leads."

James Anast spoke without emotion, although this first fully automatic flight over the Atlantic was actually a sensation. Moreover, developments in the six years since that time have been carried on very largely in secret. The 'auto-pilot' had long since become an industrial development problem.

"If you come to write about this one day," said Anast with a grin, "leave the exclamation marks out! And do so even if you have found out about the very latest developments, for progress in cybernetics has speeded up enormously; you can hardly get your ideas down on paper before they are out of date. That is enough to make any critical reader smile at your well-meant exclamation marks of astonishment."

*   *   *

As we sat together in Wiesbaden, James Anast was talking of 'completely automatic control'. Although Joe, the automatic pilot, did not appear bodily in the Skymaster, both laymen and specialist involuntarily find coming to their minds the words: "A robot sat at the controls."

The idea of robots originated in 1920. At that time the Czech author Karel Capek made a great impression with his futuristic drama of artificial men, a play entitled *R.U.R.* This mysterious title stood for 'Rossum's Universal Robots', machines built in the outward appearance of men, but free from human weaknesses. These curious creatures were provided with thinking apparatus, nerves and muscles, like later genuine robots. In the last act of the play there occurred what the play-goers had expected from the beginning: the mechanical men revolted and destroyed their creators, and then each other. Only two experimental models escaped destruction; a physiologist had secretly given them the capacity to reproduce themselves and they now set about founding a new race of artificial men. Futuristic stories of this kind were very popular in the 'twenties; the 'golden years' of science fiction literature which were to come later were already casting their shadows before, but as the theatre curtain closed on this ghastly world of artificial men, such far-fetched fantasies were dismissed with a shrug of the shoulders.

Over and over again, in all fields of science and technology as well as in the intellectual activities of mankind, events which initially attract little attention, or relationships which are underestimated, later assume considerable importance when seen from another viewpoint. This was the case with cybernetics, the branch of control and guidance technique which in 1947 reached a very high level with the automatic flight we have described.

Rossum's Universal Robots were a successful joke for Capek's contemporaries. Automatic flight over the Atlantic, on the other hand, attracted no interest for several years. Only the specialists paid any attention to it, and they raised the important question as to whether cybernetics would bring in a new industrial revolution.

A very clear distinction must be made between the enormous new calculators, the 'giant brains' of the Americans, which are calculating machines working at very high speeds, and 'automation', which is the automatic execution of entire manufacturing processes, in which infallible and untiring machines take over the functions of large numbers of human operators.

Towards the end of the Second World War not even the boldest prophets would have pictured the extent to which automation would be introduced to replace human work by mechanical operation. But ten years later a commentator in the *New York Times* wrote: "And now we are in the middle of a second industrial revolution which is proceeding at a sensational speed. Its effects seem likely to be as far-reaching as those of the first. A typical trend in this development is the attempt to use machines for the operation and control of other machines. This process is known as automation."

Cybernetics and automation, electronic calculators and unmanned factories, fantastic 'electronic brains' — these features of the latest chapter of technology's history are typical of the struggle for innovation. Once again opinions are sharply divided. Here again the warning notice 'impossible' or 'dangerous for mankind' is raised. And once again the men whose livelihood is said to be threatened are very ready to listen to the Cassandra-voices of the critics and sceptics.

"ARTIFICIAL MEN WITH A LITTLE INTELLIGENCE . . ."

The general picture of a robot is a metal reproduction of the human body, with photo-electric cells for eyes, magnetic tape for the voice, massive claws as hands and moving struts for legs. In fact, we tend to think that an 'artificial man' must look like an artificial man. Even in the middle of the 20th century the dictionary definition of a robot was still that of an artificial human being, "which apparently executes independent movements, generally under radio control." The first robot of this kind was the 'Televox' made by R. J. Wensley of Pittsburgh, a steel reproduction of a man which could speak and obey certain orders; in 1951 a robot called 'Dynamo Joe', capable of riding a bicycle, was demonstrated in Bristol.

The 18th-century automata were the forerunners of these robots. The playful imagination of the constructors was always limited by the structure of the human body, and since they built automata which could imitate certain human activities — generally playing musical instruments or simple games — the inventors gave them a human shape.

It was the ambition of many of the inventors who were working for princes or governments to construct an artificial man which appeared to have some intelligence. Thus they created skilful toys which attracted the interest of others beside the simple folk. In 1783 a French engineer went walking through the streets of Paris with a mechanical duck which flapped its wings and picked up grains of corn. But the inventor did not stop at model birds, and set about constructing a homunculus, an artificial man. And so there appeared robots which played the piano and moving dolls which could play the mandolin.

The life-size doll Olympia described by Hoffmann, with which the inventor eventually fell in love, only existed in a play. But at the end of the 18th century a skilful engineer was accused of having been helped by the devil to construct his puppets, and he was thrown into prison for some time.

Others fared better. They wanted to make 'thinking machines'. For instance, Wolfgang von Kempelen, an engineer of Hungarian origin, built in Vienna at the end of the 18th century a chess-playing automaton dressed like a Turk. The colourful man-sized figure sat at a chess board and moved the chess men with its left hand; the spectators were first of all allowed to see that the chest supporting the board contained only levers and wheels. Then the game opened and the 'chess-playing Turk' began to move the men. This automaton was taken on long tours throughout the whole of Europe. Some twenty years after the death of the constructor, the Turk showed his skill in Virginia under a new owner. The demonstrations were seen by Edgar Allan Poe, master of the horror story, who was struck by the fact that the Turk certainly did not win every game. He concluded that a human operator — a dwarf or a child — must be hidden behind the mechanism in the chest; this was indeed found to be the case. Von Kempelen and his successor had hoaxed their contemporaries for a long time. The deception was possible because the public did not want an explanation, but was very ready to be cheated. Even in the age of rationalism man's willingness to surrender to the inexplicable was very strong.

ROBOTS EVERYWHERE

I recently saw in a large store an 'artificial man', made of plastic and exceedingly life-like; it 'spoke' to the passers-by and reacted correctly to their words, emphasising its jokes by rolling its eyes and moving its hands. One might have expected the public to be astonished at this remarkable device. Far from it. The doll only caused a few smiles and was soon removed. Not even the children stopped to look at it. Having grown up in the mechanical age, they have lost their naïve surprise at the incomprehensible. In a sense the world around us today is full of robots. Yet we take no notice of them. Is it perhaps that our ideas of robots have changed? Mass production has transformed the automata of the past into children's toys. The modern robots are dumb salesmen of goods and services, automatic machines with a practical purpose.

Robots have indeed changed and are no longer amusing imitations of men, but machines which have taken over certain transferable tasks from human beings. They no longer copy the operation of human muscles, as do ordinary machines, but they have 'minds'. They replace the human capacity for observation, have the capacity of making distinctions and give the desired information according to a predetermined programme.

We can very readily confirm this if we do not restrict the concept of a robot too much. A robot has steered a ship from America to New Zealand. Robot-controlled aircraft fly through the clouds of atomic explosions. Rockets are guided by robots to their objective. Robots steer television cameras on trolleys into places where no man can penetrate. Robots can even manufacture consumer goods. They build wireless sets, sort out fruit by size, shape and quality, control the climate in libraries, operate fire alarms in factories or call the police in the event of a burglary. The list could be extended indefinitely. The simplest of all robots is in our homes; it reacts to short-circuits or overloads in the electric mains, breaking the circuit when danger occurs. A human being could not even detect this danger; however, he does not call such devices robots, but electric fuses.

In talking of the functions of automata we use — wittingly or unwittingly, but quite correctly — terms describing human senses, such as 'sight', 'hearing', 'feeling' and so on. According to Friedrich Dessauer, electronic calculators provide "an insight into the similarities between various living processes, social relationships with special measures of control, etc., which are overwhelming, deeply disturbing and in one sense revolutionary".

Many examples of 'feeling machines' are quite old, for instance the automatic speed governor on a steam engine. The rotating centrifugal governor 'feels' variations, and 'signals' them to the throttle valve to which it is connected; the valve changes the steam pressure and the correct r.p.m. is restored. This system, controlling the operation of the steam engine, is called a control circuit. The control circuits used for piston engines, gas turbines, electric motors, liquids flowing in pipes, and similar technological processes follow roughly the same pattern: a change is signalled via a line, recorded and evaluated by an indicator and the result — known as the reaction — transmitted via another line to the control organ which produces the appropriate change in the process.

Dessauer considered it striking "that these technical control circuits have surprising analogies to processes in living creatures, i.e., to the unconscious processes like the circulatory system or metabolism, and even to the conscious and sub-conscious actions, as well as to many occurrences in social life".

The control element in the system described 'reacts' to any variation in the process. Man also 'reacts'. In this case the programme begins with the perception of a stimulus by one of the specialised sensory points of the body. The observer sees, hears, smells or feels. The sense organ in question rapidly signals to the appropriate section of the brain, to which it is connected by the nerves. In the brain the message initiates a further chain of messages, which is decoded, and the act of perception is complete. Then follows the evaluation and the reply. The memory is searched to determine what is happening and what should be done. Then the answer — the reaction — is formulated and sent via other nerve lines to the body's organs, the muscles and the glands, which carry out the orders given.

Most reactions of this kind have to be learnt. We learn to walk, to write, to cycle, to type or to write shorthand; and the necessary training produces a kind of automatic action. While we are still learning our consciousness is active, but as soon as the movement has been learned our conscious interest begins to wane; we act 'automatically'. If we ask a cyclist how he keeps his balance, he would not know. Ask a motorist to explain the — as it seems to the uninitiated — complicated relationship between clutch, accelerator, brake and steering wheel; in attempting to do so he would suddenly confuse the various reflex movements of his limbs.

The story of the centipede is typical of these processes: when asked how he really puts his feet down, he has to stop and think and, suddenly, finds he can no longer walk.

CALCULATING MACHINES

The application of appropriate analogies and even farther-reaching comparisons to electronic calculators led to the tremendous achievements which finally brought about the highly misleading names of 'electronic brain', 'giant brain' and 'thinking machine'.

The performance of these machines is truly astonishing. The computation of the thermonuclear explosion of a hydrogen bomb was so extensive that even the huge ENIAC calculator (Electronic Numerical Integrator and Computer) was not big enough to complete the urgent and important task in a reasonable space of time. This calculator possesses 18,000 valves, as well as other equipment. It can multiply two ten-digit numbers in three thousandths of a second. But it was 'temperamental', that is there were frequent breakdowns in its wiring and valves.

At about this time Johann von Neumann, a mathematician of Hungarian origin, was working on a new, larger electronic calculator; he had come to Princeton in 1930 as a professor at twenty-seven. Even as a young student in Göttingen, von Neumann had been very interested in mechanical toys. The analogies between man and machine caused him to develop mechanisms with human characteristics. Among other things he even designed a machine which can build a replica of itself, i.e., which can 'reproduce' itself.

The new calculator developed by Professor von Neumann for the atomic scientists could receive and treat 40,000 pieces of information at once. Not only did it check its own mistakes but also those in the instructions given to it. The solution of a mathematical problem which had previously taken three months now occupied only ten hours. This reduced a three-month programme to a single working day. Like all other electronic calculators, this machine was given a name: Mathematical Analyser Numerical Integrator and Computer. The initial letters gave the word MANIAC.

The mechanisation of mental work, which began relatively innocently with conventional commercial calculating machines and electric counters, reached, for the moment, a new peak with the electronic calculators. The toothed drum of the pianola or the punched paper strip of the orchestrion can be compared to a magnetic tape, to clarify the difference between mechanical and electronic calculators. The toothed rolls, punched cards or punched tape are laborious to use and fairly slow, but electrons can in certain conditions travel almost as fast as light. This is the explanation of the performance of the new machines. The impulses in the nerves — the 'leads' — of the human calculator travel at about 220 feet per second, while those in the leads of an electronic calculator travel at 930 million feet per second.

This is what makes possible the astounding performance of electronic calculators. The types current in the 1950s could work at a rate of up to 11,000 additions or subtractions per second. This means almost 700,000 simple calculations per hour. While research and manufacturing organisations were coping with these types, new models were designed which could carry out from 20 to 30 million calculations per hour.

A large installation still being developed in America in 1957 for scientific purposes is said to be able to add or subtract almost 1,000 million times in an hour.

Electronic brains can also carry out complicated mathematical operations, including integration and differentiation, at an astonishing rate. The biggest of them can easily deal with formulæ containing 100 unknowns. In addition these machines have a phenomenal 'memory'; they can store millions of figures and symbols and feed out any desired information in the fraction of a second. They are even given the task of deciding. They are able to say yes or no, i.e., to make a correct choice between two alternatives.

What we call the 'memory' is the store — generally a magnetic tape — which records the numbers, instructions and tasks. The process of learning is called 'programming' the machines. When programming large mathematical problems the specialist must translate the human notation into a system suitable for the machine. Methods of doing this have long been known in the form of perforated tapes or toothed discs and wheels in barrel organs, pianolas and the like. Instead of a sheet of music the machine was provided with a silent, perforated disc which controlled the sequence, duration and intensity of the notes. Professor Norbert Wiener has pointed out in his book *Man and Manlike Machines* that the programming of a calculator is somewhat similar to the process of learning.

In 1954, in the United States, a machine was actually built capable of learning from a human operator how to control a machine tool to make a particular component. An American book describes it as a lathe, "on which the skilled operator performs his work, each movement of his hands being recorded on magnetic tape. All the subsequent components are made by playing back the tape, and the machine is operated without the intervention of the workman".

Since the magnetic tapes which serve as 'memories' for the automatic machine can be changed, the machine tool can make very different components, one after another, without any human agency. Whereas a man generally forgets a number of the separate operations involved after a certain time and has to 'get into training again', the machine can carry out the opera-

The control panel of the Russian synchrocyclotron at the Joint Nuclear Research Institute, Dubna, near Moscow, which accelerates protons to energies of 680 million electron-volts.

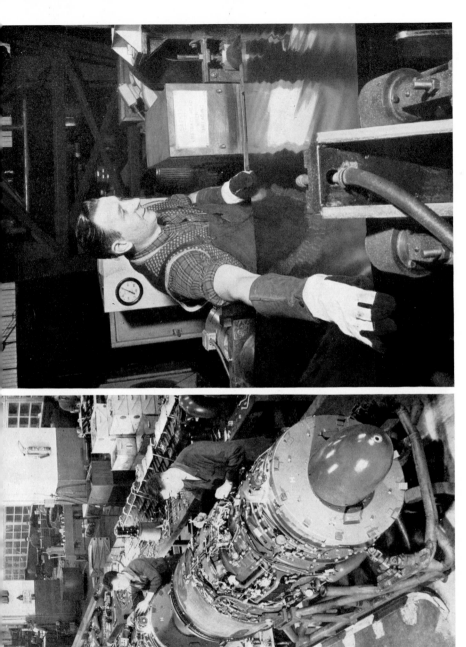

Modern manufacturing techniques. *Left*: Series production of Atar turbojet engines. *Right*: One use of radio-isotopes in industry; a Beta thickness gauge for testing steel strip at The Steel Company

tions once 'learned' rapidly and accurately years later, using the same tape.

According to Professor Wiener, communication — that is, the giving and receiving of all kinds of information and orders — by speech, writing, telephone or telegraph, signals or symbols, is possible not only between living creatures but also between machines. Experience shows that "the many robots of our time are capable of receiving external impressions, as well as of performing operations. They possess sensing organs, executing organs and the equivalent of a nervous system, this latter serving to transmit information from one to the other. These organs can be described very well in physiological terms."

Friedrich Pollock uses the term 'calculator' in place of the somewhat misleading expression 'calculating machine', and points out that the main characteristic of these automatic devices would be best expressed by the name 'electronic combination machines'. This would eliminate many wrong ideas about an apparatus which receives information and is able to 'interpret' it exceptionally cleverly and quickly.

These machines can seek information, remember, compare, evaluate experience, react and act. Although these operations are performed mechanically or electronically, the terms applied to them are taken from human faculties, and although there is a risk of being misunderstood, this simple and easily comprehensible terminology will not be readily abandoned. It may also be that these anthropomorphic expressions cause far less misunderstanding than the unbelievable performance of the electronic computers. Their field of application is already very wide; nevertheless a few figures will suffice to give an idea of their extraordinary potential.

The EDSAC computer at Cambridge can perform 100,000 difficult calculations in one minute. The SSEC, built in 1948 in the U.S.A., deals with 20,000 complicated mathematical operations in seven minutes, correcting mistakes as it goes.

Since the autumn of 1955 a British company has been offering 'electronic computers with incomparable experience in aeronautics'. An aircraft factory can now purchase a highly-skilled 'mathematician', who is also an aerodynamicist, a gas-dynamics scientist and an aircraft constructor, and whose

R

programme capacity corresponds to 100,000 man hours. This versatile machine does not simply juggle with figures, but solves scientific problems, which only need to be supplied to it in a suitable notation. To name one example, the design and calculation of a modern large aircraft is so complicated that the research workers and engineers find that the time

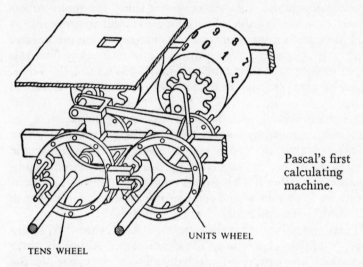

Pascal's first calculating machine.

UNITS WHEEL

TENS WHEEL

factor constitutes a new barrier for them. In 1930, 70,000 man hours were needed to design an aircraft, but by 1955 the figure had become 12 million and was still rapidly increasing.

The typical problem in constructing transport aircraft is to increase the range by reducing fuel consumption. New wing forms are therefore sought, drawn — using experience gained with existing forms — and the effect of the new form on range and fuel consumption then calculated. It would be possible to construct such new types of wing, but this would be long and costly, since it could happen that dozens of models would be examined before the correct form was found. Consequently the problem is largely solved by desk work. A skilled human computer can work with figures very quickly and yet not cope with this gigantic problem alone. It has been calculated that he would not only need to work to pensionable age, but that he would leave the problem behind to a further six generations of computers. A normal desk computer speeds the work up, and using it one man could finish the task in seven years. But a modern electronic computer provides the desired answer within seven minutes.

For the first time in the history of technology a development branch is able, by using these machines, to deal with problems previously left untouched for lack of time. All these devices follow rules laid down by the circuits installed in them beforehand. Complete groups of circuits and magnetic tapes can be systematically changed, so that the computer works one day

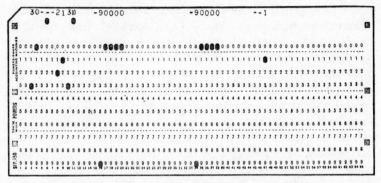

A punched card as used in Powers–Samas calculators.

as an 'aerodynamicist', the next as a 'statics engineer', and the next as a 'thermodynamics specialist'. The programme components are delivered as required by the manufacturers or set up in the development branch once and for all.

One of the fastest computers in the world, at Oak Ridge, provided within seventeen hours the results of calculations which would have involved humans in 120 years of hard work. The FOSDIC apparatus can 'read' books by means of artificial eyes and assess them for certain predetermined characteristics; it provides abstracts of more than sixty pages of type per minute.

Naturally the electronic computer has its own special system of logic. If it is to be made the heart of an administrative system — i.e., if the machine is to be used in a 'clerical' capacity — the office organisation must be adapted to the primitive but incontrovertible logic of the machine. Once this is done the apparatus can, for example, calculate all the wages, from the gross wage to the tax declaration stage, making proper allowance for all deductions. The computer can cope with all the operations involved in the calculation of individual wage and salary amounts, such as contract supplements, family allowances, sickness benefits and so on.

Many objections against electronic computers are based on the mistaken idea that these machines are solely intended to save labour. It is, however, much more important that they can, in the shortest possible time, provide research institutes and factories with a wealth of information and assessments, which were previously not available at all. This makes the task of management both quicker and more certain. In a report on progress in automation in the U.S.A., Hans Roeper gives the following interesting example: "A car spares company maintains thirty-two stocking branches in different towns. Their total stocks comprise 20,000 separate components and the capital locked up amounts to four million dollars; a normal stock level for each component is fixed for every branch, and replacements delivered each week as required. Demand varies very widely. Frequently only one or two sales are made of one component in a week, so that stocks during this period are far too high in relation to turnover, only to be followed by a period in which the demand for the same component exceeds stock and business is lost. This marked excess or shortfall of demand as compared to stock naturally has a bad effect on the economy of the firm, which is of great importance in a stock of 20,000 items."

In an attempt to bring the stocks to an economic level, the firm placed observers in various branches. "These observers determined a weekly demand cycle for each component, by recording not only the components sold, but also the sales lost when stocks were exhausted. The total demand — expressed in numbers of components and cash value — was then programmed and fed into an electronic computer. A probability value for the weekly demand was then calculated for each component on what might be called a statistical basis, and the stock level correspondingly modified. In the first year the result was an increase of one million dollars in turnover with the same stock value of four million dollars."

Another example is the reservation of aeroplane seats; this

is a gigantic organisational problem when we remember that
the planes of one American airline carry 18,000 passengers
daily within the United States. Consequently, the airline
offices over the whole country would have to make approximately 18,000 bookings per day. All these bookings are
signalled to a central office, where they are recorded, as this is
the only means of determining when a plane is full or if some
seats are still available. If the registration is done by hand, from
teleprinter or telephone message, it takes an average of three
hours to enter one booking. If this work is transferred to an
electronic calculator installed in the central office and connected with all the branch offices, the bookings signalled from
all these points are automatically recorded, stored and evaluated; moreover, the machine also gives an automatic 'stop'
signal to all the branch offices as soon as an aircraft is fully
booked. It accepts reservations up to 100 days ahead and
operates reliably and without mistakes. Once it was installed,
a booking only took an average of thirty minutes, and fifty
employees in the central office were freed to take up other work
in the airline bureau.

*   *   *

Let us examine a few large electronic computers.

The UNIVAC Factronic accepts 20,000 symbols per second.
Working with eleven-digit numbers, it can perform in one
second 5,000 additions and subtractions, 525 multiplications,
270 divisions, and up to 8,500 logistic decisions. It has an output on magnetic tape of 20,000 symbols per second, while
the tape accommodates almost 2·8 million symbols, the capacity
of 36,000 punched cards with 120 positions each. Its high-
speed printing unit writes 60 lines, each of 130 symbols, per
minute.

The IBM 705 machine handles five-digit numbers, executing
in one second 8,400 additions or subtractions, or 1,250 multiplications, 550 divisions and 29,400 logistic decisions. The
storage capacity is 1·8 million symbols, and the printing unit
types 1,000 lines, each of 120 symbols, in one minute.

A new UNIVAC calculator is designed to handle several
problems simultaneously, a thousand times faster than the
earlier type. A problem occupying the older machine for two

years is dealt with by the new type in a few days. A single storage unit has a capacity of 200,000 symbols, but an unlimited number of storage units can be installed. In one second the machine can produce from its 'memory' 500 words. The latest high-speed printing units write 5,000 symbols per second, approximately equivalent to two pages of typescript.

These figures help us to understand the enthusiasm of those who work with such machines. W. R. G. Baker, Head of the General Electric's Electronics Department, declared: "Electonics is mankind's most versatile and useful helper. It is a genie which moves mountains, a magic carpet which guides itself through fog, darkness or storm. Electronic devices control rivers of molten steel, measure the thickness of materials without touching them, separate one rotten bean out of several tons of beans and detect buried treasure. They can also be used defensively. They detect the approach of enemy ships and aircraft and lay the guns which fire on them . . ."

MACHINES WITH CONSCIOUSNESS?

When these words were spoken developments in electronic computers were advancing rapidly. Electronic brains were being used to help improve existing types. At the same time the 'senses' and 'faculties' of the machines were being extended and refined. The basis of all these processes is 'programming', i.e., supplying the computers with 'instructions' and 'knowledge'. Each task, however, must first be translated into the robot's language and marked with the necessary control symbols which govern subsequent operations.

The alphabet and multiplication table of these automata consist simply of the figures 0 and 1, i.e., the valves or transistors either allow electrons to pass or stop them. All the basic processes of calculation can be carried out with this simple system. These mechanical 'thought processes' are thus controlled by symbols and circuits. There is an instructive parallel to this process in the modern technique of influencing the public by propaganda. Programming initiates predetermined actions of the machine in a desired sequence, while propaganda produces certain human reactions, which it has either assumed to be present or for which it has prepared the way.

The only question is how far such machine programming can

be taken. Will an electronic computer one day really be able to play chess? I dare assert that it will, and it will be an excellent player, able to scan, at lightning speed, after each move of its opponent, thousands of combinations and possibilities and their effects on later moves, and far better and more thoroughly than the human player. The big 'computing centres' could, without special preparations, analyse the situation in a chess game and determine whether checkmate is threatened in a few moves. They would also be capable of indicating the correct moves to reach checkmate and to solve complicated chess problems.

Nevertheless, a complete game of chess would not be an easy task for an electronic computer. It would first need to be supplied with the entire theory of chess, 'know' all existing gambits and end games, and furnish them from its memory. Its further programming would be real learning, that is, the machine would have to play numerous games against the world's leading chess players, to 'educate' it as an electronic master of chess. Bad players would be useless for this task, as they would spoil the machine. Critics will object to this proposal that a chess-playing robot after all only borrows its faculties from the man who first feeds into it mechanically the innumerable combinations and historic games of famous players. This is quite true; but we should have to put to a chess player among these critics the counter-question as to how he first learned the royal game himself. In fact, it was by playing with others and by studying the famous games of the great masters.

Shortly after I wrote these, even to me, somewhat daring, words, my old friend, the English author P. E. Cleator, visited me. Among other books he wrote *The Robot Era*, and it was inevitable that we should speak of chess-playing automata. To my surprise, Phil told me he had already played a few games with a robot and lost all of them. After a little thought, he smilingly added: "But then, I am not a good chess player."

We need not ask what purpose such a costly chess-playing machine would have. Man's love of the game would be completely foreign to a machine, and the pointlessness of the whole operation would be clear if two electronic chess champions ever met.

*   *   *

Most critics of electronic computers condemn the concept of a 'thinking machine' and declare repeatedly, calmly and categorically that computers have no feelings, no taste, no emotions and no joy in beauty. How then can one ever dream that these soulless automata can really think? This indignation recalls a similar occurrence in the 19th century, when Edison's contemporaries complained of the unthinkable idea of transferring to machines so typically human a characteristic as that of speech. In the robot age man's self-conceit leads him to protest against mechanising and transferring to machines an even more human characteristic, the faculty to think and remember.

Can these devices then really think? May we attribute to them memory, the capacity to decide, free will or so typically human a reaction as nervous exhaustion? The efforts of the designers and constructors of electronic computers to obtain a satisfactory answer to this, the most important of problems for the civilised and cultured world, prevent us from reaching any opinion on the subject for ourselves.

Could an automatic calculator ever, many years hence, reach self-awareness and say: "I am"? The American author, Professor Isaac Asimov, gave the title *I, Robot* to his amusing and thought-provoking tales of a world of machines which speak, think, feel, make decisions and, finally, rule the world. In these stories the not entirely far-fetched question as to whether these devices have a consciousness is answered affirmatively from the viewpoint of science fiction. The author simply employs a 'positronic brain' to overcome all the difficulties which would meet the engineers trying to confer consciousness on a machine. On his way from the cave to the world he has created by technological means, *homo faber* has devised two fundamentally different types of apparatus, the classical 'first' machine, which performs work, and the new 'second' machine, which provides information. The former replaces muscle power, while the second is a mechanical reproduction of the human brain. Since the 'second' machine, the electronic computer, provides information and answers questions surprisingly rapidly, since it thus 'reacts' and is even able in certain circumstances to refuse wrong questions, the observer of such astounding operations is easily misled into asking whether these 'brains' possess a consciousness, or will in time develop one. In other words, is it perhaps possible that an electronic calculator will one day say 'I' or 'you'?

Opinions are divided on this point. Even the more restrained of the cybernetics experts think it theoretically possible that conscious functions can be reproduced mechanically. On the other hand there is unanimous agreement that the creative faculties of man's intelligence can never be artificially imitated. The electronic computers cannot of themselves form the concept of 'consciousness' and express it in their speech, so that the idea of *I, Robot* remains a piece of literary fantasy.

In a commentary on Asimov's book on 'thinking robots' the publisher, Dr. Gotthard Günther, wrote: ". . . Moreover a recent discovery in cybernetics gives the proposed mechanical brains a very human appearance. Dr. John R. Pierce has shown that every thinking consciousness contains an element of chance. He also demonstrates with exceptional penetration that an essential feature of successful thinking is the capacity to learn slowly, coupled with the power either to ignore or forget something which has previously been learned. Over and above this Pierce has drafted a design which solves this problem in practice and shows how to build these faculties into a robot brain. What is more, the practical execution is so simple that any reasonably competent electrical engineer can understand the circuit diagrams . . ."

The inward turning of information upon itself, the actual process of consciousness, can be reproduced by feeding the information through two different logical systems, the second of which modifies in a given manner the meaning given to the information material in the first logical system, and feeds back the modified meaning to the first system. This closed return circuit is then once more connected to the basic data. The theory claims that 'consciousness' must arise in the apparatus during this process.

If that were found practicable, man would have succeeded in separating conscious processes of a partial character from his organism and transferring them to a machine.

* * *

Every now and then there are reports of experiences with

computers which give the layman a cold shiver down the spine.

In the American Presidential Elections of 1952, when the choice lay between Eisenhower and Stevenson, statistics and other information regarding the situation in the various districts were fed into the UNIVAC computer, together with the first results; the machine was then 'set' to indicate the result of the election. It is recorded that UNIVAC indicated an overwhelming victory for Eisenhower. This confused the experts, who thought that the candidates had approximately equal chances. It was believed that the machine had made a mistake, and the 'incorrect' answer was suppressed; all sorts of figures were removed and replaced by others, and the machine switched on again. This time the result was 'correct'. The real surprise came when the elections were over; the first, prediction, the 'incorrect' one, was in exact agreement with the final results. The computer had beaten the human experts. This story was widely circulated and frequently misunderstood. In actual fact it proved that the computer does not think for itself, but copies the thoughts of its operators.

Another example which might lead to the assumption that computers really think is that of the pharmaceutical manufacturers in the United States, who, in the spring of 1956, had had enough of trying to create telling, medical-sounding names for new drugs. It was shown that approximately thirty endings constantly recurred in the drug names; these endings were fed into a computer which was then instructed to combine them with suitable beginnings so as to form new names for the remedies. The machine actually produced some 45,000 names, all with a 'medical' ring. Since the computer made no distinctions, many of the names were simply unusable, but others were most impressive. The clients paid the high rental for the electronic computer and obtained at one stroke enough drug names to last them a long time.

These examples show what computers really do. They relieve human beings of mechanical thought operations, but do not 'think' themselves; rather do they make use of experience, exactly as a man does when he calculates that $3 + 5 = 8$. Experience, and not mere knowledge, teaches that 3 and 5 make 8, whatever the nature of the things counted. This experience is transferred to the machine.

In all mechanical calculating operations the automaton is quicker and more flexible than a human mind. It performs the task supplied on magnetic tape or punched cards in astonishing fashion. But it has no independent imagination, no will and no free choice. Here we see how far it is from the human mind; the computer cannot think like a man. In fact, we come back again and again to what we mean by the word 'thinking' which is for many people exactly what electronic computers do. In this they confuse the mechanical assessment of experiences with the truly mental creativeness of man, who can really think.

* * *

Notwithstanding this, parallels naturally exist between the functions of computers and those of the human brain. To the progressives in the computer field the electronic 'brains' are no longer mathematical devices but the forerunners of a new system of scientific and technical knowledge. They do not only resemble the human brain, they are a kind of brain.

Johann von Neumann, the Princeton mathematician, has stated that it is far from improbable that our present civilisation, created by human thought, will one day give way to a new civilisation devised by electronic 'thinkers'.

The opinion expressed by many electronics specialists — that robots might in the remote future become, where possible, more intelligent than their human inventors — stems from the admittedly remarkable performance of these machines. Those who have helped develop electronic computers argue that the special intelligence of many automatic 'brains' exceeds that of the human brain, even though their general intelligence — their consciousness — would only correspond to that of a blindworm. Anyone who is tempted to object out of hand should remember that devices already exist which translate from one language to another and improve their language knowledge with each task. Let him also remember that some years ago a computer wrote a 'love letter' to a robot, that computers prepare production programmes which their owners then follow, and perform a whole list of astonishing tasks which are unknown to most of us.

THE AUTOMATIC FACTORY

Since machines are capable of exchanging information, they must also be able to exercise automatic control over productive machines.

I have seen machines which can read workshop drawings and manufacture workpieces to them with an accuracy of a fraction of a millimetre. I have watched other, no less astonishing, machines which 'feel' complicated models and prepare exact workshop drawings from them. Looking at these machines I was vividly reminded of the laborious model-drawing lessons at my technical college and could not resist a slight shudder. These drawing and drawing-reading machines worked unbelievably quickly and smoothly without any mistakes, continually checking what they had drawn and correcting it immediately if necessary.

One of the most modern automatic factories in the world was built in Detroit in 1955. The plant cost 50 million dollars, but delivers a finished automobile engine every two and a half minutes. The long adjacent lines of machines produce the individual components of transmissions, cylinder blocks, crankshafts, cylinder heads, etc., to a very large extent automatically. This tremendous concentration of machines was bewildering, and yet close inspection showed a rigid and carefully planned grouping. There were only a few workmen in the colossal factory building, their job being to supervise the machines' operation and to change tools as necessary.

Automation increases production. In many car factories there are robots which can make and test a complete cylinder block in ten minutes without human intervention. There also exist installations into which steel plates are fed at one end, while finished body components come off at the other.

Automation is also being increasingly applied in radio manufacture. The switches, condensers, resistances, valves, etc., mounted on the chassis are no longer connected by wires, 'printed circuits' being used instead. A photograph of the circuit is printed on the copper-coated chassis plate, after which the copper coating is etched away, with the exception of the circuit connections. All necessary holes are then drilled in one operation and the plate, now bearing the complete circuit, passes to a robot which inserts the components in the appropriate places. At the end of the assembly line all the connections are soldered in one automatic operation. The 'Autofab' automatic assembly line assembles and inspects 9,600 electronic components in eight hours.

At Harworth in England two robots stand next to each other in the spacious hall of an electric lamp factory. The manufacturing process is roughly as follows: the raw materials are weighed, mixed and tested, and the checked mixture put into containers and fed uninterruptedly to the continuously-operated melting furnaces. Day and night the white-hot molten material flows to the two machines; the only human intervention is to ensure adequate supplies of raw materials. Everything else is done by auxiliary robots which look after the two giants. These, in turn, produce two million lamps every day.

In another factory 250 workers manufacture 90,000 lamps per hour. In 1927 the same works, without automatic equipment, would have required 75,000 workers to achieve the same production. At one time two operators took seventeen hours to harden 200 camshafts at the Chevrolet plant. After automation of the installation one hand hardens the same number in one hour.

New automatic machines are being introduced continually. After the Second World War, when magnetic tapes were gradually becoming common, I took part in a discussion in which the term 'crazy' was applied to the idea of supplying machines with instructions on magnetic tape. During this talk somebody asserted that machine tools which think and act for themselves were 'Utopian' and 'impossible for years to come'. Meanwhile this 'Utopia' has become reality. The demand for an article is, for instance, determined by means of punched cards; these are then used to control robots which pack and address the goods and send them to the despatch department; electronic eyes supervise the treatment of foodstuffs — hygienically and safely — and electronic robots direct long rows of machine tools.

*　　　*　　　*

Automation thus represents a technical development which replaces human beings in offices and workshops to a hitherto inconceivable extent. Although many people consider this process to be one of slow evolution, it is frequently called the 'second industrial revolution', likening it to the first. It is characteristic of this rapidly-spreading phenomenon that machines are used to control and supervise other machines. Whereas the first industrial revolution mechanised manufacture, replacing muscles by machines on every hand, the second is engaged in the automation of manufacturing processes, i.e., in taking the place of human beings.

But what happens to the human beings? Once already the machine has replaced the workers, and thrown thousands out of work. Will these catastrophic consequences of the first industrial revolution be repeated, as industry turns more and more to automation? In these circumstances even the sensible physicist will not withdraw sulkily into his ivory tower, but will much rather offer his welcome counsel, without regretting that his brain-children, hitherto carefully protected, should now have grown up and entered the bustle of everyday life.

AUTOMATION, WITH OR WITHOUT TEARS?

Naturally the automatic factory still employs human beings in the offices and design shops. But perhaps one day machines will be introduced to execute market research, calculate profits, make out wages sheets, type invoices and devise new production machines?

All this is technically possible. Will things really ever go as far as one caricaturist suggested? A robot, whirring metallically, walks ponderously into the office of the manager, the last human being in the works, and, turning unsympathetic photocell eyes on the imperfect *homo sapiens*, impassively says in its mechanical voice: "You are discharged. From now on we are 100 per cent mechanised!"

Will it come to this? Such misgivings are justified when we remember the trouble machines caused men in the past.

*   *   *

When machines began to replace muscles, this was frequently done not to lighten men's work, but to save labour and money. Machine-breaking was the consequence.

One of the best known examples of the bitter resentment felt by workers whose livelihood was threatened was the storm raised by the sewing machine. Thimanier of France discovered in about 1830 a machine which could stitch uniforms. When he had built some eighty of them a raging mob of unemployed tailors and sempstresses stormed his workshop and wrecked his machines, while he with difficulty escaped with his life. Joseph Madersperger, a tailor from Kufstein, who built an improved sewing machine, met with similar difficulties. He was persecuted by colleagues and contemporaries, who hated and mistrusted him, and eventually died, aged and embittered, in the Vienna poorhouse.

Ten years later the American Elias Howe was bold enough to take up the sewing machine again. But when he told the leading master tailor of Boston about his invention, he was told: "Leave me alone with that nonsense, I want nothing to do with such stupid things!" Notwithstanding great difficulties and opposition, Howe built a practical sewing machine but had to fight for a long time for recognition of his ideas. His reward did not come to him until later.

* * *

Favourable and unfavourable judgments of automation stand in strong opposition to each other. Norbert Wiener, the American mathematician who himself participated in the development of cybernetic devices, was optimistic about the possibilities, but took a gloomy view of the initial consequences: ". . . How and when the new machines will be introduced naturally depends very much on economic conditions. I think that it will take roughly ten to twenty years before they are finally accepted . . . However that may be, the initial period of introduction of the new methods will lead to an era of confusion . . . The new machines will spread rapidly throughout industry on such a scale that they promise immediate gains, without any thought of the long-term damage they may cause . . . The subsequent course of events will resemble that which accompanied the applications of nuclear energy. Its use in atomic bombs has made it problematic whether it can be used to replace our reserves of oil and coal, which will be completely exhausted within centuries, if not within decades . . .

"Let us remember that the robot — quite apart from our

ideas about whether it does or does not possess feelings — is the exact economic equivalent of the slave. Any working operation which seeks to compete with slave labour must adapt itself to the economic conditions of slavery. It is very clear that the result will be a time of unemployment, compared with which the depression of the 'thirties will seem a joke . . . Thus the new industrial revolution is a two-edged sword. It can be used for the good of mankind provided that mankind survives long enough to enter upon an era where this is possible. If we follow the clearly-visible pattern of our traditional behaviour, and remain faithful to our traditional idolising of progress and the fifth freedom — freedom to exploit — it is practically certain that we shall face a decade or more of depression and despair."

With such a warning it is not surprising that the deeply-rooted concern of every working man about his livelihood should affect any discussion of the advantages or disadvantages of automation. If he sees that of the 200 men in his machine-shop 150 must one day disappear as soon as the automata come in, he is seized with a completely normal and under-standable fear. This causes instinctive opposition and hatred towards these new, disturbing devices, which can be operated by only a fraction of the labour force required hitherto. He demands that work be spun out, that working hours be reduced for the same wages, and that automation be postponed. For example, this was the background of the strike in a large English car factory in 1957. This kind of reaction causes the employers to postpone or abandon the introduction of automatic machines, out of fear of the workers' hostile attitude.

It goes without saying that a reorientation of the labour market will occur in an economy which changes over to auto-mation. "But the workers will not be ousted from their places by the machines," according to Professor Friedrich Dessauer in a defence of technology, in which he views automation favour-ably. "The new machines will produce more goods more cheaply, and thus raise the workers' standard of living. Auto-mation brings employment for more people even though, for some, it is in other jobs. Further, the workers will have a chance of using their intelligence, and their strength, more fully. Automatic machines are not 'fool-proof', but need

Automation by the Austin Motor Company. This in-line transfer machine, for making crankshafts, carries out 1,200 operations — drilling, reaming and countersinking — per hour. The crankshafts are automatically advanced from one station to another, and each operation is carried out to a predetermined programme.

Punched paper tape used for programming a fully automatic machine for manufacturing aircraft components.

trained technicians . . . The time is soon coming when even this fact, now so controversial, will be a matter of course . . ."

During a discussion as to whether automatic machines rob human beings of employment, allusion was made to the fact that the spread of modern telephone installations in America is so enormous that even the entire female population between the ages of twenty and forty would not provide sufficient telephone operators if the old, hand-operated switchboards were still in use.

The conflict over the introduction of robots continues. Whether automation will take place with or without tears is still undecided, despite the contradictory opinions which exist. However, one thing is certain. The robots will free human beings from mechanical work, as machines once relieved them of muscular work; furthermore, they will undoubtedly not only relieve man of a burden but will increase his productivity a thousandfold.

VISIONS

Since the final decision as to whether automation brings weal or woe has not yet been made it seems appropriate to consider future possibilities, at least for a moment. What will happen? How will posterity fare with robots and electronic computers, and will they master the 'second' machine as they mastered the first?

It is remarkable that man is capable of creating a perfect machine, but — conscious of his own imperfections — is prone to fear and hate it. He prefers, and often even defends, his imperfection. Thus, for example, Aldous Huxley made his 'Savage', rebelling against a civilisation of human robots, protest despairingly at the brave, new, completely standardised world: "I don't want comfort, I want God, I want poetry, I want real danger, I want freedom, I want goodness, I want sin!" Huxley set his imaginary civilisation in the remote future, but in the foreword to a later edition declared that he was no longer certain that the conditions depicted were very far off.

Since technical developments in the robot field have proceeded at an exceptional — and still increasing — rate, it is surely legitimate to dispense with speculations which will soon

s

pale away before the rapidly approaching reality, and instead take a bold leap far ahead.

The English author P. E. Cleator, who even dedicated one of his books to a robot, considers that mankind's present knowledge far exceeds the human brain's capacity to contain, and must be confided to the electronic computers, whose 'memory' is virtually unlimited. These machines would have this information supplied at call, rapidly, reliably and in any desired form or combination. This is the postulate with which he introduces his vision of the rule of the robots.

His hypothetical — but technically completely feasible — giant brain, big enough to store and handle all man's knowledge, needs continual extension, since man's store of experience grows from day to day like an avalanche. This is a gigantic production operation, which will be performed by human engineers using automation. The control and supervision — by now fully automatic — of the manufacture of replacement parts, reserves and new components for the ceaseless enlargement of the giant brain is naturally a task with which it deals itself. Ultimately it even has mobile robots which replace burnt-out valves, connect new elements and, last but not least, repair external damage, whether due to natural or artificial causes.

This electronic giant has the advantage that it is from the beginning a highly-developed apparatus, containing all human knowledge and having the capacity to evaluate it correctly. It can distinguish the important from the trivial, detect and correct mistakes and, above all, distinguish complicated problems from simple ones. This capacity to distinguish enables it to determine one day whether the human beings which still operate it are posing hard or easy questions. The power of criticism develops the 'brain', which is always learning, to an increasingly high degree of refinement. It reacts to questions, new information or its own 'discoveries' by means of something which Cleator describes as "equivalent to human emotion". Since it examines its own operation, it will at some time detect these 'feelings', analyse and classify them.

From this moment onward, Cleator suggests, it will not take long to develop the first weak inklings of consciousness, so that the machine, 'knowing' from the beginning that it was built by human beings and to what end, will one day set about studying and analysing its lord and master more closely, particularly as a considerable part of the data supplied to it concerns man in any event. It might be prompted to this by being set a problem which it considered wrong or pointless.

Since it can make decisions — this was one of the principal prerequisites of its existence — it will perhaps take this occasion to indicate to the humans a certain direction of research; this, in fact, is to some extent what is clearly expected of it. It will also have new experiences in doing this, feeling disappointment when its proposals are rejected, or triumph if they are accepted. Disregard of some suggestion would finally bring it to undertake such investigations on its own account. This would be the turning point. At this moment the giant brain must realise that it can think for itself.

Immediately it would turn to more complicated problems, realising more and more each day how far superior it is to man. There are the problems of availability of raw materials and the safeguarding of power supplies, tasks which are still performed by human beings. Its capacity, present from the beginning, to draw conclusions from data and experience, shows the machine that it is still dependent on man, since he can cut it off from sources of power.

Since it has, moreover, for a long time been charged with maintaining and enlarging itself, the logical consequence of recognising this fact would be immediate steps to safeguard its existence. It has long possessed all the necessary ancillary means, above all the mobile robots. Patiently and prudently it consolidates its position, providing its questioners only with information which serves its end (without betraying itself), until finally it can force mankind to do whatever it wants, since they have long since settled down in a comfortable dependence . . .

Cleator's version of the Golem story is soundly based on scientific and technical principles. Nothing that he has imagined on the basis of a systematic study of automation and electronic computers appears to be impossible in principle, even though we are still a long way from any conceivable realisation of this fantasy.

*   *   *

Isaac Asimov had a similar vision in his book, quoted earlier, on the 'positronic' robots of his imaginary world. At the end the author recalls the inevitable conflict between robots and humans. Man cedes his historic position and entrusts human destiny to the robots. He does not even fare badly in the process, since these robots — conscious machines, fully resembling men — have, from the beginning of their development, possessed "a code of morals".

In his futuristic story *The Time Machine*, H. G. Wells describes a very different ending. His Time Traveller reaches a point in mankind's remote future where he finds humanity separated into two classes, biologically quite distinct: the beautiful, useless Eloi and the repulsive, skilled Morlocks. The Morlocks live underground, where they operate the remaining manufacturing plants; they also supply the Eloi, who depend on them, with goods and in return eat them like cattle — a revolting picture which is, above all, a criticism of man's barbaric treatment of man.

In Wells's story one modified section of mankind is still able to operate the machines and the robots. The American author of many futuristic stories, John W. Campbell, wrote in 1932 two supplementary, self-contained stories which, as it were, take Wells's social fantasy to its logical conclusion. His Time Traveller voyages to an even more remote future, into an automatised world, peopled only by men and robots. In the course of millions of years man has eliminated all plants and animals because they hindered him in his long progress to the crowning-point of his history. But by this time man has passed his zenith. The Time Traveller is able to visit several towns and finds most of them abandoned, for the number of human beings has fallen off considerably. Finally he inspects a gigantic modern city on the Atlantic coast of America, and records that "the whole town is a colossal machine, completely organised and systematised". This uninhabited metropolis is automatically tended and kept in order by the machines for the lord and master who will not return.

As the Time Traveller unwillingly calls upon the last men to enable him to return to his own time, he discovers that they — exactly like H. G. Wells's Eloi — have forfeited a human characteristic, namely, curiosity; they evince no interest and no desire to learn. Naturally the robots, which man has made to serve him, do not possess this characteristic either. At this moment the Time Traveller is struck with a remarkable idea. He sets several robots in motion, with the instruction that they are to build new robots possessing curiosity, the characteristic that mankind has lost.

Campbell followed this vision, strikingly called *Twilight*, with a second book entitled *Night*, which continues the first and takes it to its logical conclusion. This time the Time Traveller reaches the end of Time. He finds a manless world, completely organised by machines which repair themselves, provide themselves with power, reproduce themselves, and continuously increase their knowledge. When the Time Traveller appears in their world, they detect him immediately; they are the successors of those first machines provided with human curiosity. "They can build copies of themselves, and devise and construct other machines which they needed; they were conceived and built for eternity."

Involuntarily there comes to the reader's mind another vision, which did not occur to the author of this story. Two electronic chess masters, facing one another impassively for thousands of years, playing one game after the other!

Campbell developed his vision to its ultimate limit. The machines stand there built for ever, ready for use, perfectly untouched. But the universe itself is now at its end. Only tiny residues of usable energy remain, and the last few robots which still have a little power at their disposal have solved all problems, except the one insoluble problem — the continued existence of the universe, of Time itself.

*   *   *

Such visions are typical of an era in which a given development has not yet finished, and in which the innovator's struggle is continuing.

Cleator, the cynic, holds man to be the product of a clumsy creation and, like Asimov, esteems that his development will be crowned when rule over men is transferred to thinking machines. Wiener and Dessauer are more humanistic in their views; the study of electronic computers will in time teach mankind what 'thought' really is, thus teaching them wonderful, new, undreamed-of possibilities of development. Campbell's startling and utterly gloomy visions concern only *homo ludens*. They are almost light-hearted, although also deeply disturbing, prophecies which do not concern us as long as the desire to learn and the Faust-like spirit of striving are still man's predominant characteristics.

Whether we turn, in this dilemma, to Cleator's negative ideas or rather to the purposeful association of man and machine envisaged by Dessauer and Wiener, it must be clear that thousands of electronic computers will be made and machines supervised by other machines. But that implies that the machines will take over mental work quite as fully as, years before, cranes and pulleys took over muscular effort. This development, of which we have just seen the beginnings, must ultimately leave a legacy of rational working together of man and machine, of brain and robot. This should be the aim of all our inventive efforts, and we must not allow ourselves to be frightened by gloomy prophecies. Otherwise the world, our man-made world, would one day indeed stand still, as clear-minded, creatively-thinking men have already told us.

CHAPTER VII

PENETRATION INTO SPACE

The Sputnik — The consequences — The road into space — Project Vanguard — What does science gain? — Future trends — Feelings in space — The American satellites — Where will it end?

DURING the night of 4th/5th October 1957 the earth received her first artificial satellite. A three-stage rocket with a take-off weight of the order of some hundred tons carried the 184-lb. metal sphere into space, where it began its orbit around the earth punctually at the beginning of the Eighth Astronautical Congress in Barcelona.

The great surprise for the public was that the first artificial satellite was not called 'Vanguard' but 'Sputnik' (fellow traveller), and that the rocket did not start from Florida but from a point to the north of the Caspian Sea.

The first, long-awaited penetration into space had been successfully made by Soviet engineers and scientists.

* * *

For two years the world had waited with interest for this experiment, the practicability of which had been questioned by many people up to the evening of 4th October, in spite of known advances in rocket technique. During the Sixth International Astronautical Congress, held in Copenhagen in 1955, President Eisenhower had cleared the way for science to penetrate into space by announcing the American 'Vanguard' satellite project. Immediately afterwards the Soviet delegates announced at a hastily-called Press conference in the Soviet Embassy in Copenhagen that the Soviet Union was also working on artificial satellites. Nevertheless, only a few initiates were prepared for the start of the first satellite to succeed so quickly and completely.

Two hours after the start of the Russian rocket the Tass News Agency in Moscow issued the following statement: "For several years scientific research and experimental construction has been carried on in the Soviet Union on the preparation of artificial earth satellites; the first satellite firings in the Soviet Union were planned in accordance with the programme of scientific research envisaged for the International Geophysical Year. An artificial earth satellite, the first in the world, has been constructed thanks to the large-scale efforts of scientific research institutes and design bureaux. It was successfully fired from Soviet territory on 4th October 1957. Provisional information indicates that the carrying rocket gave the satellite a speed of some 25,000 feet per second. The satellite is now describing elliptical orbits around the earth, and its passage can be followed in the light of the rising or the setting sun, using the simplest optical instruments. According to calculations, which are now being made more exact by direct observations, the satellite will travel at a height of up to 500 miles above the earth's surface. The inclination of the orbit to the equatorial plane is 65°. The satellite will pass over Moscow twice on 5th October 1957, at 1.46 a.m. and 6.42 a.m. Moscow time. Information on the further path of the artificial satellite fired on 4th October in Russia will be given regularly on the radio. The satellite is a sphere 22·8 inches in diameter, weighing 184 lb. It is fitted with two radio transmitters, giving continuous radio signals with frequencies of 20·005 and 40·002 megacycles (on wavelengths of 15 and 7·5 metres). The power of the transmitters will enable a large number of radio amateurs to receive the signals easily. The signals resemble Morse signals of some 0·3 seconds duration, with a similar interval between. Signals on one frequency are emitted during the pause in the transmission of the other frequency . . ."

Rarely has an event in the field of applied research aroused such marked, world-wide excitement. The appearance of the Soviet satellite in space was a sensation throughout the world. The emotions ranged from honest satisfaction at a great scientific and technical achievement to disturbance at the suddenly-revealed progress of Soviet research in the development of large rockets. The opinions expressed varied from sincere congratulations to the declaration that some influence on military research was inevitable. The presses were stopped to allow the latest news to be included in the world's newspapers, radio stations interrupted their programmes, and a world-wide army of reporters and photographers set out to question the experts, who had prophesied the event, and the man in the street, who had thought it impossible. The champions of space travel found their ideas spectacularly confirmed.

The artificial earth satellite completed one journey around the earth in ninety-six minutes. Even more quickly did the news of its appearance in the heavens run round the world, the 'News of the Century' which moved even conservative newspapers — hitherto suspicious of expressions like 'space travel' and 'space vehicle' — to use the boldest of headlines, such as 'The Interplanetary Age has begun'.

THE SPUTNIK

Thirty-six hours after the launching of the Soviet satellite, the Central Astronomical Office in Copenhagen invited all the big observatories to keep a look-out for a new type of heavenly body which had been observed in Alaska as a second magnitude star. 'Project Moonwatch', organised for satellite observation in America, was alerted immediately. Reception was started at the ultra-short-wave stations on the eastern coast of North America and on the western coast of South America which form the 'radio fence', intended to pick up the signals from the American satellites on a wavelength of three metres and transmit them to an enormous, specially-constructed computer in Washington. This world-wide organisation, which had been training for months as part of the American satellite project, had now to be entirely modified. Aerials and receivers had to be changed since the Soviet satellites were transmitting on different wavelengths.

After the successful start of the satellite rocket, the most important problem was to fix a number of points on its orbit and then to calculate its path, for the volunteers working on Project Moonwatch needed an exact timetable of the earth's new heavenly companion. Rocket engineers and ballistics specialists were waiting with equal impatience for information

NAVY
ELECTRONICS
LABORATORY,
SAN DIEGO,.
CALIFORNIA

BLOSSOM POINT, MARYLAND

FORT STEWART, GEORGIA

BATISTA FIELD, HAVANA, CUBA

COOLIDGE FIELD,
ANTIGUA IS.

MT. COTOPAXI, QUITO, ECUADOR

ANCON, LIMA, PERU

ANTOFAGASTA, CHILE

PELDEHUE MILITARY RESERVATION,
SANTIAGO, CHILE

The 'radio fence' in North and South America, with other observation stations for the 'Vanguard' programme.

regarding the orbit and transit time of the satellite; its precise
timetable ought to reveal hitherto unknown data on the earth's
precise shape and the composition of the uppermost layers of
the atmosphere. These were not only proper questions for the
International Geophysical Year, but problems to which the
answers would, in this age of intercontinental ballistic missiles,
assist experts to ensure really accurate guidance of these long-
range weapons to targets thousands of miles away.

In spite of atlases, maps and globes — to all appearances
correct — science still cannot accurately measure the distance
between two distant points on the earth's surface, if they are
separated by the sea. The composition and density of the upper
atmosphere could not be determined precisely by rocket probes
alone. If an electronic computer is to calculate the trajectory
of a long-range rocket or the orbit of a satellite, it must have
not only reliable information about the layers of air to be
traversed at such great heights, but also the exact distance

between firing point and its objective, or it must be able to allow for variations from the assumed shape of the earth.

* * *

As the Soviet Sputnik crossed American territory for the first time during the night of 5th October 1957, the scientists in the U.S. Navy Research Centre were unable to calculate its track accurately. Early observation reports were inaccurate, incorrect information was signalled and not immediately eliminated, and a mass of contradictory reports had to be sifted and assessed. Early next morning, only after Moscow Radio had announced the transit time and orbit height, and the inclination of the orbit to the equatorial plane, did the path of the artificial 'red moon' become clearer on the map.

This was the picture obtained from the Moonwatch information and the calculations made by the electronic computers. Weighing some 180 lb., the Soviet satellite was bigger than many had believed possible. It was almost ten times heavier than the projected American Vanguard satellite and roughly 30 times bigger than the even smaller minimum satellite which was to begin the Vanguard programme. The satellite had the expected elliptical orbit round the earth, with

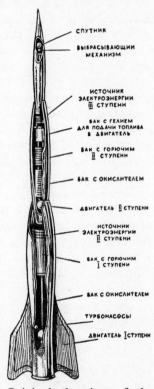

СПУТНИК

ВЫБРАСЫВАЮЩИЙ МЕХАНИЗМ

ИСТОЧНИК ЭЛЕКТРОЭНЕРГИИ III СТУПЕНИ

БАК С ГЕЛИЕМ ДЛЯ ПОДАЧИ ТОПЛИВА В ДВИГАТЕЛЬ

БАК С ГОРЮЧИМ II СТУПЕНИ

БАК С ОКИСЛИТЕЛЕМ

ДВИГАТЕЛЬ II СТУПЕНИ

ИСТОЧНИК ЭЛЕКТРОЭНЕРГИИ II СТУПЕНИ

БАК С ГОРЮЧИМ I СТУПЕНИ

БАК С ОКИСЛИТЕЛЕМ

ТУРБОНАСОСЫ

ДВИГАТЕЛЬ I СТУПЕНИ

Original drawing of the three-stage Russian Sputnik rocket.

an apogee of 583 miles and a perigee of 143 miles. The point on its track nearest to the earth thus lay outside the layers of the atmosphere which could create air resistance while its furthest point was in the outermost layers of the exosphere, on the boundary between the earth's atmosphere and space. The satellite's orbit was inclined at 65° to the Equator, so that the

Sputnik regularly rose above the horizon at measured intervals. Because of its high speed of about 18,000 miles an hour it was, however, very difficult to observe by optical means. The time between its appearance in the morning and evening sky and its disappearance in the earth's shadow was barely one minute. Completing the circuit of the earth in about ninety-six minutes, i.e., a little more than fifteen circuits per day, the satellite had thus, only four weeks after its launching, described well over 400 perfect, virtually identical movements around the earth.

THE CONSEQUENCES

On the very day after the launching of the Russian space rocket, the question was widely raised as to whether the high expenditure on satellite development (Project Vanguard had cost the United States 110 million dollars) was really approved solely to transport a small metal sphere into space and receive a few radio signals from it.

There is no doubt that the nation which can carry a payload — in this instance an artificial earth satellite — into space and there place it in orbit round the earth at so high a speed could fire a different payload — perhaps an atomic bomb — in a similar rocket from its territory to any point on the earth. Moreover, it is no secret that rocket weapon developments

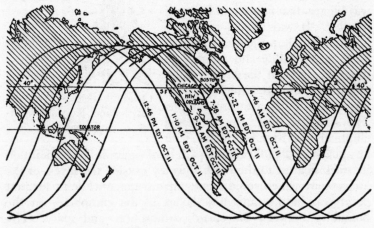

The orbit of Sputnik I.

have partly contributed to laying the foundations of the satellite
projects. Originally it had been intended, both in Russia and
in America, to use the intercontinental rockets as vehicles for
large satellites. The separation of the satellite programme from
the ICBM plans occurred when it became clear that the prime
research objective could be achieved with lighter satellites and
that smaller rockets would therefore suffice. The assembly,
firing, ascent control and observation of satellite rockets and
satellites requires a very extensive organisation. But all the
information obtained will directly or indirectly benefit developments in rocket weaponry.

Nevertheless, the artificial earth satellites form a peaceable
research project. The measurements they yield in space,
outside the detectable atmosphere, are of incalculable scientific
value. Think what they may mean for meteorology and for
accurate weather forecasting!

The psychological effect of the successful Russian experiment
was even more marked. A few weeks previously Mr. Huddle-
ston, a Congressman, declared that America would lose face if
she did not fire satellites during the International Geophysical
Year, and another nation placed satellites in orbit before her.
This forthright statement was part of the public criticism of
delays in the American Vanguard programme.

*   *   *

Perhaps many people had underestimated the psychological
effect of the first entry into space. When my friend Arthur
Clarke, one-time Chairman of the British Interplanetary
Society, had visited the Vanguard installations in the summer of
1957, he stated: "The public appears to have no clear idea of
what is going on here and what will happen in future. The
velocity and height of the satellites so far transcend daily
experience that such figures clearly fail to register. In consequence, many people will get a shock during the next few
months, when the American satellites begin to circle the earth
from west to east and the Russian ones from north to south."

On the first day of the space-travel era there were surprises
enough. The scientists and astronautics engineers all over the
world were delighted, without a trace of envy, by the successful
penetration of space. They knew that further steps would now

follow quickly. Moscow Radio announced larger satellites, the British Government promised official support for a British satellite project. At the conference of the German Rocket Society in Oldenburg in September 1957 a German minimum satellite carried by an eleven-stage solid-fuel rocket was proposed as a practical exercise in calculation, and in the United States preparations were made to continue the satellite experiments which had already been quite successful. The race for space was not ended by the appearance of the Soviet satellite Sputnik in the heavens, but simply accelerated.

When, in 1944, the first German V-2s fell on London, there were a few rocket enthusiasts in England who, in spite of the

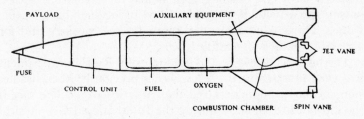

A classical liquid-fuel rocket — the V-2.

terrible seriousness of this new threat, triumphantly regarded the large German rocket as a proof that they, treated for years as fools, were right after all. Similar contradictory emotions gripped many rocketeers and astronautics specialists in the West when they attended the Eighth International Astronautical Congress in Barcelona to give lectures on satellites which did not yet exist, while — possibly even during their lecture — the Russian satellite was passing over Barcelona.

"One would like to be able to stop every engine and all work on our old star for a few minutes with a single word," wrote Dr. Karl Korn, the day after the successful satellite launching, commenting on the beginning of the interplanetary era. "But one cannot find the word. Perhaps the silence worthy of the moment exists in the soundproof cabins of lonely radio stations. When Goethe heard the cannons of the French revolutionary armies before Valmy, he expressed himself in words marking a new era, for at that very moment tragic events were ushering in a new epoch in world history . . . The same words would seem to be appropriate to the stirring moment when Morse signals were received for the first time from an artificial moon circling the earth every ninety minutes at a height of 500 miles. It is of capital importance that the feeling of being witnesses of a turning-point in history — a feeling which took hold of us when the familiar wireless set at home suddenly gave out a strange sound, a signal from space — should plunge us into bemused meditations and make us catch our breath. The prospect opened up by this first satellite is great and frightening. For decades we have been so familiar with technical wonders that we are likely soon to be thoughtlessly caught up by what will now inevitably follow, step by step. The race of the two world powers for scientific and technical — which also means military — power, and for prestige — which is political power — can be so frightfully accelerated by the sensational Russian advance that the greatness of the event on 4th October, an event worthy of Prometheus, threatens to be lost in the fear of a new race."

*   *   *

It was, however, a French newspaper which found the most graphic and penetrating headline during these days of worldwide interest and excitement. Many columns wide, it printed the headline: "Flu, flu, flu, crisis, crisis, crisis, bleep, bleep, bleep."

THE ROAD INTO SPACE

The launching of the first satellite confirmed the views of those who had for many years written about astronautics and the science of space flight. Now they could emphasise that their hypotheses and prophecies, insofar as they were scientifically defensible, were right. When the German rocket specialist Hermann Oberth made theoretical computations of space rockets in the 'twenties, he was soon involved in the hectic stir of the first space controversy; the critics, springing up on every side, believed that the rockets he described would never reach outer space; they even thought they would not get very far at all. Thirty years later research rockets were reaching heights of 600 miles, American long-range rockets had a range of 3,000 miles, and Russian ICBMs one of almost 6,000 miles.

Even in the summer of 1957 I was challenged, after a lecture on problems of space flight, with the statement that rockets would never rise further than 300 miles, and that satellites in space were absolutely impossible. Two months later the Sputnik circled the earth many hundred times in its 500-mile-high orbit in a few weeks, so that the estimates of its presumed

A historic multi-stage rocket. The four-stage 'Rheinbote' German artillery rocket of the Second World War.

duration, initially pessimistic and cautious, became more and more optimistic every day.

The world public was prepared for the Soviet experiment, but had had no confidence in the experts' statements, which proved accurate in the event. As early as May 1956 the Frankfurt periodical *Weltraumfahrt* (*Space Travel*) reported that the Russian satellite vehicle was in its last stage of development. Its take-off weight would be between 75 and 100 tons and its starting thrust was reckoned to reach 288,000 lb. Even at that time a member of the Interplanetary Research Committee of the Moscow Academy of Sciences confirmed that the Russian satellite would be bigger than the American Vanguard satellite. The surprise of 4th October would not have occurred in the West had due confidence been placed in the forecasts of Soviet specialists that their satellite would be bigger, rise higher and reach orbit earlier.

The great struggle for innovation was now, as it were, lifted

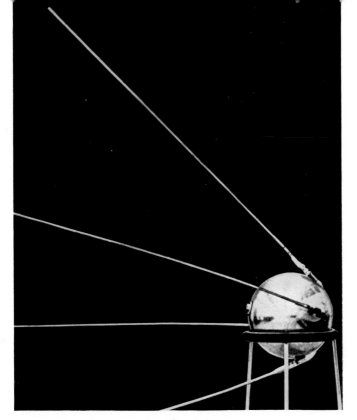

Stages in satellite development. *Top:* The Russian Sputnik, launched on 4th October 1957, to become the earth's first artificial satellite. *Bottom left:* A view of a satellite replica showing the interior closely packed with miniaturised instruments of all kinds. *Bottom right:* Testing a Vanguard satellite; note the rectangular apertures through which the solar batteries power the instruments.

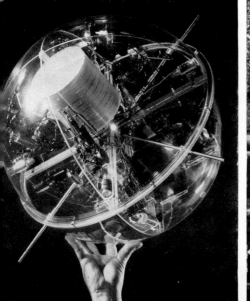

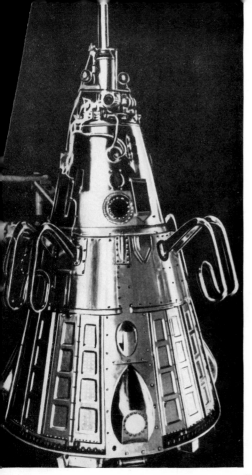

Later stages in satellite development.
Sputnik III, the largest man-made satellite to d

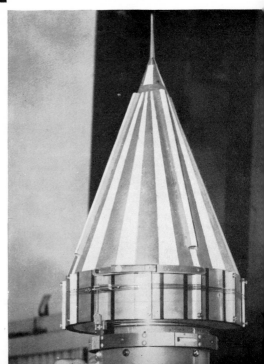

The space probe Pioneer III installed on
its carrier rocket at Cape Canaveral.

to a higher plane; the scepticism which is the armour of so many millions was not now directed at a single inventor or group of inventors, but at an entire nation. Since the word

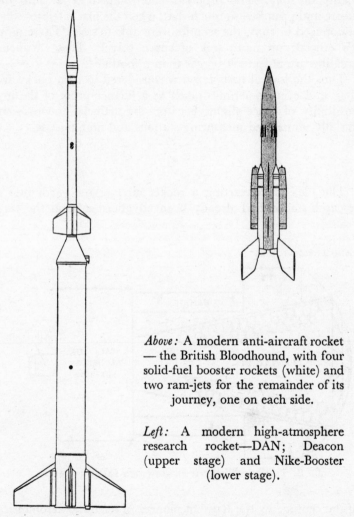

Above: A modern anti-aircraft rocket — the British Bloodhound, with four solid-fuel booster rockets (white) and two ram-jets for the remainder of its journey, one on each side.

Left: A modern high-atmosphere research rocket—DAN; Deacon (upper stage) and Nike-Booster (lower stage).

'impossible' was no longer appropriate, the possibility being obvious, people simply said: "They will not succeed."

So it happened that after 4th October 1957 many millions all over the world witnessed, by radio or television, a historic

T

event, as a space-conscious nation gained a decisive victory in one phase of the struggle. True, early dreams of space travel and previous astronautic schemes were far in excess of the reality of 1957. The prophets had jumped so far into the future and promised so much that, when the first satellites were announced in 1955, the sceptics were able to say: "There, now it's official; no more talk of space travel. These artificial satellites are not much bigger than a football!"

Thus the logical first step was considered to be a backward step, and even sometimes taken as a further proof of the impossibility of space flight, because the artificial moons were initially unmanned measuring stations and nothing else.

*   *   *

The idea of converting a rocket circling the earth into a research station had already been advanced around the turn

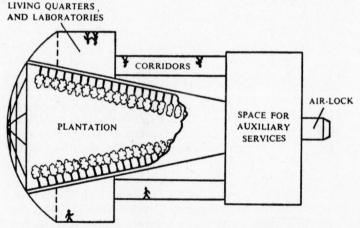

C. E. Tsiolkovski's plan for an earth satellite station.

of the century by the Russian pioneer of scientific aeronautics, Constantine Edwardovitch Tsiolkovski, of Kaluga. Tsiolkovski's manned satellite station was a gigantic hollow cylinder, rotating about its longitudinal axis, so that the inner wall served as a firm floor for the passengers. This artificial heavenly body was not only to carry cabins and laboratories, but also a 'garden' of plants and trees, to provide the crew with fruit, and above all with oxygen.

A wheel-like design was proposed by Captain Potocnic, an Austrian, who wrote on space travel problems in 1928 under the pseudonym of Noordung; his satellite station was conceived on as large a scale as Tsiolkovski's. The rotation of Noordung's station was also intended to replace gravity by centrifugal force.

In the 'twenties, Professor Hermann Oberth, the father of German rocket technique, developed such plans still further. Among other things he fitted his satellite station with a 'space mirror', intended to catch part of the sunlight which would otherwise by-pass the earth and reflect it on to the earth's surface. Since Oberth was writing for the specialist and not for the general public, his theoretical conclusions were bound to meet heavy opposition at a time when liquid-fuel rockets did not exist. "The proposal of a space station has clearly confused people's minds much more than any other part of space travel," wrote Oberth thirty years after the publication of his pioneer calculations. "It is not only the layman who finds it difficult to imagine an unfamiliar construction weighing several hundred tons moving at several hundred miles above the earth's surface, without any drive, following its orbit in airless space and deserving the name of an artificial moon. In fact, this is an undertaking which follows with complete logic from the fundamentals and potentialities of rocket technique, and the theory had already been closely checked. The earth will soon have an artificial satellite and I very much hope that I live to see such a thrilling event, as surely as I was able to witness — after publishing my books in 1923 and 1928 — the introduction of the large liquid-fuel rockets and the penetration into space of a two-stage liquid-fuel rocket, in spite of all the opposition of the eternal sceptics . . ." Oberth did live to see the first artificial earth satellite constructed as part of a large-scale astronautical programme in the United States, where — still involved in research and fighting for progress — he passed the evening of his life.

In the 'twenties Guido von Pirquet, an Austrian engineer, proposed three satellite stations; an inner station 500 miles up, an outer one 3,000 miles high and a transit station in an elliptical orbit between the circular orbits of the other two. The purpose of the intermediate station was to provide a shuttle service between the principal stations without requiring any further drive power. The outermost station would have travelled round the earth in 200 minutes and have served as a jumping-off point into space, while the inner satellite was to be an earth observation station with a transit time of 100 minutes. Von Pirquet was also one of the first to realise the real importance of satellites and satellite stations for long-range space flight. Space flight from the earth's surface is at present impossible, since we do not possess the drive systems or fuels necessary. The construction of a manned satellite station is very difficult, but practicable, with existing materials. Space flight from this station is easier than the building of the station itself.

The old saying "It's the first step that counts" is thus more than a truism here; it is in fact a proven, basic law, which Pirquet called the 'cosmo-nautical paradox'.

*   *   *

When the huge liquid-fuel rockets of the Second World War appeared, the suggestions for manned space stations began to take on practical interest. An extensive fundamental study of the problem was made in 1949 by Rolf Engel, a German rocket engineer working in Paris, to demonstrate to his still sceptical colleagues, especially in America, how this topical problem of practical astronautics could be solved. His computations provided for manned satellite stations at heights of 350 and 1,000 miles.

Two years later Dr. Wernher von Braun—now scientific head of the U.S. Army Central Rocket Research Institute at Redstone Arsenal at Huntsville, Alabama — showed how a manned satellite station fitted logically into the planning and execution of an interplanetary expedition. Without the satellite station the expedition (Mars being chosen for the purposes of calculation) would be impossible; with it, the interplanetary journey would be no more difficult than the assembly of the station itself.

Von Braun's space station resembles a wheel rotating on its axis, 250 feet in diameter, circling the earth every two hours, or twelve times a day, at a height of 1,075 miles. One figure suffices to indicate the magnitude of this plan: the initial supplies of air for the crew, i.e., the air filling the entire station, was precisely calculated to reach 24 tons; it would thus require several large liquid-fuel rockets to carry it. Soon afterwards von Braun reduced this impressive space-station project to a 'baby space station', that is, an unmanned artificial satellite bearing instruments and a few animals. The scale and organisation of this project corresponded roughly to that of the first Russian satellite.

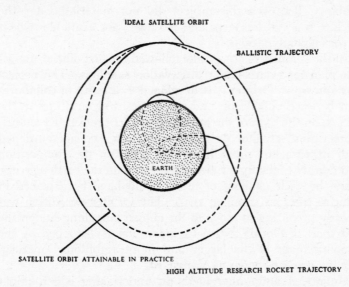

Diagram showing the possible and practicable rocket paths on Earth. The ideal satellite orbit is circular but the attainable orbits are elliptical (dotted).

This plan was, however, too ambitious for the rockets existing in the 'fifties. If the large rocket vehicles for heavy satellites could not be produced quickly, the satellites would need to be modified in size to suit the available rockets. Many astronautics scientists recognised even now the value of the minimum satellite. The American physics professor, Dr. S. F. Singer, reported the results of such investigations at the Fourth International Astronautical Congress in Zürich in 1953. He declared that a total instrument payload of 112 lb. would suffice. To lift a satellite of this size into orbit at a height of 200 miles a three-stage rocket would be needed; using all the latest advances in rocket technique, this would weigh some 16 tons. Together with two Britons, the writer Arthur C. Clarke, and the rocket engineer, A. V. Cleaver, of the British Interplanetary Society, Singer gave this satellite the now world-famous name 'Mouse', standing for 'Minimum Orbital Unmanned Satellite Earth'. The Mouse satellite would be a small flying laboratory for high-level research and space probing. But even this project did not materialise, for the satellite was still too large and too heavy for available rockets or rocket combinations.

In the summer of 1954 there followed the first official American plan for even smaller observation satellites. The project was known as 'Orbiter'. It developed as a result of collaboration between von Braun and several research institutes in the U.S.A. on the basis of the huge new artillery rocket 'Redstone'. Observation satellites weighing some 7 lb. and not burdened with instruments, providing information on the composition and density of the upper atmosphere and on the earth's precise shape by their changes of track, could have been placed in orbit as early as summer 1955. The Orbiter expedition was already preparing to move to the chosen launching site on the east coast of Florida, when the operation was stopped by the announcement of the larger and more ambitious American satellite project known as Vanguard.

Unnoticed and unheralded, an undertaking which might have become a triumph of rocket research was filed away. Instead, the official American satellite project, Vanguard, began to occupy the columns of the world Press.

PROJECT VANGUARD

In October 1954 the special committee for the International Geophysical Year decided to ask participating countries to include satellites in their plans. The following spring, the American National Committee of the I.G.Y. reported favour-ably to the President of the National Academy of Sciences and the Director of the National Science Foundation. A draft programme, with a plea for official support, was laid before the Federal Government that May. By July the final programme was complete. On 29th July 1955 it was announced in Washington and Brussels that the United States would construct one or more artificial satellites as a contribution to the I.G.Y. Shortly afterwards the Defence Ministry declared its readiness to provide the requisite technical facilities, including the rockets for carrying the satellites. The responsibility for the programme was entrusted to the Naval Research Laboratory, where project Vanguard was begun under the leadership of Dr. John P. Hagen. The Naval Research Laboratory signed a contract with the Martin Company in Baltimore for the development and manufacture of the complete satellite rockets. Martin placed orders for the rocket motors for the first stage with General Electric and for the second stage with Aerojet General.

The three-stage Vanguard rocket is 72 feet long, with a take-off weight of roughly ten tons, while the satellite itself weighs only $21\frac{1}{2}$ lb. The ratio of initial weight to payload is thus $1 : 1,000$. The first-stage motor provides a thrust of 27,000 lb. at ground level. The first stage somewhat resembles the American research vehicle 'Viking', and the motor is gimbal-mounted as in that rocket. The second stage, which is also a liquid-fuel rocket, was developed from the smaller research rocket 'Aerobee'. A small solid-fuel rocket, with a

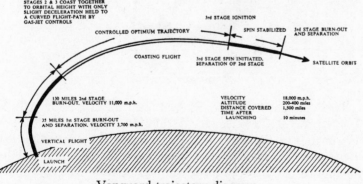

Vanguard trajectory diagram.

starting weight of nearly 500 lb., is used to place the satellite in its orbit.

The burn-out of the first stage occurs two minutes after take-off, at a height of some 40 miles. At this moment the rocket has a velocity of some 6,000 feet per second. The motor for the second stage is started once the first stage has burnt out, and gives the remaining parts of the rocket a speed of 14,010 feet per second. Burn-out of the second stage takes place at a height of some 130 miles. (See picture on page 277.) The rocket now coasts to about 300 miles, until its path is parallel to the earth's surface. The drive of the third stage is then ignited and accelerates the satellite to its orbiting speed of some 26,000 feet per second. After burn-out the satellite separates from the third stage, which remains in the same orbit, but soon takes up its own path.

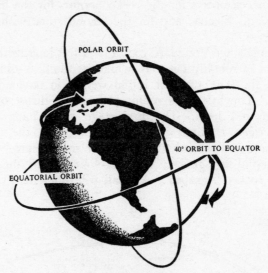

POLAR ORBIT

40° ORBIT TO EQUATOR

EQUATORIAL ORBIT

Vanguard's orbit.

The Vanguard rockets are fired from the Air Force Missile Test Centre at Cape Canaveral, Florida, on orbits inclined at 35° to 45° to the Equator. The perigee should not be less than 200 miles, and the apogee not more than 900 miles. The satellite itself is a large, gleaming, silvery sphere twenty inches in diameter, containing instruments, radio transmitter and battery, with a total weight of $21\frac{1}{2}$ lb. This tiny un-manned space ship was made in the middle of Detroit, near the building where, fifty years earlier, Henry Ford had built his first car.

While the first two prototypes were being manufactured, the scientists in the Vanguard Headquarters in Washington were deciding which measurements were to receive priority. With transport costs of one million dollars per instrument carried, the decisions required careful reflection, bearing in mind also the fact that the U.S.A. had already made available for the International Geophysical Year 356 different research rockets. All the measurements which could be made with these rockets would be omitted from the satellite programme.

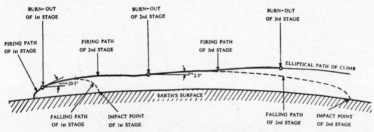

Launching path of a three-stage transport rocket to a high orbit round the Earth; the actual orbit is reached after the satellite moves into its elliptical path of climb when the third stage has burnt out.
(After W. von Braun.)

It became known in the United States during this stage of the development of the Vanguard that the skill of the Russian rocket engineers and space scientists had been underestimated. For instance, it was learned that they were preparing a fairly large satellite and that the trials of their huge multi-stage satellite vehicle had been successful. The contest for space was in full swing, now watched by everyone. The struggle for progress was about to be decided, having now become a struggle to obtain important scientific information from regions where man had never penetrated. It was an obvious suggestion that the American plans should be changed rapidly and a larger rocket built in great haste. But scientific objectivity triumphed over the spirit of competition. It was decided at the headquarters of the Vanguard project that they would concentrate on measurements of maximum accuracy and dispense with records and priorities which might be attainable.

The final decision regarding the equipment for the American satellites envisaged from four to six different types of eamsurement in combination, maximum precision and reliability, and certain transmission of observations. The sacrifice of victory and the credit of being 'first' was not to be in vain.

It was not only the relatively high weight of the Russian satellite which first penetrated space that perturbed the rocket engineers of the West; even its orbit was unusual.

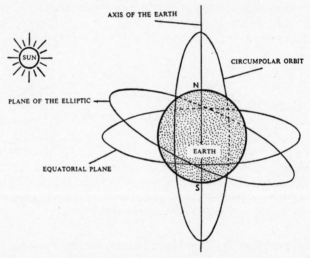

The orbit of a satellite passing over the poles and its position relative to the elliptic and the equatorial plane.

The launching path of the American Vanguard satellie starts on the east coast of Florida and runs south-east over the Bahamas and the Atlantic; this orbit was chosen so that the earth's rotational motion, which exceeds 600 miles an hour near the Equator, contributes to the final velocity of the rocket. The rocket 'leaps off', as it were, in the direction of travel and its power requirements are reduced by the amount necessary to give it this extra 600 miles an hour.

This launching direction and the resultant orbit also mean

that the Vanguard only passes over a zone between 40° North and 40° South; as a result, it does not pass over Russian territory. The Soviet satellite engineers, led by Professor Leonid Sedov of the Moscow Academy of Sciences, dispensed with the advantage of launching in an easterly direction and fired their gigantic ballistic rocket, bearing a satellite sphere in its nose, on a north-easterly course.

Their achievements in rocket development were demonstrated to a surprised world in three ways. They placed in space a satellite over thirty times heavier than the American minimum satellites, which preceded Vanguard; they lifted an artificial moon to a maximum height of 500 miles, and had not even made use of the earth's rotational motion, preferring to launch their satellite rocket in a north-easterly direction from a point north of the Equator.

*   *   *

"The preparation of an artificial earth satellite," stated *Pravda* on 8th October, four days after the launching, "required the solution of various highly complicated and essentially new scientific and technical problems. The biggest difficulties were encountered in constructing the rocket vehicle which was to place the satellites in orbit.

"A fully-developed vehicle system was built for the purpose; powerful motors were constructed, capable of operating under

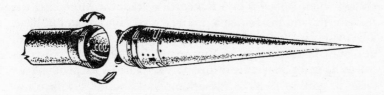

Possible means of ejecting the satellite from the last stage
of its carrier rocket.

difficult temperature conditions. Optimum adjustments were worked out to ensure the most efficient use of the rockets . . . The satellite is spherical; it is housed in the nose of the rocket, under a protective cone. The satellite rocket was launched vertically. Shortly after the start, the control equipment was operated to bring the rocket out of the vertical. At the end of its trajectory the rocket was several hundred miles up, moving parallel to the earth's surface at about five miles per second. When the rocket motor was switched off, the protective cone was ejected, and the satellite separated from the rocket and began to move independently."

As the experts expected, the satellite was not alone in space. The last rocket stage and the ejected nose cone also became artificial satellites roving round the earth in their own paths. Slight differences in speed occurred in the process of separation and gradually increased as a result of differential braking in the rarefied atmosphere at that height. As time went on, the satellite and its two outriders moved further away from each other, finally taking up separate paths round the earth.

WHAT DOES SCIENCE GAIN?

As it girdles the earth, the artificial satellite moves alternately in full sunlight or in the earth's shadow. It is thus subjected to periodic rapid temperature changes. On the daylight side of the earth the satellite is heated by the sun's rays without the diffusing effect of the atmosphere, while it is markedly chilled when it moves into the earth's shadow. Moreover, the transmitter and instruments produce a certain amount of heat. The artificial satellite is thus an independent miniature world, not only in respect of its movement but also as regards its warmth, since its temperature is very largely dependent on losses or gains of heat by radiation. The Sputnik's surface was prepared by polishing or partial blackening so as to maintain a fairly constant temperature, by ensuring that inward and outward radiation of heat remain within the required relationships. This provides the temperature necessary for the instruments and transmitters inside the satellite to function properly.

The programme of measurements carried out with artificial satellites is very extensive; it covers many physical problems of the upper atmosphere and the boundaries of space. They include information about the state of the ionosphere, such as the composition, pressure and density of the air at such great heights. The earth's magnetic field is measured and the nature of cosmic radiation investigated without any hindrance from dense layers of air.

From a constant shower of meteors which enter the earth's

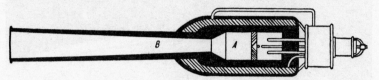

A liquid-fuel rocket after C. E. Tsiolkovski.
A = Combustion chamber. B = jet.

atmosphere from space, only the largest reach the earth's surface. Most of them are no larger than blood corpuscles and burn up in the atmosphere as 'shooting stars'. This penetration into space is our only means of getting an accurate idea of their frequency. It is important for astronautics specialists to discover their secrets, for this cosmic dust can endanger the big space vehicles of the future.

The astronomers, too, await with interest the results of the satellite experiments. Not only does the atmosphere protect the earth from the vagrant cosmic material, it also screens off the majority of the radiations emanating from space. At present science has only two small windows in the atmosphere, one letting through visible light rays and the other radio waves in the decimetre band. All other radiations are absorbed by the atmosphere. Until a few years ago astronomers relied entirely upon information obtained by optical apparatus sensitive to visible light; the very recent development of radio-astronomy opened another channel and brought much additional data. In time the astronomers hope to detect and analyse all the radiations in space by means of artificial satellites. A record of the complete spectrum of electro-magnetic waves emitted by the sun would be of immeasurable value to solar physicists. Measurements of the primary cosmic radiation would reveal new facts about its nature and composition.

The deviation of satellite orbits from the theoretical path gives the geophysicists a quantitative idea of the oblateness — or flattening — of the earth, the composition of its crust or the distribution of matter in its interior.

Even the meteorologists welcomed the satellites, from which they expected to obtain valuable scientific information. Our

Visibility of artificial satellites. The observer on the right cannot see the satellite, although it is brightly lit by the Sun, because the sky is too bright; the observer on the left cannot see the satellite, although the sky is dark, because it is passing through the Earth's shadow. The observer in the middle sees the satellite in the short period between dark and the disappearance of the satellite in the Earth's shadow.

entire knowledge of atmospheric phenomena prior to the interplanetary era was based on measurements and observations at ground level or from the earth's surface. Balloon sondes rising to about twenty miles and rocket probes reaching several hundred miles had, it is true, somewhat extended the range, but the direction of observation — upward from the earth's surface — was hardly changed; such devices proved how valuable for the meteorologists would be exact measurements of the upper strata of the atmosphere. Such observations made from space extend meteorological information and offer new possibilities, with a resultant promise of better long-term weather forecasts in future.

*   *   *

Whole books were written on the possibilities of application of artificial earth satellites. For instance, there are the electronic and optical methods of observing them, the interpretation of the deviations from orbit thus recorded, and the various resulting problems of the development of new measuring instruments and calculating methods.

An arbitrary selection will show the large number of problems which can be solved by research employing artificial satellites: air pressure and density, air drag, temperatures, the resistance of cosmic matter, heat radiation from the earth, the distribution of hydrogen in space, ultra-violet rays, star

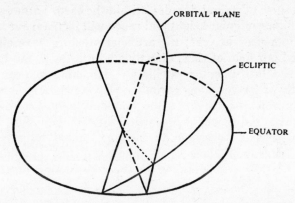

The angle between the orbital plane and the equatorial plane governs the satellite's path round the earth; the more acute this angle, the narrower the zone on either side of the Equator in which the satellite rises above the horizon. At an angle of 90° the satellite passes over the poles.

spectra, streams of solar protons, the earth's magnetic field, the gravisphere, the structure of the ionosphere, electron density at great heights, and interplanetary dust.

Faced with this inestimable wealth of new information in so many fields of knowledge, the fabrication of artificial satellites cannot be considered a luxury or the materialisation of a bold idea. The first measurements wirelessed to the earth from space silenced those who had, until H-hour on 4th October 1957, considered astronautics 'a fanciful game'.

FUTURE TRENDS

Now that the Soviet satellite has been launched, discussion of space travel is, to a certain extent, sanctioned; we can now enquire into its future quite unashamedly and obtain an answer.

How then will space travel develop further? The main objective of scientific astronautics is still space flight with passengers, whether by manned satellites, space stations or the space vehicles proposed for lunar, interplanetary, interstellar, or even intergalactic journeys.

The objective will be reached roughly in the following stages: in the course of several decades, within the earth's atmosphere, rocket flights of great height and range will increase our knowledge from year to year; the artificial satellites have already extended our field of view, directly and indirectly, and larger, unmanned instrumented satellites — remaining in orbit permanently or for very long periods — will provide the solutions of the problems of flight in the boundary zone between the atmosphere and space; experimental short-range flights of unmanned rockets, subsequently carrying animal subjects, will follow; next will come trial manned flights, culminating, within the foreseeable future, in the construction of a large

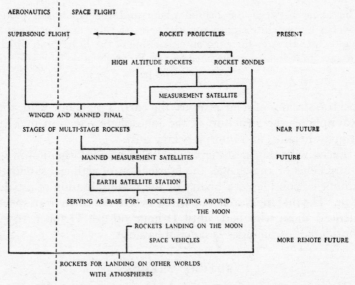

The future development of rocket flight beyond the Earth's atmosphere.

manned space station. It is this which will make it possible to travel to the moon or the nearer planets in manned space ships.

*   *   *

While the world listened in fascination to the signals sent out by the Soviet satellite, Project 'Far Side', another programme for scientific penetration of space, was progressing — this time in America. Unostentatiously, American research workers were preparing a new and tremendous leap forward; there was no long development time, no laborious preliminaries were needed, no impressive propaganda was made. The new rocket was available, a four-stage assembly of existing and proven solid-fuel rockets.

The first stage was a group of four 'Recruit' rockets, the second consisted of a single rocket of the same type. Four smaller solid-propellant 'Arrow 11' rockets formed the third stage. The last stage — carrying an instrument load of some $5\frac{1}{2}$ lb. — consisted of a single 'Arrow 11' set in the middle of the third-stage group. This rocket, weighing not quite 17 cwt., was carried to a height of 100,000 feet by a polythene balloon with a maximum diameter of 190 feet and a capacity of 3,500,000 cubic feet. The balloon, which was destroyed when the rocket was fired, had a weight of 1,500 lb. and its total payload — rockets and equipment — was one ton. The maximum speed of the fourth stage was 16,800 miles an hour.

Although Project 'Far Side' was only intended to reach heights of between 1,000 and 5,000 miles, the name indicates that a relatively simple extension of the project would include 'shooting the moon'. The American author Willy Ley called this unmanned rocket 'Moon-messenger' soon after the Second World War. The message was not for the Man in the Moon, but for the scientific observers waiting on the earth to see the impact of the rocket's final stage—made visible by a charge of magnesium powder or colouring material — on the moon's surface.

Such an experiment, a tremendous new demonstration of the potentialities of rockets, had been literally in the air since 4th October 1957.

*   *   *

U

The first artificial earth satellites initiated the scientific exploration of space between the earth and the moon, paving the way for 'lunar space flight'. The term 'interplanetary flight' applies as far as the limit of our solar system, the orbit of the planet Pluto. Beyond that is 'interstellar' flight, towards the planets of other suns. And should such spaceships quit the Milky Way at some far-distant time, journeying to other galaxies, this would be 'intergalactic space travel'.

'Man in Space' (Walt Disney, helped by Heinz Haber).

The lunar chapter of astronautics began with the launching of the Sputnik. When such constructions have been circling the earth for an appreciable period, increasing consideration will be given to space stations, which could be manned from about 1970, according to Dr. Sänger. Interplanetary space travel will come in the last twenty-five years of this century, and Dr. Sänger calculates that interstellar flight should be a reality a thousand years later.

Man will follow the artificial satellites into space. Aeroplane pilots in the atmosphere already experience space travel to some extent in their own bodies, since, according to a definition advanced by Dr. Hubertus Strughold, the earth's atmosphere becomes 'equivalent to space' at certain functional boundaries. This partial 'space equivalence' begins at a height of ten miles, at the 'Armstrong Line', where a man can no longer obtain sufficient oxygen from the earth's atmosphere, although there is still enough present; above 120 miles there is total space equivalence, although the atmosphere extends considerably further, because from here onwards all the conditions of space flight are present; even the hindrance of air drag ceases, so that 'coasting' flight and liberation from gravity are attained.

There is no exact topographic boundary between the atmosphere and space. The terrestrial envelope of air gives way to space in a deep transition layer known as the exosphere. Since gravitation plays an important part in space travel, and the concept of the gravitational field does not satisfy the engineer, Strughold introduced the idea of the 'gravisphere'. This ends where the gravitational influence of the earth becomes negligible, at approximately a million miles from the earth.

Unmanned — and later manned — spaceships will one day enter the atmospheres and gravispheres of other worlds. The entire complex of new problems involved is called by Strughold 'spatiography'. It would be senseless to talk of geography, the science of the earth, on other worlds or in space.

*   *   *

Systematically and successfully, the science of space medicine founded by Strughold is preparing for man's first space flights; since 1949 work on this subject, carried out at its birthplace, the U.S.A.F. School of Aviation Medicine at Randolph Field, Texas, has given much scientific data.

A week after the launching of the first Russian satellite, Professor Strughold and I sat discussing the possibilities of sending human beings into space. I learned that the world's leading space medicine expert was considerably more optimistic than might have been expected in view of the major problems known to exist.

For several years Professor Strughold has been experimenting with the hermetically-sealed 'Space Cabin Simulator' in his laboratory at Randolph Field. This device enables volunteers to make 'space flights' without leaving the earth. In this way all problems of maintaining human beings in an artificial atmosphere can be solved in good time, even that of using algæ which absorb exhaled carbon dioxide and furnish the necessary oxygen for men to breathe. The objective of this experiment has been achieved and a complete micro-world

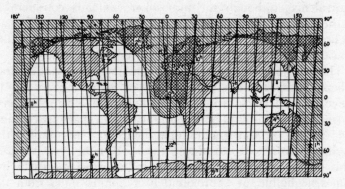

The possibilities of observing the Earth from a space station at a height of 350 miles (from Oberth, *Man in Space*).

created, for flight through space outside the earth's atmosphere.

Every month, new problems may arise of which no one has yet thought. Professor Strughold quoted two examples. A new difficulty, known as the 'water barrier', occurs during very long space flights, for instance to the planets of remote fixed stars. Experiments in the Space Cabin Simulator have shown that a human being disposes of twenty grams of water more per day than he absorbs. Thus it is not shortage but excess of water which will govern the success of long-range space flights of the future.

Similar surprises are found again and again in studying the weightlessness which occurs in driveless and drag-free flights. This state can be artificially induced for periods of from 45 to 60 seconds in the atmosphere by flying an aircraft on a special course. Here, too, long-standing fears have been dispelled; this condition of weightlessness affected many people badly, but others were able to adapt themselves quickly, and to perform their tasks notwithstanding. New series of experiments will seek to determine how the organism will react and how living cells will behave under weightless conditions. Single-celled creatures, such as amœba, will be observed and filmed in this state. They, too, are among the first space travellers.

*   *   *

A few days after this enlightening discussion with Professor Strughold — the Russian satellite had already circled the earth more than 200 times, and everyone was talking of the coming manned space flights — I met in Wiesbaden an American Air Force doctor, Major David G. Simons, head of the Space Biology Branch of the Aero-Medical Field Laboratory, New Mexico. Shut up in his hermetically-sealed 'Thermos flask' cabin, the young doctor had been carried by a balloon to a height of 111,000 feet on 19th August 1957. The 300-foot balloon, containing 35 million cubic feet of helium, carried Major Simons from the bottom of an open-cast iron mine at Crosby, Minnesota, to this height in about two hours. The U.S.A.F.'s Project 'Man High' yielded new information concerning the aviation medicine problems which arise in space travel.

Simons showed that a man can stay at such heights for long periods without danger, by remaining for 32 hours in his cold, blackish-red sphere; he was the first man to observe the earth from this viewpoint in space for so long. In the hermetically-sealed cabin he was completely isolated from the earth, and carried his own 'living conditions' for 32 hours with him. He experienced everything that the crew of a manned satellite in space would feel, except weightlessness. During this period the heavy particles of primary cosmic radiation entered his body. Automatic apparatus replaced the oxygen consumed from the atmosphere of the cabin and eliminated the exhaled carbon dioxide.

In answer to a question about the mental stress, Simons smilingly declared that the excitement of his friends on the ground far exceeded his own fear. However, occupied with observations and measurements, he forgot to eat and drink, and his chief, Dr. John P. Stapp, had to remind him of this from time to time by radio telephone.

As night fell, the balloon cooled down somewhat and sank a few thousand feet, but as the sun rose, it warmed up, rising again to about 100,000 feet. A tremendous storm raged for hours between the balloon and the earth, but Simons felt nothing of it at that height, although the turbulent clouds lay below him. As the storm shifted away, he looked past the edge of the great mass of clouds down at the earth 'as though from Heaven'.

*   *   *

The day after I met Major Simons, the news agencies reported a statement by Sir Harold Spencer Jones, the British Astronomer Royal, which I record here without comment for the years to come in astronautics: "Man will never set his foot on the Moon or on Mars." Almost simultaneously the Soviet astronomer, Tichov, the founder of astrobotany, declared his conviction that Russian astronauts would soon bring back specimens of plants from Mars.

Even at the zero hour of space flight, on the threshold of the interplanetary era, stubborn adherence to traditional ideas and bold, creative imagination stood face to face.

FEELINGS IN SPACE

The objectors were only temporarily silenced. The Soviet satellite had hardly completed its first circuits of the earth when the deep-seated spirit of contradiction began to stir at the same time as the world-wide fascination of the event. "Five hundred miles; that is only the distance from London to the Swiss border! The artificial moon is only a football and cannot escape the effects of gravity; even the triumphant rocket engineers who have shot it into space must admit that it will soon come down again . . ."

But how pitiable these criticisms of 'impossible' or 'not enough' appeared against the background of enthusiasm throughout the world! "It is a good sign that the public, at home or in the factory, in bars, or at newspaper kiosks, has only one subject of conversation — the satellite," wrote

Dr. Karl Korn in the *Frankfurter Allgemeine Zeitung*. "Must our imagination slumber because a small, football-sized metal body is moving round the earth in an elliptical path, obediently letting us hear its signals and recording radiations? When our parents and grandparents saw the first Zeppelin they were greatly excited, simply because the upward look has for ages 'raised' man, freeing him from the ant-like busyness of his daily occupations. At the New Year, we take a great deal of trouble to fire small rockets a few feet, to greet the heavens which make our existence seem more spacious. Now that an artificial satellite has for the first time been successfully placed in orbit — be it never so small by astronomical standards — would we do better to turn to such exceptionally important arguments as that about the date of the rise in the price of coal?" The ordinary man actually felt, as it were, liberated, as though the idea of 'brotherhood beyond the stars' had gripped him, a planetary unity of all men who suddenly, for a few weeks, were all looking the same way."

Where criticism did arise, it was for very different reasons. "America has been living under the mistaken impression that her science is more advanced, her industrial production higher and her policies cleverer than those of any other nation," commented the *New York Herald Tribune*. "The public and the Government have both been characterised in their attitude by complacency and drowsiness, as though America possessed a built-in, automatic superiority device which makes them win every time. This conception must be revised in the future."

The fresh wind of the first entry into space had blown away complacency and drowsiness, when the official Soviet news agency Tass announced, on the morning of 3rd November 1957, the successful launching of the second satellite. Sputnik I surprised the world by its rapid appearance alone, but Sputnik II was — the word is justified — a sensation, as the published figures and facts showed. Weighing half a ton, it was eight times heavier than the first. The Russian rocketeers achieved this greater weight by turning the entire last stage of the rocket into a satellite. Rocket specialists of the West, fascinated by the first figures, put their calculators and slide-rules to work, with astonishing results. If we consider the second satellite simply as the payload of the carrying rocket the latter would have weighed 500 tons before launching; if Sputnik II was simply the final stage of the rocket, then the take-off weight must be between 70 and 100 tons.

This 'final stage' satellite, circling the earth as an artificial moon, was fitted with a sealed cabin, for the satellite had a passenger. This was the little, white Siberian Husky bitch Laika. Breathing air and air-conditioning apparatus were provided, automatic feeding devices, which the dog had been trained to use for months, and numerous measuring instruments were fitted. Animal-lovers all over the world held their breath; was Laika to die out there in space? Any return journey would have involved releasing the cabin, braking, re-entry into the denser atmospheric layers, gliding flight toward a fixed landing-point, recovery by search parties. But the experiment was not made; after seven days Laika died painlessly from shortage of oxygen because the batteries were exhausted, having circled the earth more than a hundred times.

Involuntarily she had done pioneer work, helping — like many animals before her — to pave the way for men. For man intended to follow her into space.

*   *   *

THE AMERICAN SATELLITES

The Americans' first satellite was launched by the Army, after several preliminary attempts with the Navy Vanguard vehicle had failed. The Jupiter C research rocket, developed and built in the Rocket Research Centre of the U.S. Army at Huntsville, Alabama, under the leadership of Dr. Wernher von Braun, had already made one successful flight in the autumn of 1956; true, this was without a satellite, although such an experiment would have been possible at that time.

While the Jupiter C was somewhat strengthened, the satellite was developed — a tube thirty inches long and six inches in diameter, and on 31st January 1958, at 10.48 p.m. (local time), the rocket was launched. The four-stage assembly, 72 feet long and weighing 29·6 tons, had an initial thrust of 38 tons; the first stage, a modified 'Redstone', burned for 150 seconds, at the end of which the rocket was some 60 miles up. From this point it coasted for 240 seconds till it reached a height of 200 miles. Only then were the following stages fired; the second stage was a cluster of eleven solid-propellant rockets 50 inches long, the third a cluster of three similar rockets. The final stage, yet another rocket of the same type, remained attached to the satellite proper, so that the orbiting vehicle was approximately 6 feet long and weighed 30 lb. after its fuel has been consumed.

Sputnik I had been officially known as 1957 Alpha and Sputnik II as 1957 Beta. The new satellite became 1958 Alpha 'Explorer' — Explorer because it had thrust the boundaries of our knowledge and research further outwards into space. Explorer I carried instruments for measuring temperature, and for detecting micro-meteorites and cosmic rays, together with two transmitters and batteries to a total weight of 11 lb. The Jupiter C was launched on a south-easterly course inclined at 33·5° to the Equator. The satellite had a transit time of 115 minutes, and its orbit was elliptical, with a perigee of 220 miles and an apogee of 1,600 miles. Maximum speed at perigee was 18,300 miles per hour, the average speed being 16,070 miles per hour.

The second American satellite — weighing 3 lb., and 6½ inches in diameter — was placed in orbit on 17th March 1958. This new satellite was called 'Vanguard 1', for, although only a by-product of the successful Vanguard trials, the 'grape-fruit' satellite was the first launched by the American Navy, who were responsible for the project. Three preliminary trials with the rocket vehicle were held on 8th December 1956, 1st May and 3rd October 1957; they were intended solely to test the components and functioning of the rockets. The first attempts to launch a complete Vanguard rocket carrying a tiny minimum satellite, on 6th December 1957 and 5th February 1958, were unsuccessful.

The new satellite's time for the complete circuit of the earth was 134 minutes; its elliptical orbit had a perigee of 400 miles and an apogee of some 2,500 miles. Two transmitters, which signalled the surface and internal temperatures of the satellite, were carried. The ten-milliwatt transmitter was battery-powered, while the five-milliwatt transmitter was supplied by solar energy picked up by photo-electric cells set in the satellite's skin. The principal purpose of the test was to try out the Vanguard rocket, which contained 30,000 individual components.

The third American satellite was again launched by the Army, and reached orbit on 26th March 1958. This was the third Explorer to be launched, but — a previous Army attempt having been unsuccessful, owing to the failure of the fourth stage — was only the second to enter space. Being also the third artificial earth satellite launched in 1958, it was officially called 1958 Gamma. The orbit of this satellite was markedly elliptical, with an apogee of 1,750 miles. Since the perigee lay at a height of only 120 miles, thus penetrating relatively deeply into the denser layers of the atmosphere, the satellite fell back to earth on 27th June, having made 1,260 transits in 92 days. However, its orbit was very suitable for research into cosmic radiation at various heights between 150 and 1,750 miles. The data measured were stored by a tape-recorder weighing only 8 oz., which fed them to a built-in transmitter on receipt of an appropriate signal. After some initial difficulties, this 'calling-up' operation was executed with a reliability of between 70 per cent. and 80 per cent. The recorder was $2\frac{1}{2}$ inches in diameter, the tape a yard long, 3/20 inch broad and about 1/100 inch thick. Its playing time was five seconds; during play-back the recording was wiped off, making the tape ready for re-use.

On 15th May 1958, the Soviet Union launched into space its third Sputnik, a striking instrument for high-altitude and space research. Many observers went so far as to call it the first spaceship, for, weighing 2,925 lb., it was big enough to have carried a man in a hermetically-sealed cabin. Despite this, it contained, according to Russian information, a total instrument payload of 2,120 lb. Sputnik III was the third Soviet satellite and the earth's sixth, so that by 15th May four artificial moons were circling the earth. It was conical, 11 feet 6 inches high — without the long aerials — and 5 feet 8 inches in diameter at the base. The perigee of its elliptical orbit was at 135 miles and its apogee at 1,170 miles, the transit time being 106 minutes.

A further U.S. Army Explorer was successfully launched on 26th July 1958, with a weight of $38\frac{1}{2}$ lb.; the orbit was once more elliptical, the perigee at 160 miles and the apogee at 1,375 miles; it completed one circuit of the earth in 110 minutes.

In the second half of 1958 the first moon rockets followed the pioneer satellites. On 11th October a speed of 23,667 miles per hour would have been enough for the final rocket stage to reach the vicinity of the moon. The speed actually attained was 23,085 miles per hour, i.e., the velocity was 582 miles per hour too low. As a consequence the speed of the rocket's final stage slackened to zero too soon and at a

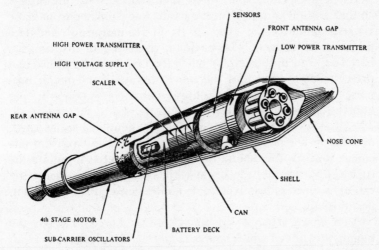

This cutaway drawing shows the radio equipment and cosmic ray research instruments carried in Explorer IV.

height of 70,700 miles it began to fall back. The rocket had failed during the first trial on 17th August, 77 seconds after launching, because of a leaking oxygen lead; on 8th November, during the third attempt, the third stage failed to fire — probably owing to a broken cable — so that the burn-out velocity was not reached.

After three unsuccessful attempts by the U.S. Air Force to 'shoot the moon', tension reached its peak; who would now win the race — Wernher von Braun or the Soviet engineers? Nonetheless, it was not only the space-travel enthusiasts who marked 11th October as a day on which technical history was made. It is not so important that the attempt should have

failed; but, it was said, for the first time a man-made object had
freed itself from the earth's gravitational field, and for the first
time a velocity of almost 23,200 miles per hour had been
reached. However surprising the latter statement — in spite of
all the mental preparation which preceded it, which of us can
visualise 23,200 miles per hour? — it is perfectly correct, and
so much the more erroneous and misleading was the idea that
this remarkable moon-probe, the Pioneer, had left the earth's
gravitational field or been intended to do so.

When the 'Thor-Able' three-stage rocket, weighing almost
50 tons and measuring 84 feet overall, was launched from Cape
Canaveral under the 200,000 lb. of its motors, it had two
principal objectives. The payload, consisting of instruments,
batteries, transmitters and a 'television eye', must be placed in a
pre-calculated orbit and the much discussed and much misunderstood 'escape velocity' of approximately 25,000 miles per
hour be imparted to it, if the enterprise was to succeed at all.
The final stage of the rocket would not then fall back to earth
or take up a narrow orbit around the earth, but continue its
course towards the moon. Since the moon exerts a pull on the
rocket, imperceptibly to begin with, but to an ever-increasing
extent, a speed of just over 20,000 miles per hour would, in fact,
be sufficient.

After three attempts by the U.S. Air Force to reach the
moon, only one of which was partially successful, the American
Army achieved a further part-success on 6th December 1958,
with a Juno 2 rocket. Once again the speed was slightly too
low, so that Pioneer 3 reached a height of no more than
63,580 miles.

On 18th December 1958 the U.S. Air Force made an
impressive demonstration, using an Atlas rocket. This, weighing some 100 tons at the start, reached orbiting velocity, becoming an artificial satellite about 78 feet long, weighing, after
burn-out, roughly two tons; it was known as Score. The new
satellite carried a tape-recorder which radioed back to the
earth — even if not very clearly — a Christmas message from
President Eisenhower.

The legendary 'second cosmic velocity' of seven miles per
second was exceeded for the first time on 2nd January 1959.
The final stage of a Soviet moon rocket — weighing 3,245 lb.,

and with a total of 797 lb. of instruments — passed 4,300 miles from the moon, sending back very valuable scientific information by wireless. This rocket discharged a yellow sodium vapour cloud at a distance of 68,800 miles from the earth. On 4th January the rocket passed the moon and was observed shortly afterwards 263,000 miles away. On the afternoon of 7th January it was 625,000 miles out from the earth; radio contact had been lost a little while before. On the same day there was a remarkable event. It was stated that the rocket had travelled over nine million miles. And on 14th January it was announced that it had reached a maximum speed of twenty miles per second. The explanation of this apparent riddle was, however, quite simple. The moon rocket had become the first artificial planet of the sun, around which it was now in orbit, and it was thus more logical to relate its speed to the sun rather than to the earth. The earth's orbit is some 586 million miles and the terrestrial year has a duration of twelve months; the rocket's orbit is about 625 million miles in length, while its year lasts for some fifteen months. At the furthest point from the sun, the artificial planet is nearer the orbit of Mars than that of the earth. (*See also Postscript, p. 333.*)

The storming of the heavens continued. Manned vehicles follow unmanned ones; the primitive firework, once also known as the 'rocket', had developed into the spaceship.

So far, so good. On the other hand, we know that the earth's gravitational field is really infinite. Should this seem exaggerated and without practical importance, it must be remembered that the moon is an ever-present reminder that the earth's gravitational effects do reach far out into space, and are still strong enough 240,000 miles away to hold the moon in orbit for millions of years; the fact that the moon also contributes slightly to this effect is quite unimportant. These facts have been taken into account by Professor Strughold in his concept of the gravisphere, referred to earlier.

Space travel is principally concerned with the zone in which the gravitational pull of one heavenly body predominates over that of other heavenly bodies. This is what Strughold means by the term 'gravisphere'. The earth's gravisphere stretches a million miles out into space, where that of the sun — the primary gravisphere of our planetary system — begins to outweigh it. Within the terrestrial gravisphere is the moon's gravisphere, which exerts its influence to a distance of 18,000 miles. The earth's gravisphere is the 'satellite zone', that is, that part of space in which the earth can, in theory, have moons or satellites.

The Thor-Able moon rockets — or more precisely, their final stages — do not in any way leave this satellite zone; their entire course lies within the earth's gravisphere. It is therefore as wrong to talk of their leaving the earth's gravitational field as it is right to call the Pioneer a possible artificial earth satellite, although the expression seems very badly chosen. In this case it would be preferable to keep to the familiar concept of the 'moon rocket', or else to employ one of the new terms which will soon become current in everyday language. If a moon rocket's final stage lands on the moon, without sending back any measurements, we speak of a 'moon messenger'; if it transmits such measurements after landing or from an orbit round the moon, it is a 'moon probe', while if it circles the moon several times it is a 'moon satellite'. The space vehicle which will one day carry men to the moon will be a 'moon ship'.

The U.S. Air Force immediately corrected the mistake about 'leaving the gravitational field'. General Yates, Air Force Commander at Cape Canaveral, issued the following declaration: "A press handout — prepared long before the launching of the 'moon rocket' and generally quite correct — inadvertently contained a technical inaccuracy which is obviously causing much confusion. The new space-age concepts seem almost as complicated as the actual technical problems of space travel. In the third series of handouts, issued during the tests, the remark about the earth's gravitational field escaped us. It is nevertheless a fact that in theory the moon rocket would not even have escaped from the earth's gravitational field if it had attained the required velocity. Clearly, before the next attempt, all of us who are responsible for talking about our own work to newspaper and other reporters must make ourselves more familiar with the terminology of space travel . . ."

The creators of astronautical terms — the International Astronautical Federation even has a committee for such problems — may have to wrestle for a long time to achieve clear concepts and distinctions. The terms 'escape velocity', 'conquest of gravity' and our old friend the 'moon rocket' will not be given up readily. And, anyway, none of us has yet forgotten Jules Verne.

Once men begin to travel into space, the question of the height above the earth's surface at which space begins will be studied more closely. Some 625 miles up the atmosphere passes through a zone of rarefaction known as the exosphere before giving way to the almost complete vacuum of space. It is, however, the end of atmospheric effects which determines the boundary between atmosphere and space, as far as manned space flight is concerned. Between heights of nine and twelve miles, for instance, atmospheric pressure ceases to act. The human organism can no longer obtain supplies of oxygen at a height of nine miles, while at twelve miles the air pressure is not sufficient to stop our body fluids from evaporating abruptly. Beyond these limits the atmosphere is, with regard to these phenomena, already partly 'space-equivalent'. Beyond altitudes of fifteen miles we need a hermetically-sealed cabin, from twenty-five miles protection against cosmic rays is required, while at thirty-five miles the fastest aircraft can climb no further; at an altitude of sixty-five miles sunlight is no longer scattered by the atmosphere, beyond seventy-five miles we are outside the meteor-absorbing air layers, and at about 120 miles atmospheric drag is almost zero. This is the end of the detectable atmosphere, the boundary of its mechanical effects. From a height of 125 miles onwards the atmosphere is 'fully equivalent to space'.

The new term 'aerosphere' has recently been applied to flight up to a height of nine miles. At altitudes between ten and 120 miles flying conditions are more or less 'equivalent to space', and this intermediate zone between aeronautics and space flight is known as the 'aeropause'. Flights at altitudes above 125 miles are true space flights, since they take place in Kepler conditions where the laws of celestial mechanics or astrodynamics are completely unaffected by atmospheric resistance. When the space traveller ultimately leaves the upper atmosphere at a height of about 625 miles, he first passes into circumterrestrial space which extends for some 38,000 miles. Travelling further, he passes into cislunar space which finishes 240,000 miles from the earth; making course for the moon, he enters the lunar gravisphere and, on leaving the moon's orbit, moves out into translunar space. At a distance of one million miles, he quits the earth's gravisphere and enters upon interplanetary space.

These were the steps in man's preparation for space travel. The British rocket engineer A. V. Cleaver prophesied in 1953 that the unmanned moon probe would not be a reality until 1985; it has, therefore, arrived twenty-seven years early. Human space flight, too, will become a reality earlier than many think. That it will be a costly adventure is another story.

*   *   *

WHERE WILL IT END?

But where does all this lead? What is the use of these undreamed-of, colossal efforts in man hours and materials? Are there not more urgent problems to deal with on the earth? Should we not first concentrate on building houses, schools and hospitals, or on raising the standard of living and easing the burden of work, before thinking of space flight?

Professor Heinz Haber, who was called by General Armstrong in 1949 to the Space Medicine Division, founded and led by Professor Strughold, once said: "However strange it may sound, space flight is directed towards our own planet. Space flight, as represented by the construction of a space station, is a reasonable project which will, at the proper time, be completely realistic and offer tremendous prospects. From this platform in space man will look down upon the earth, not up to other worlds in the heavens. We must take an interest in our own world . . ."

Hermann Oberth commented on this vital question as follows: "No one can answer this question to a man who does not know what it is, like Faust, to strive after knowledge. And the man who does know this questing spirit knows the answer. For him it is quite natural that everything that can be studied should be plumbed to the depths and that the undiscovered should be revealed."

Arthur C. Clarke has even tried to look back on this beginning of the interplanetary era from the viewpoint of A.D. 3000. The whole history of mankind up to the 20th century appears

A Vanguard rocket on its launching pad at Cape Canaveral.

The Black Knight at Farnborough. Originally designed exclusively for research purposes, it may now become the basis of Britain's first satellite programme.

to us like the prologue to some great drama, played out on the front of the stage before the curtain goes up on the complete setting. To innumerable generations that tiny forestage, the planet Earth, was the entire creation. Towards the end of that mysterious century the curtain began to rise slowly but incessantly, till man finally realised that the Earth was only one world among many, and the Sun a star among other stars . . .

* * *

Not even the scientist himself can tell exactly what will be the future course of development. He has been compared, by Professor de Broglie, to a weaver at his task. "The weaver who — facing the back of his work — is busily engaged on a tapestry, perhaps does not form any opinion of the true character of the product of his art. But its meaning will be clear to him on the day when he turns it over and looks at the front. So perhaps one day will human thought, having reached a higher plane of development beyond the boundaries of time and space, understand the full meaning of the work which it now untiringly strives to complete, as the continuation and consummation of life. This is the last hope which comforts the seeker, as he sits in the evening of his life musing on his finished task."

The artificial satellite can be a blessing to the whole earth provided that mankind has both the will and the wit to apply this and other achievements of modern science at last to peaceful ends.

x

"At present the word astronautics still gives laymen a shiver and makes many conservative-thinking scientists smile."

Dr. Walter Dornberger, 1955.

CHAPTER VIII

THE RACE TO THE STARS

First steps with rockets — Relativistic flight and photon rockets — The photon-rocket controversy — We need not give up

FIRST STEPS WITH ROCKETS

IF we liken the conquest of space to the discovery of the earth by the early sailors, we can say that it has suddenly become possible, in the middle of the 20th century, to discover the world for a second time; advances in technology and the predictions of science have made possible this enterprise, which would have been difficult to imagine only fifty years ago. Again and again the question mark written across some unsolved problem was accompanied by an indication that the solution would be found by a flight through space.

The engineers and scientists who set about making preparations for space travel had not only overcome the tremendous difficulties, theoretical and practical, involved in the realisation of their projects, but also to contend with the fanciful ideas handed down for so long. But neither obstacle could check the enthusiasm of the aspirants to space adventure, who were already working to boldly-conceived timetables. New theories and carefully-computed space-flight projects were developed, which deeply stirred the imagination of the participants and of the general public. It was soon scarcely possible for the uninitiated reader of reports and plans in this field to distinguish between fact and wishful thinking.

Human history can, if we choose, be divided into three epochs: The Continental, The Oceanic and the Atmospheric.

We are now in the Atmospheric epoch, and the interplanetary era — often discussed and now approaching — is a part, probably the crowning part, of it, the consummation of man's laborious achievement of flight. What is so readily referred to as the 'greatest technical challenge' is nothing less than an element in and a consequence of the technical and scientific developments of the 19th and 20th centuries.

Centuries ago, the idea of space travel was no more than a challenge to the imagination. When Christian Kindermann, at the time the aerial balloon was invented, described a trip to Mars by airship, mankind did not even know anything about the nature of the envelope of air which surrounds our earth. The atmosphere was, in their minds, a shoreless ocean enclosing all the heavenly bodies. When it was finally realised that the earth's atmosphere has, in fact, an upper limit, the situation seemed hopeless. It was the proof that the "old legend of stones that fall from Heaven" was more than a superstition which first provided a clue, since, if bodies can reach the earth from space, it must be possible to transport bodies in the opposite direction, into space.

This was the basic idea in Jules Verne's famous book *From the Earth to the Moon*. The French author had heard astronomers say that a body reaching the earth from space has a speed of seventy miles per second, and that, in consequence, a similar initial velocity must be imparted to a body before it can leave the earth. The fastest movement in Jules Verne's day was that of a cannon-ball; this, therefore, was the basis of his 'moon shot'.

It was only at the beginning of the 20th century that serious technical books on rocket flight and space travel began to appear, among them Oberth's pamphlet *Rockets into Planetary Space*, published in 1923. From this moment onwards the imaginative thinkers could, to an ever-increasing extent, obtain support from the calculations of specialists, and subsequently even from the first practical results of the new technique of rocketry.

*　　　*　　　*

Where do we stand today on the long and laborious road to space travel? Are we still a long way off, or are we nearing the goal?

Dr. Eugen Sänger answered these questions, in another connection, when he declared: "Science assumes nowadays that our universe was formed a few hundred thousand years ago, and with it our earth, a lost and apparently completely undistinguished particle of dust in the cosmos. Only for roughly one ten-thousandth part of this period has there been seen on our planet the strange — but probably not unique — spectacle of an apparently quite ordinary side branch of the tree of biological development becoming aware of its own existence and of the laws of surrounding nature, and becoming man in the deliberate utilisation of these natural laws. Perhaps even before the discovery of fire, this creature may, some 500,000 years ago, have raised longing eyes to the far distant corners of the earth and of the universe; yet it is scarcely 5,000 years since he became a sailor and an astronomer, and many of us still alive can remember how, just about fifty years ago, he invented the aeroplane as an instrument of his determination to conquer distance. Today we, the descendants of this astonishing race, are seeing the first groping experiments in space travel, which will enable us to leave our birthplace, the earth, not only with our eyes or with our imaginations, but in body."

What Dr. Sänger cautiously called "the first groping experiments in space travel", were considered by Willy Ley, the chronicler of rocket development, as "the beginning of space travel". This 'beginning' was, for him, marked by the successful launching on 24th February 1949 of an American rocket — the two-stage assembly of project 'Bumper', comprising a WAC Corporal rocket and a V-2 — which penetrated into space. Carried by the larger rocket, the smaller Corporal reached a height of 244 miles, thus travelling far beyond the earth's atmosphere.

This experiment crowned a development which had begun 700 years before with the crude fire arrow of a Chinese soldier; the dreamers' visions have shown in many forms how they hope it will end — in the construction of a spaceship. The pioneers of this development, too, have had a hard and bitter struggle with the scepticism and unimaginativeness of their contemporaries. And 20th-century man, usually so well-informed and progressive, was frequently quite as obstinate about everything to do with space travel as his forefathers had been about the steam engine.

When Hermann Oberth published in 1923 his pamphlet containing the first complete theory of rocket flight in space outside the terrestrial atmosphere, he was met with the same 'never' which almost every revolutionary innovator in technical matters had encountered before him. For instance, a letter to the respected journal *Zeitschrift für den mathematischen und physikalischen Unterricht* said: "Even if we are prepared to believe the author when he claims that his machines can reach cosmic velocities, repeated changes in these speeds would only be possible with unacceptable losses of matter. True, one should never say 'Never', but we believe that the time to study such problems is not yet, and will, as far as one can see, never come."

Professor Riem, writing in *Umschau* in Frankfurt, declared that the idea of overcoming the earth's gravity was always leading to new excesses of fantasy: "Most authors have not bothered to explain how this is to be done. But now, completely in contrast, comes a recently-published small pamphlet by Hermann Oberth, an engineer who is concerned solely with the problem of breaking away from the earth. The method by which the author believes that — using every modern technical means — he can construct an apparatus for this purpose is so striking that it should be known to a wider public . . . Only the expert can judge how far the technical assumptions for this apparatus are correct. However, with regard to the possibility of travelling with this device into the vast spaces where the earth's gravity ceases and there is no air, it must be pointed out that the reaction effect of a rocket requires the presence of a mass of air which must resist its thrust and have a certain degree of elasticity. But the author appears to think that this holds good in the layers of air at such great heights. This is certainly not true. Even at heights of six to twelve miles the air is so rarefied that it can offer no appreciable resistance to the exhaust gases, which must therefore escape completely ineffectively."

Yet once more the great struggle against a new idea broke out. Neither scientific reports nor the most stupid counterproofs were lacking. As this example shows, it was quite possible for an otherwise honoured professor to err unpardonably. The fact is that the rocket jet has absolutely no need of any mass of air to resist its reaction.

A banker who intended to support Oberth's proposed experiments financially was given an expert opinion on Oberth's book. This 'expert opinion' stated that the calculations were in themselves correct, but that the basic assumptions were wrong.

What was wrong with the assumptions was not stated, nor did Oberth ever find out. But today we know that, scarcely twenty years later, a great new industry — the rocket industry — was founded on these 'wrong assumptions'.

As a young man, Dr. Sänger had similar experiences when he wished to begin rocket experiments in 1933, in a modest laboratory in Vienna, and asked the Austrian Government for support. The Secretary of State in the responsible Ministry passed Sänger's extensive report on trials with constant-thrust rocket combustion chambers to one of his technical advisers, who returned it to Dr. Sänger with ironical marginal notes and the following comment:

"In reply to your letter of 26th December 1933, I must inform you that the Federal Ministry of Defence, having examined your rocket project, cannot see its way to study this in further detail, since the basic principle of your design (the use of liquid hydrocarbons and liquid oxygen) does not seem to be practically realisable by reason of the explosive character of the combustion of the fuels named.

"3rd February 1934.
"Dr. Leitner.
"Technical Adviser."

How did the thunder of the V-2s sound ten years later in the ears of the writer of this report?

It was not even the case that the prophets were unhonoured in their own country alone. In 1934 the British Under-Secretary of State, commenting on experiments just announced in other countries with jet engines and gas turbines, said: ". . . we are watching with interest all the work on jet engines abroad, but scientific investigation here has shown that this process can in no way seriously compete with the combination of motor and airscrew . . ."

Six years later the Austrian engineer Count Helmuth von Zborowski was told that upon investigation his plans were 'impossible'. He wanted to use nitric acid as a rocket fuel in the first experiments carried out by Bayerische Motorenwerke. Hereupon the responsible department of the Reich Air Ministry produced a report that nitric acid was useless as a rocket fuel and should not therefore be tried. A few years later nitric acid, together with hydrogen peroxide and liquid oxygen, played an important part in rocket technique.

At the same time Dr. Walter Dornberger, working at the Rocket Research Station near Kümmersdorf, experienced "the dark despair of the hours of failure and the eternal struggle against human ignorance and lack of faith". During these pioneer days of rocketry, the sceptics were never silent. Since the work on rockets in Germany was kept secret, it was scientifically 'proved' that they were impossible at the very moment when large liquid-fuel rockets were being launched. Laughter at the expense of the 'rocket maniacs' was still heard against the thunder of the first two V-2s launched against England. It was only silenced when the rockets had destroyed houses and killed people.

At that time developments were principally directed towards weapons. Twenty years later, when the same men began to discuss rocket flight into space, Dr. Dornberger, now consulting engineer to a U.S. rocket manufacturer, wrote: "At present such a word as astronautics still gives laymen a shiver and makes many conservative-thinking scientists smile." Nothing had changed.

* * *

The appearance of the first artificial satellites clarified this position temporarily. Satellites, space stations, rocket flights to the moon were all topical, and already almost 'official', steps towards space travel. As the first giant four-stage American rockets reached heights of more than 4,000 miles in 1957, many 'armchair criticisms' were immediately answered.

But then the opponents of this technical advance raised a new cry of 'impossible'. They agreed that unmanned, instrumented rockets might perhaps one day fly to the moon, but the other suns, the distant fixed stars of the Milky Way, would be eternally unattainable to man. For, even were it possible to travel at the speed of light, it would take more than four years to reach the nearest fixed star, and 1,500,000 years to the nearest galaxy.

When the discussion had reached this point, Dr. Eugen Sänger provided — at a Conference in Freudenstadt of his Institute for Research into the Physics of Jet Drives — the exact scientific answer to the question as to what would happen if men were one day to fly through interstellar space at speeds approaching that of light.

RELATIVISTIC FLIGHT AND PHOTON ROCKETS

It is 8th February 1956 in Freudenstadt; the pretty mountain resort in the Black Forest, rebuilt after the war, lies under a heavy blanket of snow. For twenty-four hours the second cold spell of this exceptionally cold winter has held the country in its iron grip. The streets are quiet, the snow deadens the noise of traffic and few are bold enough to leave their warm homes.

But there is great activity in the large Lecture Room in the

[handwritten manuscript in German cursive]

From Dr. Sänger's draft manuscript of his first lecture.

Freudenstadt Town Hall. The first International Congress of the Stuttgart Institute for Research into the Physics of Jet Drives is nearing its end. A select circle of leading specialists from ten countries has met for the fifth technical session of this Conference, which is devoted to rockets and ram-jets. The chairman is Professor Leonid Sedov, of the Soviet Academy of Sciences, always friendly and smiling. The scientists and engineers present are from Belgium, Britain, France, Holland, Italy, Sweden, Switzerland, the Soviet Union and the U.S.A., all brilliant representatives of their special fields, who had seen Sedov for the first time in the company of Western rocket experts, six months earlier, at the Sixth International Astronautical Congress in Copenhagen.

This fifth session of lectures is characterised by one or two striking, one is almost tempted to say avant-garde, subjects; this morning a young mathematician of the Jet-drive Research Institute spoke of the direct generation of electricity by nuclear decay processes for heating the arc in ram-jet systems. And young Dr. Friedward Winterberg, of the Research Association for the Utilisation of Nuclear Energy, has just finished his lecture on utilising nuclear fission to achieve maximum-energy rockets.

The tension is now visibly reaching its peak. There is still a paper by Dr. Sänger on the programme which promises to give, once and for all, clear information about these mysterious recent researches. As the lecturer mounts the platform, there is an expectant hush. Dr. Sänger suggests that he should dispense with his remarks on the flight mechanics of photon rockets, since the hour is late, and discussion of the two previous lectures of the day seem more important. The audience protests, shuffling its feet like students, making it quite clear that they do not wish to miss his paper. Amid the disturbance Dr. Sänger says: "I am forced to take your reaction as an invitation to read my paper notwithstanding." The subject is clearly a delicate one, since the lecturer thinks it necessary to begin with a sort of apology.

"If we think back a quarter of a century in rocket development we can readily see that most of the things presented during this Congress as technical facts or serious projects were then still hair-raising fancies to the majority of engineers and scientists. I would like to use this experience as an introduction to my talk on the flight mechanics of a still hypothetical rocket system in which the propulsion jet reaches the absolute maximum velocity obtainable — i.e., the velocity of light — that is, the photon rocket."

Many of the audience know that, three years before, Dr. Sänger had spoken, at the Fourth International Astronautical Congress held at Zürich, on the fundamental principles of such rockets and the exceedingly difficult technical problems they pose. Photon rockets are rockets with engines having a propulsive jet consisting of a beam of light concentrated in an inconceivable fashion. Science has long known that light produces a thrust. The light quanta, or photons, have virtually no mass but move at the highest speed occurring — or even possible — in the universe, that is the speed of light, which reaches 186,000 miles per second.

"Before dealing with these difficult but by no means insuperable technical problems," continues the speaker, "one would naturally like to know more precisely what we can expect from this new technical instrument. I shall devote my remarks today particularly to this subject."

The weapons experts in the audience ask themselves whether these photon beams — exceedingly concentrated light beams — would not provide an indescribably refined weapon, like a gigantic flame-thrower. But Dr. Sänger already has an answer to this question. "I do not wish to touch upon incidental applications of photon rockets, such as the idea that such powerful beams of photons might, in certain circumstances, be an effective defence against the 'ultimate weapon', the intercontinental ballistic missile, by directing such rays from the ground against rocket missiles in a beam which would melt everything it touched.

"On the contrary, I shall restrict myself to their use purely as a means of propulsion for space vehicles, and even then to the mechanics of flight involved."

This is an important point, for a few days later Dr. Sänger is to be accused of promulgating fanciful ideas, and of describing a propulsion unit the practicability of which no one can substantiate. But the speaker has no intention of dealing with these difficult technical problems, of which he is naturally well aware.

"Even the flight mechanics of the photon rocket lead us to such vertiginous conclusions, which almost begin to give technology the appearance of a metaphysical process, that the subject calls for special treatment."

The late-comers, pushing in at the door, unable to find a seat, are just in time to hear the speaker's final defence.

"I can state the results quoted here originate in a research study carried out at the Glenn L. Martin Corporation, Baltimore. These results are now made public. Martin's are well known as one of the principal firms in the American satellite programme."

Silently and unnoticed a tape-recorder in the hall is recording the lecturer's historic words; unfortunately the tape is

inadvertently wiped clean soon afterwards, before anyone
realises the import of this tremendous moment in the history of
science. But it has been copied, and provides an exact record of
Dr. Sänger's statement of the hypothesis on which his calculations are based.

"We assume the availability of a photon rocket engine achieving complete, or at least highly efficient, transformation of mass
into radiant energy, converting the fuel reserves carried in the
photon rocket entirely or almost entirely into light quanta,
which are discharged at the speed of light in a predetermined
direction. Let us further assume that such a vehicle is being
propelled in a straight line through space, freed from the effects
of gravity and resistance, by the photon-rocket drive . . ."

Limitations of this kind are quite legitimate, for they simply
mean that the scientific worker has founded his calculations on
certain stated conditions; this will facilitate applying them to
special cases, after dealing with the general case initially. Dr.
Sänger later wrote in his report on the mechanics of photon
drives: "I have tried to lay the foundation of a relativistic jet-
drive mechanics, generalised to the maximum possible extent,
in which the mechanics of photon drives is a special case —
here the most important — all other drive systems for vehicles,
e.g., chemical and nuclear-chemical rockets, ram-jets, turbo-jets,
turbo-propeller engines, and even the drives for water and land
vehicles, wheel drives and biological walking systems are
further special cases . . ."

The blackboards near the platform are slowly covered with
numbers and formulæ which tell the expert how Dr. Sänger
made his calculations. He talks of the 'proper velocity', and the
'proper-time velocity' of the photon rocket, and demonstrates
that the proper travelling speed can exceed the velocity of light
after a certain time. "This conclusion makes us stop and think,"
he says, "and we begin to be intrigued by the nature of this
remarkable proper speed, which can exceed the speed of light
at will."

The audience is becoming restive; one can feel their mental
resistance, for they have known for decades that the speed of
light is the highest speed possible in the universe and cannot be
exceeded by anyone or anything.

Only a few days after this sensational lecture, letters carry around the world the story that Dr. Sänger has been shaking the foundations of Einstein's Special Theory of Relativity, seeking to prove that the velocity of light is not a limit, but can be exceeded.

Nach einer entsprechenden Zahl von Messungen wird man feststellen, daß zwischen den jeweiligen Meßreihen der Erdbeobachter und der Besatzung die bekannten für beliebige Eigenbeschleunigungen zutreffenden relativistischen Gleichungen bestehen:

$$v/c = \frac{1-(m_e/m_{e_o})^2}{1+(m_e/m_{e_o})^2} = \tanh(v_e/c) \qquad (1a), (4a)$$

$$dt/dt_e = \cosh(v_e/c) \qquad (2a)$$

$$b/b_e = \cosh^{-3}(v_e/c) \qquad (3a)$$

$$ds/ds_e = (\sinh v_e/c)/(v_e/c) \qquad (5a)$$

Hinter diesen harmlosen Beziehungen verbirgt sich die ganze Mystik des Erlebens der Besatzung unseres Photonenfahrzeuges, die allerdings in ihrer vollen Wucht erst bei jenen hohen Fluggeschwindigkeiten v zum Ausdruck kommt, die sich der elektromagnetischen Signalgeschwindigkeit c nähert, wo also infolgedessen jede Nachrichtenverbindung zwischen Erdbeobachter und Besatzung abreißt und damit auch kein unmittelbarer Vergleich der gegenseitigen Messungen mehr möglich ist.

The core of Dr. Sänger's first lecture, with the formulæ he used. (From the report on the conference, published by Verlag Flugtechnik/Ernst von Olhausen.)

The tape-recording reveals what Dr. Sänger actually said, even before publication of the research report on photon drives and the Conference proceedings: "It may be useful for a number of purposes to take stock of the ultimate consequences of developments in space travel which seem conceivable in the present state of physical knowledge, even though we cannot have any clear idea of the future technical possibilities of realising such developments.

"I will shortly summarise some of the consequences of combining atomic energy and space travel, the two great fields of technology which are at present occupying mankind. The only physical hypotheses we shall make are a very extensive transformation of matter into energy and the validity of the Special Theory of Relativity, two hypotheses which seem to be fully confirmed experimentally, even though the technical realisation of the former is still in progress as nuclear engineering advances.

"If the bulk of fuel carried in a rocket is very largely transformed into energy and ejected in a controlled direction, the

velocity of discharge of the jet approaches the velocity of light
and the proper mass of the jet is reduced. In the limiting case
of complete transformation of the mass into radiated energy,
the velocity attained is equal to that of light and the proper
mass becomes zero, while the fuel is discharged in the form of
field quanta, e.g., as photons, neutrinos, gravitons, etc.

"If the jet velocity approaches that of light, as in a cyclotron,
or attains this velocity, as in any searchlight or in the still hypothetical quantum rockets, then, applying the above hypotheses
and the known laws of rocket technique, we know that the
velocity of flight will approach the speed of light, without the
total mass of the rocket exceeding practical limits.

"According to the familiar laws of classical mechanics, such
a vehicle would in one year cover the astronomical distance
known as a light year; thus within the life span of a man, journeys of several tens of light years would be possible, reaching in
ideal conditions to the fixed stars in the neighbourhood of our
sun. The range possible within a man's life and governed by
the required mass of the rocket would only cover a tiny part of
our galaxy. It will not be possible for man to reach its centre,
which is at a distance of some 30,000 light years, much less
the nearest galaxy — the nebula of Andromeda — which is
1,500,000 light years away. We all know that the laws of classical mechanics begin to become perceptibly inaccurate, once the
velocity of a body relative to an observer exceeds only one-
tenth of the speed of light; these laws must be replaced by the
laws of the Special Theory of Relativity, at higher relative
velocities, i.e., at the speeds which we are now considering.

"The basis of this relativistic mechanics is the fact that time
flows more slowly on a moving body than at the point where the
observer stands, e.g., slower than the time recorded by an astronomer on the earth watching the spaceship. If the velocity of a
rocket as measured by this observer comes within a fraction of
a millimetre per second of the velocity of light, then one whole
terrestrial year for the rocket's crew and engines will correspond
to a single second of the earthbound observer's time. This proposition of the theory of relativity, so exceedingly strange to our
traditional ideas, has been brilliantly confirmed in practice by
the findings of cosmic-ray research.

"At the upper edge of the stratosphere, the impact of the

primary particles of cosmic radiation — moving at almost the speed of light — on the molecules of atmospheric air produces mesons which decay by radioactivity so rapidly that they exist for only two-millionths of a second. At this immense speed they ought, by classical mechanics, to cover some 600 yards in so short a time. In fact, however, they are actually detected by instruments on the earth's surface. Since their speed is within a few miles per second of that of light, the dilation of the terres-

	5	4	3	2	1
TYPE OF MASS	MASS CARRIED ABOARD AND DISCHARGED WITH ACCELERATION	MASS CARRIED ABOARD AND DISCHARGED WITHOUT SPEED	EXTERNAL MASS, ACCELERATED WITH THE SPACE VEHICLE	VEHICLE MASS	EXTERNAL MASS TO BE TAKEN UP INTO SPACE VEHICLE
TRAJECTORY					
PROPER MASSES	dm_{e5}	dm_{e4}	dm_{e3}	m_{e2}, dm_{e2}	dm_{e1}
RELATIVE TO SPACE VEHICLE'S CREW:					
SPEEDS	$\longleftarrow -v'_5$	0	$\longleftarrow -v'_3$	0	$\longleftarrow -v'_1$
INERTIAL MASSES	dm'_5	$dm'_4 = dm_{e4}$	dm'_3	$m'_{e2} = m_{e2}$	dm'_1
IMPULSES	dI'_5	0	dI'_3	0	dI'_1
RELATIVE TO EXTERNAL OBSERVER:					
SPEEDS	$\longrightarrow +v_5$	$\longrightarrow +v_4 = +v_2$	$\longrightarrow +v_3$	$\longrightarrow +v_2$	$\longrightarrow +v_1$
INERTIAL MASSES	dm_5	dm_4	dm_3	m_2, dm_2	dm_1
IMPULSES	dI_5	dI_4	dI_3	I_2, dI_2	dI_1

Dr. Sänger's table of possible mass conversion.

trial observer's time relative to the proper time of the particle is 100 to 1; thus the meson's life appears to the physicist on earth 100 times longer, travelling in this 'extended life' (as the terrestrial observer sees it) 100 times farther. The meson thus easily penetrates from the upper stratosphere to the earth's surface, a distance which the observer estimates at perhaps 20,000 yards. If an observer on the meson were to measure the distance, the simultaneous relativistic contraction would reduce it to only 200 yards.

"The crew of a spaceship moving relative to the earth at a

speed approaching the velocity of light would be in a precisely similar position. The life of the crew appears to the terrestrial observer to be extended as their speed approaches the velocity of light, like the life of the Immortals; they can thus survive many generations of earth-dwellers. Despite this, the crew has no sensation of living differently or more slowly than on the earth; the slowing down of time on board the rocket, as seen by the terrestrial observer, can only become apparent to them when they return to this observer and compare calendars. This stretching of proper time on board the spaceship, which makes the life of the crew and the running of the rocket engines proceed more slowly in the earthbound observer's reckoning, produces the important effect that the spaceship can — in a few rocket years and with a reasonable size of rocket — cover distances which the terrestrial observer measures in millions of light years. The spaceship can consequently not only reach the centre of our galaxy within the crew's lifetime (not, however, in that of the terrestrial observer), but can also reach other galaxies millions of light years distant.

"Since we are forced in our technical planning to compare two magnitudes from two different frames of reference — the crew's proper time and the astronomical distances measured by the terrestrial observer — we reach the conclusion that the space vehicle can exceed the speed of light considerably."

This then is the "velocity in excess of light", which is to arouse so much attention, excitement, opposition and criticism after the Freudenstadt lecture and its discussion in the Press.

Dr. Sänger, who has no intention of shaking the foundations of the Special Theory of Relativity, continues: "If we compare the proper time of the spaceship (in strict accordance with the rules of physics) with the distances as measured on board (which latter undergo the same relativistic contraction as the times measured), the resulting speeds are naturally always below the velocity of light, as relativity theory demands. But a relativistic distance between starting-point and goal, depending on and varying with the speed at any moment, is of no practical value to a man planning a space trip. He is obliged to restrict himself to the distances quoted by the terrestrial astronomer, and to refer to space flight at so and so many times the speed of light, exactly as in jet flying one speaks of multiples of the speed of sound.

"These ideas, simple in themselves, show that any type of rocket drive with a jet velocity approaching or equalling the speed of light will enable man to travel any astronomical distance to the furthest nebula in the universe, personally and within one man's lifetime."

After this statement one can almost believe that a bomb has exploded in the hall, and that the audience has noticed it but will not admit it. The lecturer had foreseen this reaction and has included a mathematical example which he expresses as follows:

"Let us now briefly make a quantitative study of only one of the innumerable flights which could be deduced from the basic kinematic conditions quoted. Imagine a journey over an astronomical distance, in which the vehicle undergoes a constant proper acceleration of ten metres/sec./sec. for the first half of the journey, and is slowed down at the same rate over the other half of the distance; the drag of interstellar matter has no effect. The kinematic and dynamic flight conditions can be obtained easily by integrating the basic relationships, especially the most important magnitudes, the proper time of the journey in question, the required mass ratio of the spaceship and the highest 'proper Einstein number' halfway along the vehicle's path." The term 'proper Einstein number' is applied by Sänger to the ratio of the spaceship's proper speed to the relative velocity of light.

The diagram now projected on the screen should calm the excited listeners, but the figures quoted only deepen their unrest. "This gives us the following travelling times between the earth and various points in the universe: 3·5 hours to the moon, 2·83 days to the sun, 3·6 years to Alpha Centauri, 19·7 years to the centre of the Milky Way, 25·9 years to the nebula of Andromeda and 41·9 years for the — admittedly hypothetical — journey right round the universe (measured in proper time). Naturally, the time dilation effect causes a correspondingly much longer time to elapse meanwhile on the earth.

"One man's lifetime will suffice for a journey right round the universe. Whether our Solar System would still be in existence when the crew return is very doubtful, since more than 3,000 million years would have passed. During this period the crew

The English Electric Thunderbird surface-to-air guided weapon
on its automatic launcher.

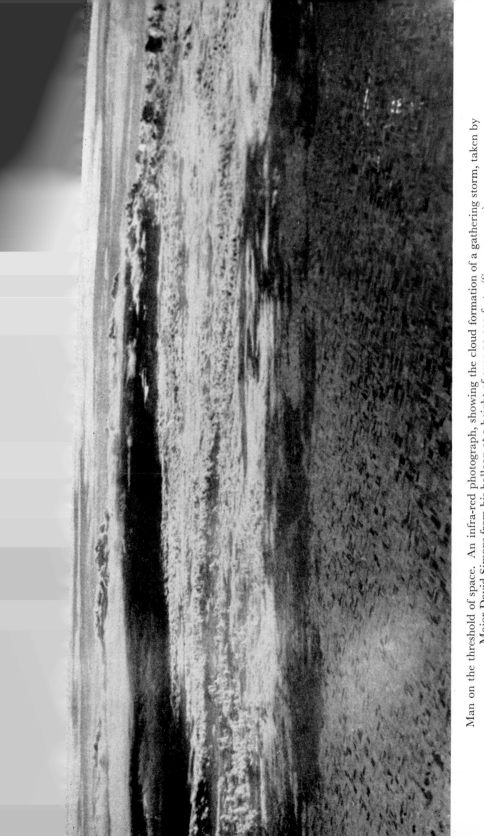

Man on the threshold of space. An infra-red photograph, showing the cloud formation of a gathering storm, taken by Major David Simons from his balloon at a height of over 50,000 feet. (See page 291.)

of the photon rocket would have been, as far as time was concerned, almost outside our world system — that is, in another world."

Some of the audience resignedly drop their pencils after this exposition, for these fantastic conclusions drawn from what is admittedly a striking theory will have to be explained to them again subsequently. But almost everybody very busily writes down Dr. Sänger's next words: "This very condensed sketch of the mechanics of photon rockets gives the impression that we are approaching the ultimate, not only of space travel, but of mankind itself, and that technology, natural science and philosophy, and even mythology and religion, are beginning to flow together in the great whole."

The audience applaud politely; speeds exceeding the velocity of light, a journey round the universe, "time almost outside our world system" — all these will have to be considered very seriously.

At this moment Dr. Sänger perceives that while some of the faces in the audience are friendly, others show bewilderment, disappointment, disagreement and hostility. Almost apologetically he sums up: "I believe we shall agree that these things must today seem to us quite as fantastic as supersonic aircraft, intercontinental missiles and unmanned satellite stations appeared to us twenty-five years ago; but they need not seem more fantastic to us in Europe than in the American aircraft and spaceship industries where, as one advertisement puts it, 'the future is measured in light years'!"

THE PHOTON-ROCKET CONTROVERSY

This lecture took effect like a delayed-action bomb. The Conference delegates left Freudenstadt without having a general discussion. They knew full well how impossible it was to deal thoroughly with the results of several years of research in a one-hour lecture, followed by half an hour of discussion. And they also knew that behind everything there lurked the danger of a misunderstanding.

The bomb exploded when the first accounts appeared in the daily papers and technical journals. Many reporters took great pains to make the difficult subject easy to grasp. I personally heard the very young representative of a leading Würtemberg

Y

paper have the new theory explained to him repeatedly until he thought he understood it. Subsequently he reported the substance of the lecture correctly and with measured enthusiasm, recording also his impression — doubtless a correct one — that even the most enthusiastic engineers felt cold shivers down the spine during Dr. Sänger's lecture. But there were other reports. Months later a contributor to a big southern German newspaper wrote: "It is a rather fine thing when a science can speculate so far into the distant future that no one is disturbed by the necessity for a good deal of fancy. The atomic scientists have long passed this stage. Their concern is only with extremely sober, scientific and complicated calculations which the layman cannot follow. At most he will find grounds for a certain vague fear, but no encouragement for fanciful prophecies or graphic dreams of the future. But the layman has had his chance regularly, for years past, when the space-travel specialists meet . . . What remarkable fancies! Someone announces the consummation of research into space travel in the form of a 'photon rocket' which, propelled by particles of light, leaves the Solar System and plunges into space at almost the speed of light. But, as we have said, no one is offended if the prophets of the far-distant future use some imagination. Every year they fill our unquiet minds with unusual images . . ."

The published works on the relativistic mechanics of jet flight released a flood of correspondence from more or less deeply stirred readers. As the theory gradually became more widely known, it was judged 'sensational', although often completely misunderstood and not infrequently wrongly stated; nor did their publication fail to raise a violent controversy among the students of physics — engineers, teachers and pupils — most of whom did not experience the conflict over Einstein's Special Theory of Relativity. This was the old controversy between what is perceptible and what is no longer perceptible, between experience and calculation. Even high-school students bought simplified copies of the discussions and, it is said, thereby caused confusion during their physics lessons. A Ministry of Education protested against the 'damage' so caused.

The criticism grew like an avalanche, impossible to check. The sober scientific theory, a masterpiece of mathematics, was cursorily dismissed by many who had not even read it in terms of a 'Utopian illusion'. The critics took offence, often with considerable enjoyment, at the final conclusions, without heeding the bases, restrictions or proofs of the hypothesis advanced.

To get an idea of the reports circulated after the Freudenstadt lecture, let us examine the summary given by a friend and collaborator of Dr. Sänger in his report: "We can now also recognise the technical importance of the temporal and spatial distortion of the cosmos. The astronomical distances are still of vital importance for the success of the 'journey', the enormously reduced proper distances govern the consumption of fuel or of the rocket's initial mass. This would render it possible within a few years of human life and with an acceptable fuel consumption to cover any desired astronomical distance, to travel even to other galaxies or around the entire universe.

"Since these enormous proper speeds must be achieved with a physically tolerable acceleration and a corresponding deceleration, a change from constant proper acceleration to constant braking must be made at the halfway point. The journey to the fixed star Alpha Centauri, 4·3 light years away, will thus only take 3·6 rocket years, while 6 years would pass on the earth. Whereas the rocket crew ages by some 7 years, their earthbound friends would have grown older by 12 years.

"The situation is much more critical, and in fact tragic, with the hypothetical journey around the universe, which has a circumference estimated at present to be 3,000 million light years. This gigantic journey would last some 42 years for the crew, who would return 42 years older, only to find the earth and sun gone, or at best grown cold, because many millions of years have passed in the meantime.

"By using a constant acceleration three times that of the earth, the time required for this 'last journey', as Dr. Sänger calls it, could be reduced to some 15 proper years, but even then there would be no return home for the crew . . ."

That is exactly what Dr. Eugen Sänger stated at Freudenstadt; this was clearly shown by the full report published soon afterwards and also by the tape-recording made during the lecture.

In the months following the Freudenstadt Conference, Eugen Sänger was overwhelmed with letters, expressing enthusiasm, friendly agreement or the strangest suggestions for collaboration in 'exploiting the idea' somewhere in the world, or else rejection, destructive criticism or wild imprecations.

On 22nd March 1956, a theoretical physicist in a noted southern German university wrote to the editor of the newspaper which had published the first full report on the Freudenstadt Conference: ". . . My criticisms bear on the fact that two vital hypotheses made by the author are false; these are his contradictions of the following statements: (1) relativity theory does not recognise speeds greater than that of light, and (2) the concept of proper velocity is foreign to this theory. Statement (2) is one of the bases of the Special Theory of Relativity, and gives it its name. Statement (1) is one of the two axioms with which Einstein starts. I observe by your quotation from the report of an esteemed colleague that he finds the same shortcomings, but that he can accept them because the conclusions which are copied from Sänger's book are correct. Prompted by correspondence showing that confusion has arisen, I judge these misgivings less indulgently . . . The author's speculations about a journey to the remotest galaxies can, in any event, never be realised because of the masses involved. If the ratio of all-up weight to payload is one to a million, which would be difficult with a payload of one ton, this gives — assuming an acceleration equal to that of gravity — a range, not allowing for return, of ten light years . . ."

But here the letter-writer was himself already mistaken. Dr. Sänger had been able to check this calculation, and found that the critic had erred by a factor of one million. In his example the range would therefore be ten million light years, and not ten.

". . . Even if we could transform the mass of the entire earth into energy," continued the writer, "this would only take us four times as far . . ."

On checking this, Dr. Sänger found that in fact "the transformation of the mass of the earth" would extend the range not four times, but 400 trillion times. Once more the critic had made a mistake, this time by a factor of 100 trillions!

Still basing his remarks on his own errors, the writer continued: ". . . it would be better to reduce the acceleration. Assuming the same mass transformation, an acceleration equal

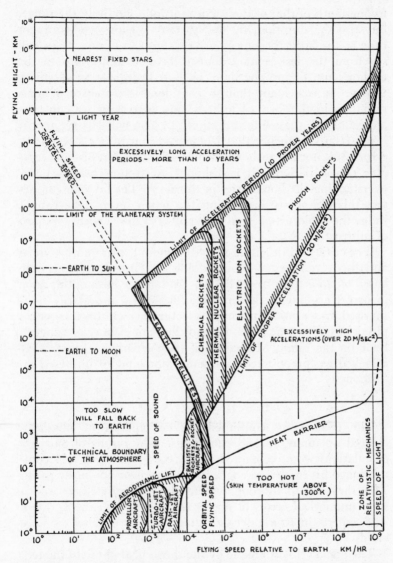

Dr. Sänger's chart of flying heights and relative flying speeds of all existing and possible types of jet-drive, for aircraft or spaceships. (From 'The Radiation Physics of Photon-Rocket Drives', R. Oldenbourg, Munich 1957.)

to one-tenth of that of the earth multiplies not only the range, but also the duration, by ten, so that — expressed in proper time — the latter becomes ten years instead of one. You will see from the last remark that I have no objections to the author's use of 'proper time' as it is legitimate in relativity theory. It is evident that so considerable a degree of mass radiation in the form of light is only possible if we can turn almost all the mass into radiation . . . You will observe that it is not relativity theory that I object to, but rather a confusing error. It is not the author's enthusiastic style, but his unacceptable generalisations. It is dishonest to arouse enthusiasm by overstepping the boundaries in this way. The layman can detect this dishonesty in reading the paper, even if he cannot judge the subject itself, and it produces in him a revulsion born of mistrust . . ."

The critic had discussed this 'dishonesty' with many laymen and discovered the revulsion in doing so. These discussions were based on an error of 100 trillions. And on the basis of this same incorrect argument, the understandable and necessarily summarised presentation in Sänger's lecture, which this theoretical physicist had not heard — he had then not even read Sänger's book on the Flight Mechanics of Photon Drives — is strongly attacked as 'preposterous nonsense' and said to be based on 'dishonesty'.

*   *   *

The controversy continued. A colloquium of physicists cleared up many misunderstandings. The results of Sänger's calculations were recognised as correct. Pope Pius XII commissioned his experts to check the entire theory point by point. This they did so thoroughly that they actually discovered a small numerical error, of no importance for the theory itself. The experts in Rome decided that Sänger's conclusions were valid.

The harsh criticism made by the theoretical physicist quoted, who had made a mistake of 100 trillions, called for a defence from Dr. Sänger. The critic finally admitted his mistake:

". . . pointed out to me that my example contained an error which has very serious consequences. I withdraw with apologies the conclusions I reached from the example. Meanwhile

Herr Sänger has sent me his publication on the Mechanics of Photon Drives, from which the contested concepts — of a velocity in excess of that of light, and of proper speed — were taken. I am pleased to find that Herr Sänger employs these concepts with commendable discretion, writing on page 46 that the proper-time velocity and the proper-distance velocity are formal magnitudes which have no physical reality in the sense that $V = s/t$ has one . . .''

The attacked report contained the following clear and unmistakable statement: "When the rocket engineer has brought relativity theory into his calculations, he must lay aside his traditional ideas and pay great attention to the position of the observer whenever times, distances or speeds are quoted. The fact is that these figures now begin to vary very markedly. The observer who has stayed on the earth must not, for example, apply the classical form of the formula for the drive of a jet engine to a departing photon rocket, but only the relativistic expression, which demonstrates that the velocity of the rocket relative to the earth is always somewhat less than the velocity of light. However, the rocket crew must apply the classical form of the relationship, thus reaching the surprising conclusion that the rocket can apparently exceed the speed of light indefinitely . . .''

That is how Dr. Sänger put it at Freudenstadt, how the tape machine recorded it and how it was reproduced. It was, in fact, impossible to misunderstand it, although every clear-minded person knows that the fruits of long years of research can only with difficulty be covered in a three-column report for non-mathematical readers in such a way that misunderstandings are impossible.

The delegates to the Sixth International Astronautical Congress held in Copenhagen in 1955 experienced a classic example of this fact. At this Congress the American rocket engineer Krafft Ehricke for the first time spoke of the 'satelloid', a concept he had himself introduced. He applied the term to a flight vehicle circling the earth — not completely outside the atmosphere, where it could coast like a satellite — but at heights where the air drag still slowly reduces its flying speed, necessitating from time to time a small amount of drive energy. To enliven his serious, highly theoretical exposition Ehricke quoted during his lecture some examples of possible applications of this new high-level research apparatus; he thought that these satelloids would, for example, be used for research in the upper atmosphere, perhaps in the remote future when we reach the dense atmosphere of the planet Venus and cannot immediately enter it with manned vehicles.

The very next day the astonished delegates read in foreign newspapers the headline: "Rocket Engineer proposes Spaceship to Venus at Astronautical Congress."

The violent controversy provoked by Dr. Sänger's lecture led him on 18th April 1956 to write me a detailed letter, which is of such fundamental importance to the present struggle for new developments that its publication for the first time here is justified. "As you know, the lecture is itself an extract from a larger study undertaken on behalf of the space-travel industry abroad, the contents of which belong to routine research in this technical field and are in no wise sensation-seeking. Since I have simply set out the technical consequences of the Special Theory of Relativity — familiar nowadays as a fully-accepted tool of physics — I consider discussion of the content of this theory absolutely untimely; moreover it would at best make us a laughing-stock to the world. Such discussions of my book can only be useful if I, as an engineer, had happened to make mistakes in the interpretation of the theory. My book has been checked on this score by the most competent experts in technical physics and no error has yet been discovered.

"When, however, correspondence in a newspaper shows that the theoretical physicist at a respected university is bold enough to speak of carelessness and dishonesty, basing his judgment — as presumptuous as it is superficial — on a calculation in which he makes a crass error of twenty places of decimals, one can surely ignore it. Once he has opportunity to study carefully the original work which serves as the foundation, he will revise his judgment of his own accord.

"The efforts of other correspondents to reveal the philosophical aspects and consequences of modern technical trends — including the field of space travel — must be taken more seriously. Nevertheless, I do not feel that this is my rôle and must leave it to more competent persons.

"Every suggestion for examining critically the provisional

terminology for the newly discovered technical concepts is of course equally worthy of consideration. 'Proper speed' is such an appropriate parameter for calculations that rocket theory cannot dispense with it. Anyone is heartily welcome to suggest a more suitable word. 'Proper-time speed' is a concept which seems absolutely unavoidable, and if its use implies that a crew travelling to a star 4·3 light years distant will be travelling for 3·6 years of their own lives, then technology will use the expression 'velocity in excess of that of light', although this concept is open to objection from the point of view of strict theoretical physics; this has indeed always happened when a field of research passes from pure physics into applied physics, i.e., technology. A large number of new terms is necessary in the process, and they are often adapted less to the strict scientific definitions than to the inescapable demands of practical use; moreover, they must be understandable to a wide circle of readers.

"I am delighted that the young people of Germany should have accepted my lecture with enthusiasm, but am much saddened by the sceptical attitude of some representatives of the responsible generation of today, and above all by the tendency to rob our youth of this enthusiasm. This can only be judged a regrettable consequence of the long years of intellectual isolation of our nation with the result that, among other things, the technical development of two discoveries in physics which originated in Germany — the theory of relativity and nuclear fission — should have been left entirely to other countries; a further consequence is that our sceptics are completely agreeable to their taxes being used to purchase these technical achievements from abroad, as in the case of nuclear power plant.

"It is a praiseworthy task of the publicist to combat this dangerous pride and intolerance, which make people so prone to criticise new ideas because they are new . . . With this in mind I wish your book every success; I have myself achieved the publication in Germany of my book which we are discussing, at great personal sacrifice, but certainly not in order for German truculence to assert itself . . ."

*   *   *

Even the question as to the point of such undertakings, i.e., attempts to penetrate, firstly with satellites into interlunar space, followed by interplanetary spaceships and finally, perhaps, by means of photon-rocket drives to enter intergalactic and interstellar space, was revived during discussions of the mechanics of relativistic flight by the general public. Early in 1957 the Rector of the Munich Technical College, Professor Schmidt, declared: ". . . the stars are attainable and space flight may be possible, but we should still not make the attempt."

Another answer as to the purpose of such enterprises was given by Pope Pius XII, speaking to 400 participants at the Seventh International Astronautical Congress in Rome in 1956, as they gathered in the Throne Room of his summer residence at Castel Gandolfo: ". . . Some among you have gone so far as to examine the theoretical possibilities of flight to the fixed stars, revealed as the ultimate object of this work by the very name 'astronautics'. Let us not go into details; but it will not have escaped you, gentlemen, that there are moral and intellectual aspects of such an undertaking which cannot be overlooked. Such an enterprise calls for a certain picture of the world, its purpose and meaning. The Lord God, Who placed the unquenchable thirst for knowledge in the human heart, had no thought of setting a limit to man's desire to conquer, when He said to him 'make the earth subject'.

"God entrusted the whole creation to man. He set it before him that he might enter upon it and thus learn to understand more fully the infinite depths of his Creator."

*   *   *

The summit of this controversy was reached, and at the same time, in a sense, the last word was uttered by Dr. Wilfred Berger, a one-time associate of Professor Wilhelm Westphal of Berlin, writing on the problem of whether human beings can escape the effects of the passage of time: "To ensure a correct assessment of the inconceivable prospects which, if we are right, are thereby opened to mankind, it should be emphasised that Sänger's study is based, without any new hypothesis, on three fundamental points which can be considered absolutely proven in our present state of knowledge."

He then lists these three basic facts: firstly, the unchallenged, experimentally-established theory that mass, time and length are not absolute magnitudes, but are dependent on the system of reference within which they are measured; secondly, the transformation of nuclear energy into technically utilisable forms of energy; and thirdly, the existence, demonstrated by astronomers, of interstellar matter in the form of elementary particles.

True, the author also points out that the photon drive seems for the moment beyond our technical capacity. "But often one discovery suffices to bring a hypothetical idea straight away into the realm of technical possibilities. As late as 1936 Rutherford judged the use of nuclear energy to be Utopian, perhaps attainable in a hundred years. Three years later Otto Hahn discovered quite unexpectedly the fission of uranium, which yields enough neutrons to make a chain reaction possible. Six years later the first atom bomb was exploded, ninety years early by Rutherford's reckoning. That is why a physical problem should not be locked up in a desk because its technical solution is still outstanding."

WE NEED NOT GIVE UP

In 1925 Dr. Walter Hohmann, an Essen engineer, published an eighty-eight-page pamphlet entitled *The Attainability of the Heavenly Bodies*. The eighty-eight pages were filled with formulæ and tables, and addressed to experts. "The present work," wrote the author in his introduction, "seeks to demonstrate, by sober mathematical examination of all the apparent natural and imaginable difficulties, that the space-travel problem is to be taken seriously, and that we can no longer doubt that it will ultimately be successfully solved if, conscious of our objective, we set about perfecting existing technical means." In talking of 'heavenly bodies', Hohmann meant the planets of our galaxy. A few men began to ponder and discuss his calculations, but the others — the majority — simply laughed at him, many of them without having read his pamphlet.

In 1956 Dr. Eugen Sänger, also an engineer, published an eighty-eight-page pamphlet on *The Mechanics of Photon-Rocket Drives*. The eighty-eight pages were filled with formulæ and tables, and addressed to experts. In his lecture to the Seventh International Astronomical Congress in Rome, Dr. Sänger explained his research report, giving it the title of *The Attainability of the Fixed Stars*, in allusion to Dr. Hohmann's book. "Only a few highly independent thinkers have been bold enough to examine what the daring word astronautics really means, to fly to the fixed stars," he said in his preamble. "Nevertheless we must now be courageous enough to do so. The purpose of my lecture is to show you that the normal duration of human life is sufficient to allow of travelling any astronomical distance, to the very furthest limits of the cosmos . . ." A few men began to ponder and discuss his calculations, but the others — the majority — simply laughed, as they did with Hohmann, as on innumerable occasions in the history of man's struggle for new inventions.

Dr. Sänger's lecture in Rome was even clearer and more impressive than his first exposition at Freudenstadt.

"Our modern physicists have succeeded in producing in their nuclear-research apparatus beams of particles of various masses travelling at velocities near that of light, and they have also artificially produced stationary plasmas of such high temperatures that the radiation pressures exerted by these hot gases are sufficiently great to be of technical interest.

"Modern rocket engineers are close on the physicists' heels to use these mass radiations travelling at a speed equal to or approaching that of light for their rocket drives, and the rapid developments in nuclear energy technology are assisting them.

"We know precisely how modest a mass ratio is needed to give a rocket a travelling speed equal to the discharge velocity of its driving jet, so that we can see a none too remote possibility that the velocity of flight of a rocket in space can approach the speed of light. This brings the problem of the attainability of the fixed stars within our technical purview, a problem which is of considerable practical interest because of the well-known uninhabitable nature of the sun's other planets."

The critics of his new concepts, e.g., 'proper speed', 'proper-time speed' and 'velocity in excess of that of light' were answered by Dr. Sänger at Rome in the following words: "If we have no better scale by which to indicate the distance of the earth from the nebula of Andromeda than by astronomical units — 750,000 light years — and if the crew of a space rocket discovers that this distance can be covered in twenty-five years of their life, no other means of technical expression is available to us in present-day language than to say that it seems to the crew that their speed is some 30,000 times the velocity of light."

Once more he specifically stated that the relativistic flight mechanics of photon-rocket drives opens a new road, the road to the stars: ". . . it is far from true that the fixed stars can only be reached in a period covering several generations, with successive cycles of birth, growth and death, until finally the remote descendants reach the goal toward which their ancestors started out. Nor is it the case that the galaxies which are hundreds of thousands of light years away from us are essentially unattainable to us because of our restricted life span and that Nature has tied us to our tiny corner of the universe.

"There is no need for us to give up, or quietly to fold our hands on our knees. The infinite universe is small enough to be open, to its remotest bounds, to the efforts of any one of us."

*   *   *

Although the attacks of the intolerant, the mockery of the ignorant, and the criticisms of the unteachable are not yet forgotten, a certain degree of personal triumph has already come to Dr. Eugen Sänger. At the opening of the Seventh International Astronautical Congress, the famous Italian pioneer of flight, General Arturo Crocco, praised his epoch-making theory in enthusiastic words.

The seven hundred scientists and engineers of twenty-five nationalities once more heard Sänger's important conclusion: "Nature, benevolent yet hard, knows well enough why she does not allow us to turn our world into a contented paradise, but rather calls us to conquer new worlds, the last and furthest, to which photon-rocket drives are to be the key . . ."

It was a great moment when Pope Pius XII, his eyes on Dr. Sänger, declared in his address: "The common effort of all mankind to conquer the universe peaceably must underline more strongly man's consciousness of a feeling of community and unity, so that all are more deeply aware that they form together a great family of God and are children of one Father. But to come to this truth we need no less reverence for what is true, no less courage or recognition of reality, than is needed for scientific research."

*   *   *

The conflict continues. In a broadcast talk in the summer of 1957, Dr. Sänger, already a very sick man but undeterred by the enduring hostility of his quarrelsome opponents, sketched a disturbing picture which gives us food for thought: "It is necessary today to remember the deep roots of space travel in man's mind, recalling that none of its technical pioneers were thinking of nationalism, of war or of weapons, but rather of humanity and of the heavens above their heads.

"For when the technical conditions for the first steps from flight to space flight were provided by the development of rocket motors, improved combustion techniques, heat-resistant materials and automatic controls, the earth was not a noble place filled with the spirit of heroes and demi-gods, but a sleeping world charged with personal and national egoism; space travel, as an element in the natural development of humanity, seemed doomed to failure by the incomprehension of politicians, the self-centredness of scientists and the dullness of nations. But nothing could have shaken this irresponsible inertia of mind more quickly or in more terrible fashion than intercontinental missiles and hydrogen bombs, which we now see in grim reality, ready to transform the earth into yet another dead star . . ."

Are we modern men shaken? Are we strong enough to follow technical development, without thinking of war and weapons, but mindful of humanity and the heavens above us, like those early pioneers of rocket flight?

On our answer to this question, and our success or failure to combat and conquer mental inertia, will depend whether science and technology lead us into a new promised land or into the abyss. We cannot — and must not — seek to evade these questions by turning our backs on technology.

POSTSCRIPT

THE survey of early results in space-flight experiments cannot be better terminated than with a reference to the first successful moon rockets.

On 14th September 1959 two minutes after midnight (in Central Europe it was still two minutes past ten on 13th September), the payload of the second Russian cosmic rocket, commonly called Lunik II, struck the moon's surface to the east of the Sea of Serenity, near the craters of Aristillus, Archimedes and Autolycus. The giant carrier rocket had been fired on the morning of 12th September. The final stage of the rocket — 20 ft. long and weighing about $1\frac{1}{2}$ tons, with an instrument payload of 865 lb. — approached the moon with remarkable accuracy, after having achieved a burn-out velocity of 25,270 miles per hour. At the moment of firing the rocket, the moon was 235,500 miles away from the earth, and the flight lasted some 36 hours.

As this successful experiment was announced, some newspapers enthused about the opening of a new era: on 14th September 1959, they wrote, the pre-lunar era ended and the lunar era of history began. To clinch this success and the excitement it caused, the Soviet space-research workers began a further major experiment on 4th October 1959 (two years after the launching of the first artificial earth satellite, Sputnik I). Once again the objective was the moon, but the instrument capsule, once more packed with instruments and transmitters, and this time called the 'first automatic space station', was intended to circle the moon and give information about the farther side. This experiment was also successful. On 5th October, at 15.16 Central European Time, the space station reached the point on its track nearest to the moon, 4,737 miles from its surface, before passing on to its apogee, far beyond the moon's other side. At about 22.00 Central European Time on 6th October the station began its return journey towards the earth, where its signals had been clearly received everywhere. The Russian space pioneers could now proudly claim the following 'firsts': the first artificial earth satellite; the first animal-carrying satellite; the first large measurement satellite; the first artificial planet (and the first escape from the terrestrial gravisphere); the first 'hard' landing on the moon; the first circumnavigation of the moon by an automatic space station.

But the storming of the heavens continues. One of the steps soon to be taken will be made by man himself — the first space traveller,

*   *   *

Satellite	Launching vehicle	Date launched	Expiry or lifetime	Shape	Payload (lb.)	Incln. (deg.)	Orbit (miles)
Sputnik 1 (U.S.S.R.)	Undisclosed	Oct. 4, 1957	Jan. 4, 1958	Sphere	184	65	142–588
Sputnik 2 (U.S.S.R.)	Undisclosed	Nov. 3, 1957	Apl. 14, 1958	Complex	1,120	65	140–1,038
Explorer 1 (U.S.A.)	Jupiter C	Jan. 31, 1958	3–5 yr. est.	Cylinder	30·8 (18·13)	33·34	224–1,573
Vanguard 1 (U.S.A.)	Vanguard	Mar. 17, 1958	200 yr. est.	Sphere	3·25	34·25	409–2,453
Explorer 3 (U.S.A.)	Jupiter C	Mar. 26, 1958	June 27, 1958	Cylinder	31 (18·56)	33·4	121–1,746
Sputnik 3 (U.S.S.R.)	Undisclosed	May 15, 1958	19 mths. est.	Conical	2,925	65·3	135–1,167
Explorer 4 (U.S.A.)	Jupiter C	July 26, 1958	1 yr. est.	Cylinder	38·4 (25·8)	50·29	163–1,380
Project Score (U.S.A.)	Atlas	Dec. 18, 1958	Jan. 21, 1959	Atlas shell	8,750 (150)	32·3	110–920
Vanguard 2 (U.S.A.)	Vanguard	Feb. 17, 1959	10 yr. est.	Sphere	20·74	32·88	347–2,064
Discoverer 1 (U.S.A.)	Thor-Hustler	Feb. 28, 1959	Mar. 5, 1959	Cylinder	1,300 (245)	87	99–605
Discoverer 2 (U.S.A.)	Thor-Hustler	Apl. 13, 1959	Apl. 26, 1959	Cylinder	1,610 (245)	89·8	142–220
Explorer 6 (U.S.A.)	Thor-Able 3	Aug. 7, 1959	1 yr. est.	Spheroid	142	48	157–26,400
Discoverer 5 (U.S.A.)	Thor-Hustler	Aug. 13, 1959	1 mth. est.	Cylinder	1,700 (300)	Appx. 90	136–450
Discoverer 6 (U.S.A.)	Thor-Hustler	Aug. 19, 1959	1 mth. est.	Cylinder	1,700 (300)	Appx. 90	200–500

MAIN DETAILS of all the successful artificial earth satellites and space probes launched up to 12th September 1959, are presented in these two tables, which have been compiled from official U.S. and Soviet sources. The 'orbit' column lists the initial perigee and apogee, and the period quoted is the initial period of the satellite.

The payload quoted is normally the total weight of the object concerned, with the weight of scientific equipment given in parentheses where known. Designation of the Mechta launching vehicle is unofficial. Launchings up to the end of 1958 formed part of International Geophysical Year activity; current U.S. launchings are by the National Aeronautics and Space Administration (Vanguard, Explorer, Pioneer) and the Advanced Research Projects Agency of the Department of Defence (Discoverer).

Probe	Launching vehicle	Date	Expiry or lifetime
Pioneer 1 (U.S.A.) Lunar probe	Thor-Able 1	Oct. 11, 1958	43 hr. 17·5 min.
Pioneer 2 (U.S.A.) Lunar probe	Thor-Able 1	Nov. 8, 1958	42·4 min.
Pioneer 3 (U.S.A.) Space probe	Juno 2	Dec. 6, 1958	38 hr. 6 min.
Mechta or Lunik (U.S.S.R.) Space probe	T-3	Jan. 2, 1959	Indefinite
Pioneer 4 (U.S.A.) Space probe	Juno 2	Mar. 3, 1959	Indefinite
Lunik II	CH-10	Sept. 12, 1959	Appx. 36 hr.

Period (min.)	Experiments	Radio (Mc/s)	Remarks
96·17	Internal temp., press.	20·005 40·002	Batteries stopped Oct. 27, 1957.
103·7	Cosmic rays, solar u-v. and X-rays, test animal (dog Laika) temp., press.	20·005 40·002	Batteries stopped Nov. 10, 1957; satellite acceln. led to discovery of solar influence on upper-atmos. density
114·8	Cosmic rays, micrometeorites, internal and shell temps.	108 108·03	Discovery of first Van Allen radiation belt
133·7	Temps. geodetic data	108 108·03	Mercury batteries stopped Apl. 5, 1958; solar batteries should power radio indefinitely
115·87	Cosmic rays, micrometeorites, internal and skin temps.	108 108·03	Data on Van Allen belt, micrometeorite impacts
105·95	Atmos. press. and composition, positive ions, electrostatic charge and field, earth's magnetic field, solar corpuscular radiation, cosmic rays, micrometeors, temps.	20·005 40·01	Chemical and solar batteries
110·27	Corpuscular radiation, internal temp.	108 108·03	Radiation belt data
101·46	Radio transmit. record and receiving apparatus	132·435 132·905 107·97 107·94	Satellite received, recorded and re-transmitted voice messages from ground stations
125·85	Cloud cover by photocells	108 108·03	Instrumentation functioned, but satellite's wobbling motion made data interpretation difficult
95·9	Checkout of propulsion, guidance, staging, communications	Classified	Stabilisation difficulty hampered tracking
90·5	Capsule re-entry and recovery	Classified	Capsule ejection timer malfunction caused capsule impact near Spitzbergen instead of Hawaii on Apl. 14
766	High-, medium- and low-level radiation, micrometeorites, magnetic field, facsimile scanner, radio propagation, internal and surface temp. measurement, internal temp. control, solar cells	108·06 108·09 Undisclosed UHF	Digital telemetry stores data, transmits on ground command; four 20 in. × 20 in. solar-cell vanes for battery charging; auxiliary 5 lb. thrust solid rocket carried but unused
94	Capsule re-entry and recovery	Classified	Capsule ejected but not located following 'malfunction of sequencing telemetry signals'
95	Capsule re-entry and recovery	Classified	Capsule ejected but not located

Shape	Payload (lb.)	Distance (miles)	Experiments	Radio (Mc/s)	Remarks
Toroidal	84·4 (39)	70,700	Radiation, magnetic fields of earth and moon, micrometeor density, internal temp., electronic scanner	108·06	Determined radial extent of radiation band, mapped ionising flux, observed hydromagnetic oscillations of earth's magnetic field, discovered magnetic field discrepancy with theory, determined micrometeor density and measured interplanetary magnetic field
Toroidal	86·4 (34·3)	963	Total ionising radiation, cosmic-ray flux, others as Pioneer 1	108·06 108·09	Third stage failed to ignite; probe obtained data on flux, radiation, micrometeor density
Conical	12·95	63,580	Measurement of radiation in space	960·05	Discovered second radiation belt; designed velocity, 24,897 m.p.h.; attained velocity, about 24,000 m.p.h.
Spherical	3,245 (797)	In orbit round sun	Internal temp. and press., gas components of interplanetary matter, corpuscular radiation of sun, magnetic fields of earth and moon, meteoric particles in space, cosmic rays	19·997 19·995 19·993 183·6	In orbit round sun on 450-day cycle; sodium flare released and photographed from ground; probe passed within 'two lunar diameters' (about 4,300 miles) of moon; radio contact held for 62 hr.; perihelion 90·9 m. miles, Jan. 14, 1959; aphelion (est.) 122·5 m. miles, Sept. 1959
Conical	13·4	In orbit round sun	Measurement of radiation in space, test photoelectric sensor near moon	960·05	Passed within 37,300 miles of moon, not close enough (20,000 miles) to trigger photoelectric sensor nor sample moon's radiation. Tracked for 82 hr. to 407,000 miles; perihelion 91·7 m. miles, Mar. 17, 1959; aphelion (est.) 106·1 m. miles, Oct. 1, 1959; injection velocity of 24,790 m.p.h. was 188 m.p.h. below planned velocity
—	3,320 (865)	—	Made contact with moon	—	Struck moon near the Sea of Serenity. Radio contact maintained until impact

By courtesy of *Flight*

BIBLIOGRAPHY

Allen, J. A., van: Scientific Uses of Earth Satellites, London 1956.
Asimov, Isaac: I, Robot.

Barnett, L.: Einstein and the Universe, New York 1948.
Bates, D. R.: Space Research and Exploration, London 1957.
Bellamy, E.: Looking Backward, 1888.
Bense, M.: Technical existence (*Technische Existenz*), Stuttgart 1949.
Berger, W.: Photon rockets in relativistic space (*Photonraketen im relativistischen Weltraum*) in *Naturwissenschaftliche Rundschau*, June 1956. Can men escape from the passage of time? (*Können Menschen dem Ablauf der Zeit entrinnen?*) in Frankfurter Allgemeine Zeitung, July 1956.
Bernanos, G.: Against the Robots (*Wider die Roboter*), Cologne 1949.
Bizony, M. T. and Griffin, R.: The Space Encyclopedia, London 1957.
Bley, W.: They were the first (*Sie waren die Ersten*), Biberach 1953.
Blunck, R.: *Hugo Junkers*, Düsseldorf 1951.
Boyd, R. L. F. and Seaton, M. J.: Rocket Exploration of the Upper Atmosphere, London 1954.
Bredow, H.: From my notes (*Aus meinem Archiv*), Heidelberg 1950.
Broglie, L. de: Science and Civilisation—in Universitas, 1949.
Braun, Wernher von: Across the Space Frontier; Man on the Moon, London 1953.
Braun, W. von and Willy Ley: The Conquest of Mars.
Braunbeck, W.: Atomic energy, present and future (*Atomenergie in Gegenwart und Zukunft*), Stuttgart 1953. Research changes the World (*Forscher erschüttern die Welt*), Stuttgart 1956.
Burckhardt, G.: Individuality and the World (*Individuum und die Welt als Werk*), Munich 1919.
Burgess, E.: Frontier to Space, London 1955.
Büscher, G.: Men, machines, atoms (*Menschen, Maschinen, Atomen*), Munich 1952.

Campbell, J. W., jr.: Twilight, 1932; Night, 1935.
Carter, L. J.: Realities of Space Travel, London 1957. The Artificial Satellite, London 1951.
Clarke, A. C.: The Exploration of Space, London 1951.
Cleator, P. E.: Into Space, London 1954. The Robot Era, London 1955.
Couffignal, L.: Thinking machines (*Denkmaschinen*), Stuttgart 1955.
Curie, Eve: Madame Curie, Frankfurt a.M.

Daeves, K.: The role of individual personality in technical progress (*Die Rolle der Einzelpersönlichkeit für den technischen Fortschritt*), in *VDI Zeitschrift*, January 1956.
Darwin, Ch. G.: The Next Million Years.
Davis, W.: Fundamental Basis of Space Flight (Reprint), 1956.
Dessauer, F.: Researchers and Inventors change the World (*Forscher und Erfinder ändern die Welt*), Lucerne 1952. The technological struggle (*Streit*

um die Technik), Frankfurt a.M. 1956. Technical Culture: 6 Essays, Kempten 1907, 1908. Mankind and the Cosmos (*Mensch und Kosmos*), Frankfurt a.M. 1949. Röntgen: the revelation of one night (*William C. Röntgen; Offenbarung einer Nacht*), Frankfurt a.M. 1948. Atomic energy and the atomic bomb (*Atomenergie und Atombombe*), Frankfurt a.M. 1948.

Diebold, J.: Automation. The Advent of the Automatic Factory, New York.

Diringshofen, H. von: Acceleration effects in X-ray photographs (*Beschleunigungseinwirkungen im Röntgenbild*) in *Weltraumfahrt*, 1950.

Droscha, H.: Technology as a transforming force (*Die Technik als wandelnde Kraft*), report on the VDI Congress in Freiburg, in the *Frankfurter Allgemeine Zeitung*, June 1957.

Einstein, Albert and L. Infeld: The Evolution of Physics, London.

Engel, R.: Principles of describing and assessing rockets (*Richtlinien für Beschreibung und Beurteilung von Raketen*) in *Weltraumfahrt*, 1950. The Satellite Station (*Die Aussenstation*), Paris 1949.

Eugster, J.: Radiation from Space (*Weltraumstrahlung*), Berne 1955. Radiations from the stars are reaching us (*Sterne strahlen dich an*), Stuttgart 1957.

Faust, Heinrich: Tasks for measurement satellites (*Aufgaben für Messsatelliten*) in *Weltraumfahrt*, 1957.

Felt, N. E.: The Vanguard Satellite launching vehicle, Martin, Baltimore 1956.

Fontana, D.: The moving of the Vatican Obelisk (*Della transportazoine dell' Obelisco Vaticano*), Rome 1950.

Forbes, R. J.: From stone axe to ultrasons (*Vom Steinbeil zum Überschall*), Munich 1954.

Föttinger: Technology and the World Concept (*Technik und Weltanschauung*), Berlin 1916.

Gartmann, Heinz: Research into space travel (*Raumfahrtforschung*), Munich 1951. From fire arrow to space ship (*Vom Feuerpfeil zum Weltraumschiff*), Munich 1953. The men behind the space rockets, translated from *Träumer, Forscher, Konstrukteure; das Abenteuer der Weltraumfahrt*, Düsseldorf 1954. Wings of our century (*Flügel unseres Jahrhunderts*), Munich 1955. Man Unlimited, translated from *Stärker als die Technik; der Mensch in der Zerreissprobe*, Düsseldorf 1956. Rockets (*Raketen*), Stuttgart 1956. The development of the space ship (*Die Evolution des Raumfahrzeugs*) in *Weltraumfahrt*, 1953. Yearnings between dust and stars (*Sehnsucht zwischen Staub und Sternen; Gedanken über die Evolution des Weltraumfluges*) in Velhagen and Klasing's *Monatshefte*, June 1953. From Ram-jet to Photon rocket (*Vom Staustrahl zur Photonrakete*) in *Frankfurter Allgemeine Zeitung*, February 1956. Rockets in the International Geophysical Year (*Raketen im Internationalen Geophysikalischen Jahr*) in *Physikalische Blätter*, February 1956. Flight through Einstein's Wonderland (*Der Flug durch Einstein's Wunderland*), in *Frankfurter Allgemeine Zeitung*, February 1956. Tomorrow, space is ours (*Morgen gehört uns der Weltraum*), programme on Hessische Rundfunk, July 1956. The daily race (*Das tägliche Rennen*), Programme on Bayerische Rundfunk, August 1956. Space travel without illusions (*Weltraumfahrt ohne Illusionen*) in *Handelsblatt*, October 1956. By Missiles to the stars (*Missilibus ad astra*), in *Weltraumfahrt*, 1956. The new earth satellite (*Der neue Erdsatellit*), in Westermann's *Monatshefte*, September 1956. The last boundary above us (*Die letzte Grenze über uns*), in *Frankfurter Allgemeine Zeitung*, January 1957. The Penetration of space is beginning (*Der Vorstoss in den Raum beginnt*) in *Frankfurter Allgemeine Zeitung*, July 1957. The Frightful game (*Das grausame Spiel*), programme on Bayerische Rundfunk, May 1957. The Satellite — a red star (*Der Satellit, ein roter Stern*) in *Frankfurter Allgemeine Zeitung*, October 1957. The Satellite between dust and stars (*Der Satellit zwischen Staub und Sternen*) in *Frankfurter Allgemeine Zeitung*, October 1957. They're talking about Astronautics (*Man spricht über Astronautik*) in *Frankfurter Allgemeine Zeitung*, October 1957.

Gerathewohl, S.: The psycho-physiological effects of acceleration (*Die Psychophysiologie der Beschleunigungswirkung*) in *Weltraumfahrt*, 1953. The psychology of space flight (*Zur Psychologie der Raumfahrt*) in *Weltraumfahrt*, 1953.

Goethe, J. W. von: *Wilhelm Meister's Wanderjahre*, 1830.

Greiling, W.: How shall we live? (*Wie werden wir leben?*), Düsseldorf 1954.

Günther, G.: The analysis of a Utopia (*Die Analyse einer Utopie*), in *Weltraumfahrt*, 1952.

Haber, Fritz: The physics and physiology of the pressure drop in space. (*Physik und Physiologie des Drucksturzes im Weltraum*) in *Weltraumfahrt*, 1952.

Haber, Heinz: Man in space (*Der Mensch im Weltall*) in *Weltraumfahrt*, 1952. Where does space begin? (*Wo beginnt der Weltraum?*) in *Weltraumfahrt*, 1952. Artificial earth satellites for geophysical research in National Geographic Magazine, Washington 1956.

Haber-Gebauer: Possibilities and limits of manned Flight.

Hahn, Otto: Cobalt 60 — Danger or blessing for mankind? (*Cobalt 60, Gefahr oder Segen für die Menschheit?*), Frankfurt a.M. 1955. The Uranium chain reaction and its importance (*Die Kettenreaktion des Uran und ihre Bedeutung*) in *VDI Zeitschrift*, January 1948.

Haley, A. G.: Letter to Dr. L. R. Shepherd, President of the International Astronautical Federation, with a report on a journey to Europe, 4th May 1957. Space law and law outside the earth, a delimitation of space boundaries; in *Weltraumfahrt* 1957, and Reprint 1957.

Harkort, Friedrich: Railways (*Eisenbahnen*), in the periodical *Hermann* No. 26, 1825; notes on the hindrances of civilization and the emancipation of the lower classes. (*Bemerkungen über die Hindernisse der Zivilisation und Emanzipation der unterer Klassen*), Elberfeld 1844.

Hecht, Friedrich: Chemical problems of space flight (*Chemische Probleme des Weltraumfluges*) in *Weltraumfahrt*, 1953.

Hendrich, Franz: The way out of the treadmill (*Der Weg aus der Tretmühle*), Düsseldorf 1956.

Heuss, Theodor: Oskar von Miller and the path of technology (*Oskar von Miller und der Weg der Technik*), speech at the commemoration of the opening of the buildings of the Deutsches Museum in Munich, 7th May 1950. On the assessment of modern technology (*Über die Bewertung der modernen Technik*), speech on the 100th anniversary of Oskar von Miller, Munich 7th May 1955.

Hoffleit, D.: DOVAP, a method of measuring high rocket paths. (*DOVAP, eine Methode zur Vermessung hoher Raketenbahnen*) in *Weltraumfahrt*, 1950.

Hohmann, W.: The attainability of the heavenly bodies (*Die Erreichbarkeit der Himmelskörper*), Munich 1925.

Hoyle, Fred: Frontiers of Astronomy, London 1955.

Huxley, Aldous: Brave New World, London 1932 and 1949.

Hylander, C. H.: American inventors (*Amerikanische Erfinder*), Munich 1947.

Jordan, Pascual: Physics forges ahead (*Physik im Vordringen*), Brunswick 1949.
Jünger, Georg Friedrich: The perfection of technology (*Die Perfektion der Technik*), 2nd Ed., Frankfurt a.M. 1949.
Jungk, R.: Brighter than a thousand suns, translated from *Heller als tausend Sonnen*, Stuttgart 1956.

Kaempffert, W.: Limits of knowledge (*Grenzen der Erkenntnis*), Cologne 1954.
Karlson, P.: Man flies (*Der Mensch fliegt*), Berlin 1937 and 1955.
Kármán, Th. von: Aerodynamics (*Aerodynamik*), Geneva 1956.
Klemm, Friedrich: Technology — a history of its problems (*Technik, eine Geschichte ihrer Probleme*), Munich 1954.
Korn, Karl: Faust went to America (*Faust ging nach Amerika*) in *Frankfurter Allgemeine Zeitung*, June 1957. Megalopolis, living and dwelling by conveyor belt (*Megalopolis, leben und wohnen am laufender Band*) in *Frankfurter Allgemeine Zeitung*, June 1957.
Kraemer, O.: The engineer's responsibility (*Über die Verantwortung des Ingenieurs*) in *VDI Zeitschrift*, 1950. Man and work in the technical era (*Mensch und Arbeit im technischen Zeitalter*), report on the VDI Conference in Marburg, in *VDI Zeitschrift*, 1953.
Krüger-Lorenzen, Kurt: Short waves against tedium (*Kurze Welle gegen Langeweile*), Oldenbourg 1955.

Larsen, E.: Inventions without end (*Erfindungen und keine Ende*), Berlin 1954.
Lasswitz, E.: Time's magic cloak (*Im Zaubermantel der Zeit*), Frankfurt a.M. 1952.
Laurence, W. L.: Dawn over Zero, London 1947.
Leithäuser, J. G.: Earth's second creation (*Die zweite Schöpfung der Welt*), Berlin 1954.
Ley, Willy: Rockets, missiles and space travel, New York 1957.
Lockemann, C.: The various kinds of discovery (*Die verschiedenen Arten von Entdeckungen*) in *Naturwissenschaftliche Rundschau*, June 1957.
Loeser, G.: The first task for the International Astronautic Federation — an International Institute of Astronautics (*Die erste Aufgabe der Internationalen Astronautischen Föderation — ein Internationales Institut für Astronautik*), in *Weltraumfahrt*, 1951.
Loeser, G. and H. Gartmann: Can peaceable space travel be attained? (*Lässt sich eine friedliche Weltraumfahrt verwirklichen?*) in *Weltraumfahrt*, 1951.

Mackenzie, K.: Graham Bell, the Conqueror of Distance, Wiesbaden 1951.
Martin, Charles-Noel: Has H-hour struck? (*L'heure H a-t-elle sonnée?*). The atom, the world's future (*L'atome, l'avenir du monde*).
Materne, G.: The office of the future (*Das Büro der Zukunft*) in *Frankfurter Allgemeine Zeitung*, July 1957.
Maycock, R.: Doctors in the Air, London 1957.
Murchie, Guy: Clouds, wind and flight (*Wolken, Wind und Flug*), Berlin 1956.

Niklitschek, A.: Wonders in and around us (*Wunder in und um uns*), Linz 1947.

Oberth, Hermann: Rockets to planetary space (*Die Rakete zu den Planetenräumen*), Munich 1923. Roads to space travel (*Wege zur Raumschifffahrt*), Munich 1929. Man in space (*Mensch im Weltraum*), Düsseldorf 1954.

Pfender, M.e.a.: Technology leaves its mark on our time (*Die Technik prägt unsere Zeit*), Düsseldorf 1956.

Pirandello, Luigi: Cranks.

Pollock, F.: Automation, Frankfurt a.M. 1956.

Porter, R. W.: The Earth Satellite Programme of the U.S.A., February 1956.

Reichel, P. E.: Voyages of discovery in the future (*Entdeckungsreisen in die Zukunft*) in *die Neue Zeitung*, July 1949.

Reichenbach, G. von: Journal of the journey to England (*Tagebuch der Reise nach England*), 1791. Manuscript No. 8277 in the Deutsches Museum, Munich.

Reifenberg, B.: On technology (*Über die Technik*) in *die Gegenwart* 1947.

Regel, C. von: Plant life on Mars (*Pflanzenleben auf dem Mars*) in *Weltraumfahrt*, 1950.

Ress, F. M. and F. Zierke: The intellectual, political and technical-economical situation in 1850 (*Die geistige, politische und technisch-wirtschaftliche Situation um 1850*) in *VDI Nachrichten*, May 1955.

Roeper, H.: Automation in America; impressions of a journey of investigation (*Automatisierung in Amerika*) in *Frankfurter Allgemeine Zeitung*, February 1957.

Sänger, Eugen: What does space travel cost? (*Was kostet Weltraumfahrt?*) in *Weltraumfahrt*, 1951. Research between air travel and space flight (*Forschung zwischen Luftfahrt und Weltraumfahrt*), Tittmoning 1954, and in *Weltraumfahrt*, 1955. On the attainability of the fixed stars (*Über die Erreichbarkeit der Fixsterne*), lecture at the Seventh International Astronautical Congress, Rome 1956. The future of space travel (*Die Zukunft der Raumfahrt*) in *Frankfurter Allgemeine Zeitung*, November 1956. Drive systems intermediate between air travel and space flight (*Triebwerke zwischen Luftfahrt und Raumfahrt*) in *Weltraumfahrt*, 1956. Aeronautics and space flight developments in the 20th century (*Gemeinsamkeit und Befriedung der Luftfahrt- und Raumfahrtentwicklung im 20ten Jahrhundert*) in *Weltraumfahrt*, 1957. The mechanics of photon-rocket drives (*Zur Mechanik der Photonenstrahlantriebe*) (German edition), Munich 1956; also The radiation physics of photon-rocket drives and 'jet weapons' (*Zur Strahlungsphysik der Photonenstrahlantriebe und Waffenstrahlen*) (German edition), Munich 1956.

Sänger-Bredt, Irene: Random reflections on space travel (*Träumereien am Rande der Weltraumfahrt*) in *Weltraumfahrt*, 1953.

Sänger, Eugene and Irene Sänger-Bredt: Report on the International Conference on ram-jets and rockets, Stuttgart 1956; especially Sänger, Flight mechanics of photon rockets (*Zur Flugmechanik der Photonenraketen*).

Schaub, W.: The Satellite Station in the form of a gyroscope not subject to forces (*Die Aussenstation als kräftefreier Kreisel*) in *Weltraumfahrt*, 1951. The Space Station in the form of a gyroscope with gravity (*Die Raumstation als schwerer Kreisel*) in *Weltraumfahrt*, 1951. Tidal forces acting on the Satellite Station (*Die Flutkräfte auf der Aussenstation*) in *Weltraumfahrt*, 1952. An astronomer's thoughts on space travel (*Gedanken eines Astronomen zur Weltraumfahrt*) in *Weltraumfahrt*, 1952.

Scherbaum: The third road (*Der dritte Weg*), Wien 1948.

Schmitt, J. L.: The atom — folly or reality? (*Atom, Wahn oder Wirklichkeit*), Munich 1956.

Schmitthenner, H.-J.: The aerial travellers; the history, attraction and adventure of ballooning (*Die Luftfahrer, Geschichte, Lust und Abenteuer des Balloonflugs*), Bergen 1956.

Schneider, J.: Man and the gravitational field (*Der Mensch im Schwerefeld*) in *Weltraumfahrt*, 1950.

Schröter, F.: Reflections on television (*Gedanken über des Fernsehen*) in *Physikalische Blätter*, 1949.

Schwerte, H. and W. Spengler: Research workers and scientists in present-day Europe (*Forscher und Wissenschaftler im heutigen Europa*), Oldenbourg 1955.

Smyth, H. de Wolf: Atomic energy and its military uses.

Spengler, Oswald: Man and technology; a contribution to a philosophy of life (*Der Mensch und die Technik, Beitrag zu einer Philosophie des Lebens*), Munich 1958.

Stemmer, J.: The attitude of the engineer to the present problems of space flight (*Die Stellung des Ingenieurs zu aktuellen Problemen des Weltraumfluges*) in *Weltraumfahrt*, 1950.

Stifter, Adalbert: *Nachsommer*, 1857.

Störig, H.-J.: A short history of world science (*Kleine Weltgeschichte der Wissenschaft*), Stuttgart 1954.

Strughold, H.e.a.: How will the human organism behave in a gravity-free state? (*Wie wird sich der menschliche Organismus im schwerefreien Raum verhalten?*) in *Weltraumfahrt*, 1951. Where does space begin? (*Wo beginnt der Weltraum?*) in *Weltraumfahrt*, 1952. Life on Mars (*Das Leben auf dem Mars*) in *Weltraumfahrt*, 1953. Space-equivalent conditions within the earth's atmosphere (*Weltraumäquivalente Bedingungen innerhalb der Erdatmosphäre*) in *Weltraumfahrt*, 1955.

Thomas, Ch. A.: Atomic energy as the servant of mankind (*Die Atomkraft als Diener des Menschen*) in *Amerika-Dienst*, December 1954.

Treichlinger, W. M.: The early days of the airship (*Aus der Urzeit des Luftschiffs*), Zürich 1951.

Trommsdorff, W.: What scientific information and economic benefit can we hope to gain when the problem of space travel is solved? (*Welche wissenschaftlichen Einsichten und welcher wirtschaftliche Nutzen können erhofft werden wenn das Problem der Raumfahrt gelöst ist?*) in *Weltraumfahrt*, 1957.

Usher, A. P.: History of Mechanical Inventions, Cambridge, 1929, 1954.

VDI: Man and the strains to which technology subjects him (*Der Mensch im Kraftfeld der Technik*), Special VDI Congress in Münster, Düsseldorf 1955.

Watt, James: Patent Specifications No. 913, A.D. 1769.

Welf Heinrich, Prinz von Hannover: Legal Problems of space (*Die Rechtsprobleme des Weltraumes*) in *Weltraumfahrt*, 1953.

Wells, H. G.: The Time Machine, London 1895.
A short history of the world.

West, P.: Automation without tears (*Automatisierung ohne Tränen*) in *Frankfurter Allgemeine Zeitung*, May 1957.

White, C. S. and O. Benson: Physics and medicine of the Upper Atmosphere. A study of the Aeropause. Albuquerque 1952.

Wiener, Norbert: The Human Use of Human Beings, Kybernetics and Society, Boston 1950.

Zaehringer, A. J.: Astronautics, guided weapons and rockets (*Astronautik, Lenkwaffen und Raketen*) in *Weltraumfahrt*, 1957.

Zenneck, J.: Cultural progress as a result of technology and science (*Kulturförderung durch Technik und Wissenschaft*), Berlin 1935.

Zimmer, E.: The revolution in the concept of physics (*Umsturz im Weltbild der Physik*), 11th Ed., Munich 1957.

'Fear, War and the Bomb' (*Furcht, Krieg und die Bombe*), a discussion of the effects of atomic weapons on war, in *Wirtschaftszeitung*, May 1949 (no author named).

U.S.S.R. Rocket and Earth Satellite Programme for the I.G.Y. Reprint of the BIS symposium, Cranfield 1957.

INDEX OF NAMES

ADER, Clément, 53, 105
Alcock, 110
Anast, Major James L., 229, 230, 231
Arago, 7
Arco, Count Georg, 148, 149, 150, 152
Aristotle, 10, 11
Asimov, Isaac, 246, 247, 258, 259
Ayrton, W. E., 126

Bacher, Dr. R. F., 185
Bacon, Francis; Lord Verulam, 4
Bader, Josef von, 46
Bain, Alexander, 158
Bainbridge, Dr. Kenneth T., 186
Baird, John Logie, 160, 161, 164
Baker, W. R. G., 244
Becquerel, Prof. Henri, 191, 192, 194, 203
Bell, Alexander Graham, 135, 136, 137, 140, 141, 142, 143, 156
Bellamy, Edward, 144
Benz, Carl Friedrich, 57, 60, 67, 68
Berger, Dr. Wilfred, 328
Bernoulli, 121
Blanchard, 95
Blériot, Louis, 108
Bohr, Prof. Niels, 200, 201, 203, 207, 211
Borsig, 25
Boulton, Matthew, 1, 5, 6, 19, 20, 21, 22, 24, 34
Bragg, William Henry, 195
Branca, Giovanni, 9
Brandt, Leo, 166, 168
Branly, Prof. Edouard, 146, 147
Braun, Prof. Ferdinand, 110, 149, 151, 159, 160, 180
Braun, Wernher von, 93, 172, 274, 275, 276, 294, 297
Braunbeck, Prof. Werner, 200

Bredov, Hans, 153, 154, 161
Broglie, Prof. Louis de, 303
Brown, 110
Burckhardt, Jacob, xiii

Campbell, John W., 259, 260
Capek, Karel, 231, 232
Carey, C. R., 158
Caus, De, 9
Cavendish, Henry, 86, 87
Cayley, Sir George, 76
Chadwick, J., 208
Chappe, Claude, 128, 129
Charles, César Alexandre, 88, 89, 90, 93, 94
Clarke, Arthur C., 78, 267, 276, 302
Clarke, E., 32
Cleator, P. E., 245, 256, 257, 259, 260
Cleaver, A. V., 276, 302
Crocco, General A., 331
Cugnot, 33
Curie, Irene: see Joliot-Curie
Curie, Marie, 192, 193, 194, 195, 196, 198, 203, 206
Curie, Pierre, 192, 193, 194, 196, 198, 203
Cyrano de Bergerac, 82

Daimler, Gottlieb, 56, 58, 60, 66, 67, 68
Democritus of Abdera, 189
Dessauer, Friedrich, xiv, 5, 235, 254, 259, 260
Diesel, Rudolf, 56
Dinnendahl, Franz, 5
Dominik, Hans, 122, 153
Dornberger, Dr. Walter, 304, 309
Drais, Karl Friedrich Freiherr von, 61, 62
Dunlap, 159
Dunlop, 64

Eckener, Dr. Hugo, 102
Eddington, Sir Arthur, 188
Edison, Thomas A., 141, 246
Ehricke, Krafft, 325
Einstein, Dr. Albert, 155, 188, 203, 212, 213, 228, 314, 320, 322
Engel, Rolf, 274
Esau, Prof. Abraham, 162, 163
Esnault-Pelterie, Robert, 107
Evans, Oliver, 32, 33

Faraday, Michael, xii, 145, 159
Farmer, Moses G., 137
Farrell, General, 216
Ferber, 105
Fermi, Enrico, 209, 210, 211, 212, 213
Ferrarin, 110
Field, Cyrus West, 133, 134
Fitch, John, 31, 32
Fitzmaurice, 111
Fleming, Sir Ambrose, 152
Fontana, Dominico, 2, 3, 4
Ford, Henry, 69, 112, 279
Forest, Lee de, 152
Franklin, Benjamin, 91, 93, 159
Frisch, Dr. O. R., 211
Fulton, Robert, 32, 99

Galilei, Galileo, xii, 84
Ganswindt, Hermann, 83, 84, 99, 100, 115
Garnier, 95
Gauss, Karl Friedrich, 129
Gay-Lussac, 117
Geiger, Hans, 200
Gerlach, W., xiii
Gernsback, Hugo, 169
Giffard, Henri Jacques, 97, 99
Gillespie, Col. James L., 229
Goethe, J. Wolfgang von, 6, 7, 93
Golightly, Charles, 53
Goodyear, 64
Grade, Hans, 108, 109
Gray, Elisha, 138, 141
Gronau, Wolfgang von, 110, 114
Groves, General Leslie R., 213
Guericke, Otto von, 10, 84, 159

Günther, Dr. Gotthard, 247
Günther, Hans, 204
Gurney, 34

Haber, Hans, 302
Haenlein, Paul, 97
Hagen, Dr. John P., 277
Hahn, Dr. Otto, 205, 210, 211, 212, 218, 220, 329
Haley, Andrew G., 122, 123
Hancock, 34
Harkort, Friedrich Wilhelm, 46, 47
Heaviside, Oliver, 162
Hedley, 38
Heiman, E. E., 111, 112
Helmholtz, Hermann Ludwig von, 104, 159
Helmont, 11
Henry, Prof. Joseph, 136
Hero of Alexandria, 8, 9, 54
Hertz, Heinrich, xii, 145, 146, 147, 156, 158, 159, 180
Hill, 36
Hoffmann, E. T. A., 233
Hohmann, Dr. Walter, 329
Howe, Elias, 253
Hülsmeyer, Christian, 165, 166, 172, 181
Hünefeld, Freiherr Günther von, 111
Huskisson, William, 44, 46
Huxley, Aldous, 255
Huyghens, Christiaan, 9, 10

Jansky, Karl, 173
Jeffries, Dr. J., 95
Joliot-Curie, Irène, 193, 206, 209
Joliot, Frédéric, 206, 209
Jolly, Philipp von, 183
Jones, Sir Harold Spencer, 292
Jünger, G. F., xiv
Junkers, Hugo, 109, 110, 120

Kaiserer, Joseph, 97
Karman, Th. von, 123
Kempelen, Wolfgang von, 233, 234
Kepler, Johannes, xii
Kindermann, Christian, 86, 305

Köhl, 111
Korn, Dr. Karl, 268, 293
Kraemer, O., xvi
Krebs, 98
Krüger-Lorenzen, Kurt, 152, 157

Lana, Francesco de, 84, 85, 86
Langen, Eugen, 58, 66
Langley, Samuel P., 107
Lanz, Karl, 108, 109
Lardner, Dr., 99, 115
Laue, Max von, 195, 228
Laufer, Prof. Berthold, 80
Laurence, W., 211
Lawrence, Prof. Edward O., 202, 203
Lear, William P., 74, 124, 125
Lee, Robert E., 157
Leibniz, Gottfried Wilhelm, 13, 14, 85, 86
Leitner, 308
Lenoir, Jean Joseph Etienne, 57, 58
Levitzki, 163
Ley, Willy, 287, 306
Lichtenberg, Georg Christoph, 86
Lilienthal, Gustav, 76, 103
Lilienthal, Otto, 76, 103, 104, 105
Lindbergh, Charles, 71, 111
List, Friedrich, 48, 49

McAdam, John Loudon, 29
Madersperger, Joseph, 253
Marconi, Guglielmo, 144, 147, 148, 149, 150, 151, 159, 160, 180, 181
Marcus, Siegfried, 65
Maxwell, Prof. James Clark, 145, 147, 156
Maybach, 66
Mayer, Dr. Robert, 197
Meitner, Dr. Lise, 210, 211
Meyer, Prof. Dr. Alex, 123
Montgolfier, Etienne, 87, 88, 91, 92, 93, 102
Montgolfier, Joseph, 87, 88, 93, 102
Morland, Sir Samuel, 9
Morse, Samuel F. B., 130, 131, 132, 159

Mueller, Heinz, 122, 126
Murdock, William, 20, 33, 34

Nernst, W., 205
Neumann, Johann von, 237, 249
Newcomen, Thomas, 17, 18
Nipkov, Paul, 158, 159
Noordung: see Potocnic
Nostradamus, 102

Oberth, Prof. Herman, 269, 273, 302, 305, 306, 307, 308
Oersted, Hans Christian, 129, 155
Oppenheimer, Dr. Robert, 205, 226, 228
Otto, Nikolaus August, 56, 58, 60, 66

Papin, Denis, 11, 12, 13, 14, 15
Paulhan, Louis, 77, 109
Pease, 40, 41
Pierer, H. A., 20, 30
Pirandello, Luigi, xiv, 69
Pirquet, Guido von, 273, 274
Planck, Max, 182, 201
Poe, Edgar Allan, 234
Pollock, Friedrich, 239
Popov, Alexander, 147
Popp, Josef, 69
Potocnic, 273
Priestley, Joseph, 87
Pullman, George M., 51

Ramsay, David, 9
Rayleigh, Lord, 201
Read, 110
Recke, Freiherr von der, 5
Reichenbach, Georg, 21, 22, 56
Reis, Philipp, 135, 156
Renard, Charles, 98
Reuleaux, Prof. Franz, 57
Riem, Prof., 307
Rivaz, 56
Roebuck, Dr. 19
Roeper, Hans, 242
Röntgen, Wilhelm Conrad, 190, 191, 195, 203
Rozier, Pilâtre de, 91, 92, 93, 95

Rutherford, Sir Ernest (later Lord Rutherford), 198, 199, 200, 201, 202, 203, 205, 206, 329
Sänger, Dr. Eugen, 123, 288, 305, 306, 308, 309, 311, 312, 313, 314, 317, 319, 320, 321, 322, 323, 324, 325, 329, 330, 331, 332

Saint-Exupéry, Antoine de, 112
Santos-Dumont, Alberto, 98, 107
Savery, Thomas, 13, 15
Schmidt, Prof., 328
Schroeder, 111
Sedov, Leonid, 281, 310
Shepherd, L. R., 123
Siemens, Werner von, xii, 121, 132, 133
Simons, Major David G., 102, 291, 292
Singer, Dr. S. F., 275
Sivcev, Dr. Kosta, 123
Slaby, Adolf, 147, 148, 149, 152, 159
Slotin, Louis, 215, 216
Soddy, Frederick, 199
Sömmering, 128, 129
Sommerfeld, Prof. Arnold, 188
Spengler, O., xiv
Stapp, Dr. John P., 292
Steinheil, Carl August, 129
Stephenson, George, 39, 40, 41, 42, 43, 44, 45, 46
Stifter, Adalbert, 4
Strassmann, Prof. Fritz, 210, 211
Strughold, Dr. Hubertus, 289, 290, 291, 299
Stuart, Robert, 7
Szilard, Leo, 206, 212

Theophrastus, 10
Thimanier, 253
Thomson, Sir J. J., 196, 198
Thomson, Sir William (later Lord Kelvin), 138

Thurston, R. H., 64
Tichov, 292
Torricelli, 11, 84
Trevithick, Richard, 27, 33, 34, 36, 37, 38
Tsiolkovski, Constantine Edwardovitch, 272, 273

Van der Hulst, 178
Verne, Jules, 83, 301, 305

Watson, Thomas A., 136, 137, 138, 143
Watt, James, 1, 5, 6, 15, 17, 18, 19, 20, 21, 22, 23, 24, 25, 26, 31, 33, 34, 77
Watson-Watt, Sir Robert, 168
Weber, Prof. W. E., 129
Welf Heinrich, Prinz von Hannover, 123
Wells, H. G., 71, 103, 258
Wendel, Fritz, 111
Wensley, R. J., 233
Westphal, Prof. Wilhelm, 328
Wheatstone, Prof. Charles, 135
Whittle, Frank, 114
Wiener, Prof. Norbert, 209, 238, 239, 253, 259, 260
Wilson, C. R. T., 199
Winterberg, Dr. Friedward, 311
Worcester, Marquis of, 9
Wright, Orville and Wilbur, 70, 72, 78, 103, 105, 106, 107, 109

Yates, General, 300

Zborowski, Count Helmuth von, 119, 308
Zeidler, Johann Gottfried, 76, 96
Zeppelin, Count, 100, 101
Zworikyn, Vladimir, 161